Towards a habitable world

TOWARDS
A HABITABLE WORLD

Task - Problems and methods - Acceleration

BY

J. VAN ETTINGER
Managing Director of Bouwcentrum

PUBLISHED FOR BOUWCENTRUM ROTTERDAM

BY

ELSEVIER PUBLISHING COMPANY

1 9 6 0   Amsterdam / London / New York / Princeton

SOLE DISTRIBUTORS FOR THE UNITED STATES OF NORTH AMERICA:

D. VAN NOSTRAND COMPANY, INC.

120 Alexander Street, Princeton, N. J. (Princeton Office)

257 Fourth Avenue, New York 10, N.Y.

SOLE DISTRIBUTORS FOR CANADA:

D. VAN NOSTRAND COMPANY (CANADA) LTD.

25 Hollinger Road, Toronto 16.

SOLE DISTRIBUTORS FOR THE BRITISH COMMONWEALTH EXCLUDING CANADA:

D. VAN NOSTRAND COMPANY LTD.

358 Kensington High Street, London W.14.

Library of Congress Catalog Card Number 60-8703

Printed in the Netherlands

by

N. V. Drukkerij Koch & Knuttel, Gouda

To my wife

Acknowledgements

When, after a five-years struggle with the extensive subject matter treated in this book, I wrote the last word, I wanted to immediately lay down my pen but I was unable to do so, because of the strong urge I experienced to thank all those who, consciously or unconsciously, have assisted me in producing this book.

It has not been an easy task for me to combine the writing of this book with the very busy and varied task of managing Bouwcentrum and also with my daily obligations in the sphere of statistics. Yet I could not have written it if I had not been in a position to perform this highly diversified work and if I had not had the great advantage of many contacts with experts from practically all the countries in the world. I am greatly indebted to all those with whom I have had the good fortune to collaborate during the last ten years within the framework of the now rapidly developing International Council for Building Research, Studies and Documentation (C.I.B.).

Moreover, I experienced a great stimulation from my regular visits to other countries and from the intensive exchange of thought resulting from lectures, addresses and discussions.

All this has made a substantial contribution to my international experience and has made me realise that building is one of the most important world problems of our time.

With regard to the actual work involved during the last five years in the compilation of this book I wish to express my appreciation of the generous help which I have received in many respects and due acknowledgement is made to

J. Tinbergen, J. B. D. Derksen, H. C. Bos,
A. R. van der Burg, J. Sittig,

for their valuable assistance with the subjects of international aid, econometrics and statistics.

Although this book gives expression to my personal ideas, I fully realise the great help I have had from members of the staff of Bouwcentrum and its associated institutes. In this connection special acknowledgement is due to

A. L. G. M. Rombouts, H. O. Eckardt,
F. H. J. Nierstrasz, J. P. A. Holtzer, C. Stempels,

for their co-operation in functional matters; to

W. Valderpoort, A. Volbeda, H. van Bremen,

for their advice on the subjects of building engineering and building physics; to

E. S. Beek, W. J. van Nieuwkerk,
A. K. Vissers, J. van Zwet,

for making available their considerable practical experience in building organisation and building economics; to

K. L. de Vries, H. Th. van Schaik, J. de Geus,

for their valuable comments and criticism of the original manuscript and the exchange of ideas on the subject of transmission of knowledge; to

H. O. Eckardt, W. A. Brekelmans,

for attending to the typography and the illustrations in close collaboration with the publisher's staff and to

R. M. Wormer

for the design of the dust cover; to

Miss M. M Verzuu, Miss E. J. van Hoboken,
Mrs. H. E. Kalshoven-Brester,

for their great effort in typing and retyping the many drafts of the manuscript.

Furthermore, I would like to express my gratitude to Mr. H. Hooper for the effort and careful attention he has devoted to the translation of the manuscript.

Finally, I should like to thank the publishers, Messrs. Elsevier Publishing Company, Amsterdam, and their staff, and the printers, Messrs. Koch & Knuttel, Gouda, before whom, I am sure, I have often placed difficult tasks, which they have fulfilled with enthusiasm and skill.

Table of contents

page

Part one: THE TASK

1 And yet . . .   3

*in the year 2000 more than 5 milliard people | rapidly rising expectations
are utterly incompatible with hunger, sickness and slums | enormous technical
possibilities | many dangers | an unbalanced world | hope and much despair |
and yet . . .*

2 Everybody wants to live   7

*all people have one thing in common: the will to "live" | to live means to
live together, to adapt space, to build | many people have no reasonable chance |
something must be done*

3 Dangers threatening progress   13

*famine, disease, slums | rapid growth of the world population | war and
revolution | "mass-society" | primitive social control | domination of engineer-
ing | failure of housing policy threatens the individual, the family and society*

4 Towards a habitable world   27

*man is formed by family life and school education | a dwelling of optimum
quality a necessity | schools an integral part of our town planning | "builders"
wanted | a milliard new dwellings alone must be built in this century | the
world can afford this investment, provided national incomes continue to rise
and armaments expenditure shows a relative decrease*

5 The decisive choice   39

*two questions | one answer: we must | we must build | greater forces to be mo-
bilised | a practical ideal | stimulating effect of visible achievement | a world
problem*

Part two: PROBLEMS AND METHODS

6 More and better building   47

*more efficient use of the existing building capacity with a fair distribution |
more by fewer obstructions | more by more means | more but also better |
optimum quality | towards industrialisation of the building industry | the
principle: standardisation based on functional quality | looking ahead | active
planning | rational programming, design and production | a play in many acts*

7 Construire c'est prévoir   63

*human action directed to the future | man wants to control the future |
growing power | many uncertainties | the descriptive statistics | facts more
important than opinions | the probability theory | describing more than is
observed | the stochastic statistics | discovering and controlling influences |
the decisionics | the most favourable policy*

8 Building is planning   77

spontaneous co-ordination or conscious planning | building programmes part of a general development policy | the design of development | battle against shortages | breaking through the vicious circle | the physical planning | careful use of the available space | changing functions of cities | lacking knowledge | need for traffic research | the social-economic planning of building | continuity of building | basic data for planning building activity

9 Building is programming   105

the initial idea | a study and a decision to build | the basic programme | the programme of requirements | the quality factors | the functional analysis | the functional synthesis | the general functional study | the application | the individual functional study

10 Building is designing   127

the "aristocratic" quality | the optimum quality | the optimum number of types | the physical requirements | finish of walls, ceiling and floor | grouping of space and building units | the load-bearing structure | the choice of building materials | the technical and functional life of buildings | minimisation of the "all-in" costs | the industrial designer | forms and aspects of forms | the task of the architect | the fine arts | the objective and subjective qualities of the design

11 Building is rational production   177

the limited influence of the contractor | the necessity for coordination of programme, design and production | the influence of the public authorities | the organisation of production within the limitations | human aspects | specialisation and coordination | work study | planning | quality control | personnel relations | safety inspection | maintenance of machines and equipment | administration | the barriers broken by feedback | influencing the townplan and the design | the task of the central and local authorities | teamwork

Part three: ACCELERATION

12 Building research and development   207

the aim: better living conditions | accidental discovery, linear invention, multi-dimensional planning | arrears in building research | basic problems: the skeleton of building activity | functional research: usefulness | technical research: realisation of functional requirements, technological basis of production | organisation research: large scale framework and efficient production | development work: from prototype to mass production

13 Transmission of knowledge   223

a problem of integration of knowledge and practice | the sources and the users | documentation and storage of knowledge | transmission of knowledge by uni-lateral and multi-lateral methods | aids: sound, written word, image | the barriers: resistance to change, linguistic barriers

page

14 Documentation   237

independence of time and space | unity in multiplicity by classification and standardisation | from unplanned reading towards planned reading by sign-posting | from undirected knowledge towards directed knowledge by active documentation | storage in the practitioner's office and information centre | basic and special subject-training of building documentalists

15 Building information centres   251

different types of information centres | the stages on the road from theory to practice | Bouwcentrum an all-round building information centre | the supply of knowledge | the production of knowledge | the transformation of knowledge | the transmission of knowledge

16 Acceleration   267

fundamental unbalance | accelerated change on well-planned basis a necessity | basic conditions: mutual trust, reduction in cost of armaments, transfer of income and knowledge, birth control | acceleration of public and private capital movement from rich to poor countries | economic and social investments | acceleration of international exchange of building knowledge | a long range U.N. programme of concerted international action in the field of low-cost housing and related community facilities

17 Our building programme   313

a thousand million dwellings to be built in this century | extension of low-cost housing in the period 1958—1969 | distribution of investments | international aid and extra building programme | towards a habitable world | more favourable conditions for development of the individual and the relations between individuals

XI

Part one: THE TASK

1

And yet . . .

in the year 2000 more than 5 milliard people | rapidly rising expectations are utterly incompatible with hunger, sickness and slums | enormous technical possibilities | many dangers | an unbalanced world | hope and much despair | and yet . . .

Man and society are faced with the great problem that the world population – already numbering 2.8 milliard – is growing very rapidly and in the year 2000 will in all probability number more than 5 milliard people. They are also faced with the disturbing fact that only a quarter of the world population is adequately fed and properly housed. This minority, therefore, finds itself opposite an overwhelming force of poverty and almost insoluble problems.

It is not a simple matter to convince these 700 million people that great sacrifices will be required of them to make the world habitable for all within the span of a few generations. They must be persuaded, despite the worries and unfulfilled desires which each one of them will undoubtedly have, not to concentrate solely on achieving greater prosperity and a higher standard of physical and mental health for themselves and a few others who are dear to them.

They should realise that we are in the middle of a revolution of rapidly rising expectations.

The poor of the world are ever more clearly exhibiting a strong desire for an existence worthy of mankind and are beginning to see that misery need not necessarily be part of their lot.

Rapidly rising expectations are utterly incompatible with hunger, sickness and slums and for those who find themselves in this situation it is difficult to understand that the world can only be freed of slums within the span of a few generations by a considerably stepped-up constructional effort and that destruction of valuable things invariably reduces the world's potential and thus also the ultimate chance of achieving this aim.

There is not much time left to prevent irreparable damage being done, the more so because a new world is coming into being, which is at once smaller and greater and in which interdependence strongly increases.

Smaller, because the rapid development of transport enables us to travel from one end of the world to the other in a matter of days, while a steady stream of products from distant countries reaches our markets every day.

3

Smaller also, because the first signs of space travel are noticeable and our planet is more and more being seen and understood against the background of – by our earthly standards – almost infinite interplanetary space.

Greater, because events in the remotest places are brought into our personal sphere by telephone, telegraph, radio and television in a very short time. With great speed they are brought inside our circle, inside the world of our interests and inner anxieties, whereby we become physically involved. Greater also, because the successful launching of guided missiles and satellites tends to bring space, which hitherto could only be explored by virtue of light rays, within the sphere of actual discovery, thus in a way making this space belong to the earth.

Hence, for the technically initiated, the interested laymen and those addicted to science-fiction there is every reason to live in what seems a world of technical ecstasy. For them the world of tomorrow with its enormous technical possibilities is already here. This is not difficult to understand, because in laboratories and to some extent also in practice the taming of atomic energy is in full swing. The rapid development of cybernetics and of practical electronic equipment lays the foundation for a substantial piece of automation, while the launching of guided missiles and satellites once more bring phantasies of Jules Verne within the sphere of technical accomplishment.

Many people may feel themselves attracted to all this, but more than anything else they feel themselves threatened, because in effect the dangers are brought home to them every day, while the advantages are to them at most a vague expectation.

In the technically developed countries mankind has indeed succeeded in creating, through the rapid progress made in the last hundred years, important material foundations, which are essential for a full and creative life. But this technical development is not founded on a conscious effort to achieve a balanced material development and, worse still, while struggling and being rightly proud of much that has been achieved, sight has been lost of what really matters: mankind itself. This has resulted in an unbalanced world, in which a bewildering growth of technical knowledge in some respects goes hand in hand with technical backwardness in other respects and is accompanied by a primitive social technique and immature psychological relationships. This situation of unbalance is likely to deteriorate even further owing to the rapid process of development in which the world finds itself, while interdependence is constantly growing.

The unbalance is threatening to assume alarming proportions, because precisely in those countries where development has lagged behind most and where with an excessive supply of labour only very limited capital investment is possible, the population is growing fastest owing to the marked drop in the death rate.

Hence, it must be realised without delay that our constructional activities to make the world habitable for everyone in the shortest possible time must be greatly accelerated for two reasons. Firstly we must make up existing arrears and secondly we must keep pace with the accelerated growth of the population.

Many villages and towns present in time and space a striking illustration of backwardness and unbalance. For those who go through life not like a tourist it is generally not a very inspiring sight. How often is it not that one sees a dilapidated house combined with television aerial, car or motor-scooter? How often is it not found that backwardness, chaos and ugliness constitute serious obstacles to the development of an existence worthy of mankind? Fortunately, it can also be seen in villages and towns and even in industrial areas and on the highways how the life of man can be favourably influenced by engineering, order and beauty.

Thus, the world of to-day is a strange mixture of achievement and much failure, of order and much chaos, of hope and much despair. For most people it is usually too difficult to see through the obvious weaknesses of our enlarged society and – despite terror, misery, smallness and indifference – to retain a clear picture of a possible better society.

This is all the more apparent when we consider that in recent years numerous conflicts have once more clearly illustrated how difficult it is to live as good neighbours in our smaller world. To achieve this the "mental" gaps, which among other things are associated with differences in way of life and language, would first have to be considerably reduced.

It is not surprising, therefore, that to many the world of to-day is very complicated and confused. Confronted with chaos every day, they can only react with cynicism, sarcasm, indifference or amazement if someone says optimistically: "and yet . . . !", because he feels that, in spite of everything, a pregnant answer lies hidden in humanity. An answer which conjures up an idealistic picture of a world habitable for all, where usefulness, order and beauty go hand in hand. An answer must be given, even if we know that it can only be realised in part, because man cannot live without hope for the future. This hope has the effect of a blood transfusion and creates new energy, which we will need on the road ahead of us, a road which – if we wish it – will lead to a better life.

2   Everybody wants to live

all people have one thing in common: the will to "live" | to live means to live together, to adapt space, to build | many people have no reasonable chance | something must be done

Since the beginning of the first world war mankind has had to face a variety of terrible events and conflicts, armed on the one hand with a rapidly growing technology and knowledge of physics and on the other hand struggling along with a complex of out-of-date and inadequate notions about human society, law and justice. During the last hundred years we have looked rather too much through the microscope and too little through the window of everyday life. Consequently, our way of thinking, our skill and our actions exhibit a high degree of disproportionality. Many important matters closely associated with the progress of human life, such as building, have been neglected.

At first the rapid progress made in the spheres of engineering and science filled us with pride and optimism, but more and more we are beginning to experience a feeling of anxiety and with all our efforts we are still vaguely wondering whether there is any sense in life at all.

This feeling became very strong indeed when in World War II millions of people were deprived of their homes and important buildings, so that literally and figuratively they sat on the ruins of what was once a human society. The feeling of anxiety is even more prevalent to-day, seeing that – technically speaking – we have become so expert at the art of destruction that we can wipe out more in a second than we can build in a hundred years.

Despite all this, some of us live on more or less indifferently under the motto "let's enjoy ourselves while we can", while others withdraw into their ivory towers. However, there are more and more men and women who are not lost in the crowd or in themselves and they are fortunately not confined to any particular rank, social standing, religion, race or the like. Irrespective of the magnitude of their talents, they are prepared to ask more of themselves than others would ask of them or they would ask of others, in order to attempt in some way or other to improve something with which they have come into contact, knowing that all people on this earth have at least one thing in common, whatever their station in life.

7

The statesman who in weak health performs a responsible task, sometimes involving the fate of millions of people. *The Olympic champion* who in excellent health puts in years of training and concentration to take a tenth of a second off the world record. *The Asian farmer*, often physically weakened, who in a superhuman struggle with nature and practically without technical aids tries to raise from less than an acre sufficient food to keep himself and his family alive, until their lives are prematurely cut off as a result of an unbalanced diet. *The housewife in a slum district*, who, as by a stealthily approaching disease, is threatened by a growing lack of the most primitive comfort and on behalf of her family often struggles against dirt and social ruin.

What have they in common with all the others who live and work, who are hungry, ambitious, sick, healthy, resigned, indifferent, purposeful, happy or whatever else they can be?

What they have in common is the will to live, despite everything they go through. Their family, their work or their hobbies can form their basic interests in life. Sometimes man derives the strength to go on from that which surpasses all things temporal.

They want to live, live differently, live better, they just want to "live". What they mean by this and what they desire from life differs as much as one human being differs from another and as the conditions under which they live differ.

Often the desires they cherish are apparently simple and reasonable. A little more and a little better food for the children, a good doctor for the family, a little less worry to make ends meet and a better chance to get on in the world for themselves and those who are dear to them.

Sometimes it is a better house that would make all the difference, a quiet corner, a good book and an easy chair or a pipe and sufficient tobacco. Sometimes it is an evening dress, a motor-scooter, a television set, a sailing yacht or even a trip to the Mediterranean for which there is a strong desire.

With all these dreams, wishes, desires and requirements – irrespective of whether they are simple or extravagant, materialistic or otherwise, an unattainable end or just another phase on the road that lies ahead – it should nevertheless be realised that the really important things in life are seldom thrown in our lap like presents in a Christmas stocking. As far as these things are concerned, man must make his own life. He must make his life in a world in which fate has placed him at an arbitrary time and place. His chance lies in the acknowledgement and enforcement of the inherent, true and human qualities of the individual [1].

By knowing himself he can utilise the capacity for goodness and creative-

---

[1] Dr. Erich Fromm: *Man for Himself*, London 1949.

ness anchored in his being. But the chances he has to "live" are only partly determined individually, since the collective bodies to which he belongs are also very important in this respect, *i.e.* family, school, church, work team, street, neighbourhood, town, country and the world as a whole. To live usually means to live together with others in a community.

We can certainly adapt ourselves to some extent to what mother earth has to offer us in the way of space, climate and raw materials, but it is precisely by building that we must adapt the space available to man to deliver him from the whims of nature.

Adapted space is necessary for agriculture and horticulture and is achieved by means of irrigation works, drainage, dikes and many other works of construction; otherwise the struggle against nature to free mankind of the scourge of hunger will remain just a game of poker with life itself at stake.

An adequate supply of raw materials and power can be ensured by open-cast and underground mining, by drilling and by constructing dams.

In properly conditioned factories and work-shops the production of numerous indispensable goods can take place without interruption under sound working conditions.

The erection of buildings for government administration and for commerce provides adapted space where man learns to control and develop further the more and more complicated life in town and country.

In the efficiently planned residential area with sufficient schools, churches, hospitals, shops, theatres, sports grounds and other facilities the individual, the family and the community as a whole are given a fair chance to come to healthy development.

Between all these various types of space – built-in, transformed in some other way or left almost in its natural state – communications are required to promote contact between human beings and to make possible transport of goods and the performance of services.

To this end we must construct highways, railways, ports, airfields and numerous buildings associated with transport of human beings and goods. The special provisions in the way of adapted space for telegraph, telephone and wireless communications are also of the utmost importance in this respect.

The individual buildings are, of course, important, but the way in which they are grouped together to form a balanced whole in villages and cities is equally important in order that the functions of housing, work, recreation and transport can, jointly and severally, freely develop. From the early stages of human life mankind – more or less conscious of all this – has been building for human communities. In a village or city it is not sufficient to express the common will to live, but life in all its aspects must be given the chance to develop by providing all types of buildings.

It is quite intolerable that the greater part of the world population lives in constant fear of hunger and the results thereof and that every minute of the day children are born in slum dwellings, such as are found in New York, London, Paris, Cairo and in practically all other cities and also in rural districts.

In view of the strong influence which the social background has on a young person throughout the rest of his life, it will be clear that not all people have a reasonable chance and that many are bound to fail, because they lack the extra energy required to work themselves up from an inferior social standard. Hence, it is unfortunate that there should be such great social differences.

This is all the more unfortunate, because in this world of increasing differentiation on the one hand and a resulting greater need for integration on the other, each human being with reasonable intelligence, with at least some talent and with energy is urgently needed to prepare the way for others by laying the foundations for a happy and prosperous life.

It is a terrifying thought that much of what could become available in the way of human knowledge and skill is now being turned to crime or used in some other way contrary to the interests of positive development. It is not solely for the sake of "equal opportunities" that the right to work for everyone who wants to work must be recognised, thus making widespread unemployment unacceptable, but also because it is gradually being realised that we are faced with an enormous task and that both from an individual and from a collective point of view it is no longer justified – either socially or economically – that part of the population is barred from the labour process.

It is a regrettable circumstance that in some cases minor unemployment constitutes a greater incentive to raise the labour output and will thus more easily result in a higher production than full employment and intelligent organisation. A lot of people still have to learn, without the threat of dismissal, to furnish a satisfactory labour output of their own free will, thereby justifying their own wage and contributing towards the prosperity of others.

It is gradually being appreciated that much remains to be done solely on account of the fact that some countries are in certain respects hundreds if not thousands of years behind compared with other countries. It is becoming clearer that timely and efficient aid to underdeveloped countries and particularly the promotion of mutual understanding might well prove to be two of the decisive factors for the future chances of life.

To qualify certain conditions as unfortunate and unacceptable is one thing, but to create new possibilities to put an end to these conditions is quite another. It is certain that any action to change untenable conditions must be based on a growing realisation that something must be done. It is also certain that we shall have to "build" a lot to make the whole world "habitable", thus creating the conditions necessary for everyone on this earth to "live".

3 Dangers threatening progress

*famine, disease, slums | rapid growth of the world popula-
tion | war and revolution | "mass-society" | primitive
social control | domination of engineering | failure of hous-
ing policy threatens the individual, the family and
society*

When a human being comes into this world the stage is already set for
him. His first lines are prompted, but from then on he is expected to
stand on his own feet. Fortunately, there are many aids which will assist
him to play his part: consciousness, *i.e.* the capacity to remember the past
and to anticipate the future and to denote objects and actions by symbols;
reason, enabling him to understand the world and imagination, with which
he can by far surpass the range of his senses.

Biologically, however, man is weaker than the animal, since he lacks
a fixed system of instincts with which he can adapt himself to the surrounding world.

Yet, he is capable of adapting himself to a certain extent to the space
available to him on earth by utilising the direct possibilities of life, such
as eating fruits, roots and tubers, hunting and fishing, sleeping in a cave
which happens to be available in the rocks or building primitive craft to
sail the oceans.

He can, however, also endeavour to acquire more than the earth directly
offers him by reorganising the earth by building and adapting the available
space to the growing number of inhabitants with their growing requirements.

The evolution of man shows us a constant interaction between these
two forms of adaptation, causing him to move away farther and farther
from the original more harmonious relationship with nature. He builds himself a world of his own, in which he endeavours to develop his life.

On this long road man is constantly surrounded by numerous dangers,
threatening his future. Whatever ideas one may have about the world and
its whys and wherefores, it is certainly not true that these dangers lie
outside the personal sphere of human responsibility, as if they were subject
to some mystic inevitability. Whether or not man will succeed in keeping
the dangers surrounding him under control depends to some extent also
on what wisdom, or stupidity for that matter, he is capable of bringing forth.
It is necessary, therefore, that man should realise more fully that, although

13

he cannot entirely foresee and control the future, the answer to the question of whether he can achieve a world habitable for everyone largely lies in his own hands.

The principal dangers which have always beset mankind are famine, disease, war and revolution.

Hence, the first condition for building a healthy community is to fight starvation. Starvation in all its forms still holds the lugubrious record of having caused the largest number of deaths. Despite all our knowledge and skill we have still not succeeded in conquering this enemy, which strikes at our world day in day out.

Formerly, starvation was regarded as a lack of sufficient food to satisfy the appetite and "to die of starvation" was understood only in the literal sense. The expression was used only in connection with the emaciated creatures who died in a famine for example. Josué de Castro [1], however, uses the term starvation in the modern sense, denoting the lack of any one of the forty constituents of food which are essential for human health. According to an American Commission, 85 per cent of the world population suffers from starvation in this sense.

The importance of food in daily life in some parts of the world is illustrated by the fact that Chinese farmers greet each other with the words "Have you eaten?" and when they take a fattened pig to the market the animal is tied to a pole and carried by two men all the way for fear that it will lose weight by walking.

Plans have been made or are being worked out to raise the food standard of all nations. In 1946 Lord Boyd Orr, then Director of the F.A.O., the Food and Agricultural Organization of the United Nations, tabled a proposal to establish a World Food Council, which would have to take the financial and technical measures necessary to reduce human privation and thus create a real demand on the world market. But unfortunately the time was not yet ripe for such a step and the plan was not realised. Owing to the lack of special powers the F.A.O. had to confine itself, as Le Gros Clark put it, to functioning as a world brain for all matters relating to production, distribution and consumption of foodstuffs and other products of land and sea.

In incidental cases much is being done, of course, within the framework of international technical assistance and the enthusiasm shown by the many experts carrying out their difficult and often thankless task in the hunger regions deserves a great deal of praise, but a comprehensive, clearly defined world action with a realistic long-term plan is still lacking. In this plan the greatest possible attention should be given to the essential

[1] Josué de Castro: *The Geography of Hunger*, London 1952.

14

transformation of the available space by hydraulic and civil engineering and the efficient use of such transformed space.

The primary object of the plan should not be to achieve greater productivity in the production of raw materials for export, but it should be primarily directed to development of the country on its own behalf.

The realisation of such a plan would require technical assistance directed to rational and scientific land use, reclamation of exhausted soil, industrial processing of local products and to projects for electrification, irrigation and transport.

The application of engineering and science in a suitable form and in assimilated quantities – due allowance being made for the specific nature and the local conditions of the population – as the Milbank Fund study [1] puts it, makes it possible to effect the economic liberation of such countries. Freed of the fear of hunger and while building, they will be transformed into areas with high productivity and full employment within the framework of a growing world economy.

With the aid of rather conservative calculations Robert Salter and Homer Shantz, experts of the American Agricultural Department, have demonstrated that about three hectares of arable land are available per head of the world population and according to the present-day views of agricultural and food experts about 0.8 hectare can furnish the indispensable constituents of a rational diet for one person. Hence, the physical possibilities for feeding a world population considerably greater than the present one are indeed available, but we have omitted to make full use of and improve our knowledge of engineering and science in the battle against hunger [2].

This battle against hunger in all its forms must be waged with all available means not only to make up for the present arrears, but because the accelerated drop in the death rate in recent decennia has made it more than likely that the world population will double itself during the period from 1958 to 2000.

The space available for food supply will consequently have to be quickly adapted on a world-wide scale to meet human requirements. At the same time a solution will have to be found to the difficult problem of regional agricultural surpluses.

Great sacrifices will have to be made, but it should be realised that we are concerned here with the most elementary principle of the development of a healthy society, in which free men can live together in peace.

Food may be essential for maintaining human health, but the battle against sickness should also be waged on many other fronts. It is the task

[1] *Milbank Memorial Fund, International Approaches to Problems of Undeveloped Areas.*
[2] *Colin Clark has calculated that the earth can provide enough food to feed 10 × the present world population, i.e. 28 milliard people (Nature, May 1958, World Population).*

of the World Health Organisation to promote the creation of adequate health care in all countries and to assist in establishing this care as much as lies in its power and, of course, as much as will be required by the countries concerned.

The recent history of health care in the Western countries has shown what can be achieved by purification of drinking water, improvement of sewage disposal and further application of available knowledge and experience gained elsewhere.

The growing international co-operation in the sphere of health care is one of the most encouraging pages in the world history of our century.

In this connection mention should be made of the Pan-American Sanitary Bureau founded in 1902, the International Health Department of the Rockefeller Foundation established in 1913, the Health Organisation of the League of Nations founded in 1933 and its Malaria Commission and finally the World Health Organisation of the United Nations referred to above, which in collaboration with many others is engaged in making the world a healthy place to live in. The funds of the International Bank for Reconstruction and Development are certainly not wasted if they are used for capital investments in essential projects on behalf of public hygiene, such as domestic water supply systems, because the economic power of a country is very closely associated with the health of its population [1].

Public health in the underdeveloped countries would benefit considerably if it were possible to build large numbers of simple but hygienic residential areas, efficient schools and a network of buildings of different size for health care.

Hence, it is building that is required. It will gradually reduce the dangers threatening the lives of many and at the same time introduce on earth a new and visible element of hope in the often hopeless world of the poor.

It is an urgent necessity that this matter should be given the closest attention, because both in the rural districts and in the large cities the housing conditions are untenable and the people in the underdeveloped areas are in serious danger. The following description of village housing, characteristic of India [2], speaks volumes:

"The village houses do offer some sort of shelter against sun and rain to dwellers, but they have no latrines, no protected water supply and no public cleansing. Men and cattle live in close proximity; mosquitoes and flies swarm; and rats abound in the huts and hovels. The interior of the house is generally clean, but the surroundings are dirty. The village pond

[1] G. E. A. Winslow: *The Cost of Sickness and the Price of Health;* World Health Organisation, Geneva 1951.

[2] *Ministry of Health (India), Report on the Environment Hygiene Committee, Simla 1950.*

16

is green with algae and is constantly polluted. The river is also used for all purposes and is polluted. The soil is polluted. The village school is noisy, poorly furnished and often devoid of urinals, latrines and drinking water. Hospitals and dispensaries are miles away, badly built, ill-equipped and inaccessible to the sick. The village market is held on the open ground, which is sodden in rains. Public eating houses are uncommon, but an insanitary tea shop or "coffee hotel" is easily found".

The shocking housing conditions in the large cities are clearly demonstrated in an account by the Bombay Housing Panel [1]:

"There are rooms so dark that even during the day the inmates cannot see each other in passages or in the single living rooms without the help of a light or fire. Fresh air is completely lacking. Very often there is no passage of air from room to room, many of which are built back to back. Ventilation is of the poorest standard imaginable. The single room serves as a living room, bedroom, sick-room, kitchen, dining room, etc. and to add to this the number of persons living in the single room ranges from four to ten. The sallow complexion, the emaciated body, the pale faces of the inmates immediately tell their tale. If further proof were needed, one has only to study the official vital statistics to understand the extent of the toll in human life taken by this ill-conceived housing, a good deal of which, even by the present inadequate and long obsolete standards laid down by the Old Municipal Act of 1888, can be classed as unfit for human habitation. It is tolerated because there is no alternative housing available and the inmates would be on the streets if the tenements are declared and marked unfit for human habitation".

Without wishing to detract in any way from the valuable efforts made in many spheres, it is evident that the task with which we are faced is enormous, seeing that nearly 200 million families [2] in the world live in

TABLE 1

STANDARDS OF LIVING IN OUR PRESENT-DAY WORLD

	Developed areas	Intermediate areas	Underdeveloped areas
Part of world population	1/5	<1/6	2/3
Annual income per head of population in U.S. dollars	461	154	41
Nourishment in calories per head per day	3040	2760	2150
Number of doctors per 100,000 inhabitants	106	78	17
Expected life at birth in years	63	52	30

[1] Housing Panel (Bombay), The Greater Bombay Scheme, Bombay 1946.
[2] See table 6, page 32.

this way. For a great part of the world it will be necessary to break the vicious circle of poverty, hunger and sickness, as may be seen from table 1. The figures in this table date back to about 1950 [1]:

During the last few decennia remarkable results have been achieved in various parts of the world, thanks to the efforts of the large organisations engaged in international health care. The miraculous results obtained in combatting malaria with D.D.T. deserve special mention. On the other hand, great victories have also been achieved with sulpha drugs, antibiotics and the like in the battle against various diseases. These results are all the more remarkable on account of the low cost per person. The amount which an American spends on a single haircut is enough to give a family in Bombay twelve months protection against malaria. There is no doubt that these successes have to a large extent been responsible for the accelerated drop in the death rate.

TABLE 2

AVERAGE DROP IN DEATH RATE [2]

Period	Expressed as a percentage of the figure for the previous period
1925 — 1929	6.0
1930 — 1934	4.6
1935 — 1939	6.3
1940 — 1944	8.5
1945 — 1949	19.2
1950 — 1954	20.1

The result of this accelerated drop in the death rate is beginning to cause great anxiety. Quite rightly, it is being asked whether the improvement in health care is not taking us from one untenable situation into another. Naturally, this cannot be used as an argument against the con-

TABLE 3

RATE OF INCREASE OF THE WORLD POPULATION [3]

Year	World population (in millions)	Average increase in previous period in %	Number of years required to double world population
1800	906		
1850	1171	0.53	135
1900	1608	0.64	110
1930	2013	0.75	93
1950	2476	1.04	67
1955	2691	1.68	42

[1] G. E. A. Winslow: The Cost of Sickness and the Price of Health; World Health Organisation, Geneva 1951.

[2] Figures of 18 noir-industrial countries from various parts of the world computed by Dr. Kingsley Davis.

[3] Statistical data in tables 3 and 4 from Statistical Yearbook United Nations.

18

tinuation of world health care or the battle against hunger. It is certain, however, that the rapid growth of the world population will not only aggravate the known problems, but will in addition place us before new, hitherto unforeseen difficulties.

The rate at which the world population is increasing at the present time has already had almost intolerable consequences and any further rapid rise in this rate would amount to a catastrophe.

The rapid growth of the world population is even more dangerous because the greatest increase chiefly occurs in places where it leads to the most serious difficulties, namely in the underdeveloped areas. In these areas there is already great poverty and certainly no shortage of manpower. Owing to the unequal increase in the various parts of the world, as illustrated in the table below, the difference in prosperity between the rich and the poor areas is threatening to become even more pronounced. Unless

TABLE 4

REGIONAL DIFFERENCES IN THE INCREASE OF THE POPULATION

Area	Annual increase in population expressed as a percentage (period 1951 — 1955)
World	1.7
Africa	2.2
North America	1.7
Central and South America	2.4
Asia	1.7
Europe	0.7
Oceania	2.3
U.S.S.R.	1.7

there is a marked drop in the birth rate, it looks as if we must come to the intolerable conclusion that the death rate should rise again rapidly.

What makes the situation even more difficult is that the people concerned are becoming more and more aware of this poverty. Modern means of communication enable them to see how others live without hunger and sickness and with a good chance to get on in the world.

They no longer regard this poverty as something unavoidable and expectations are raised to the effect that a better standard of living is possible also for them. In this dynamic era one can hardly ask these people to have patience for a few more centuries. Their world will also have to be changed noticeably in the not too distant future.

It is clear that serious shortages are not only a danger to the lives of the people suffering them, but constitute one of the most important causes of other threats to mankind, namely war and revolution. It is fortunate, therefore, that during the last few decennia hunger and sickness and the misery associated with them, which still harass the greater part of the world, have been receiving the attention they deserve, albeit in limited circles.

War and revolution have always been volubly and loudly discussed. Their praise has been sung in poetry, they have been proclaimed as factors of selection and attempts have even been made to prove on scientific grounds that wars are essential and in accordance with the laws of nature.

The calamities which during the last fifty years have cost the lives of millions do not particularly lend themselves to poetical glorification and the only aspect which from the point of view of the victims could be remotely associated with selection is perhaps the fact that in modern warfare they are selected indiscriminately from among men and women, adults and children, old people and babies, soldiers and officers, labourers and intellectuals.

This has made war lose its attraction for everyone, the more so since no one can derive any permanent gain from it. In regard to the technique of warfare the trend of development is such that to most countries full participation in the rearmament race means economic ruin, while both the continuation of experiments with nuclear weapons and the starting of a modern war amount to suicide.

"The weapons have become too expensive and too dangerous." said Mac-Millan, the British Prime Minister, in March 1957 before he and his experts left for the Bermudas to discuss world politics with President Eisenhower. This is indeed the last word after thousands of years of wars and other armed conflicts, but it is by no means certain that we have become wise enough to prevent our ruin.

It is certain, however, that if man wants to dispose of the great dangers surrounding him and to strive energetically for a healthier society, he must establish two basic conditions, viz. peace and freedom from the fear of war. In this connection it should be borne in mind that freedom and independent civilisation are other basic conditions for that society. These, however, are not threatened by force of arms alone. Much that is valuable is also threatened in other ways. The cause of this lies in the rate at which many old relationships are wholly or partly being dissolved or threaten to turn into new relationships without the most valuable and indispensable qualities of the old being integrated in the new.

In this newly developing "mass-society" the crowd has in recent decennia suddenly come to the fore. Everything has become noticeably fuller. The cities are full of people, the houses full of occupants, the schools full of children. The hospitals are full of patients, the streets full of pedestrians and motor cars. What was never a difficulty before the first world war is now almost a constant worry: to find a place.

Formerly a crowd, if it existed at all, remained unnoticed. It stood in the background of the social stage, but now it has advanced up to the foot-lights and has become the leading actor.

There need be no danger in this at all, provided this leading part involves that with all available means the masses are absorbed in the effort to attain greater prosperity and a better chance of a happy life. In any case the possibility of achieving this should not be confined to a small minority, as was often the case in former times and still is in many parts of the world.

Yet, in another respect there is a great danger in the trend outlined above, especially in the unity of purpose of the masses (not to be confused with the workers), which promotes the formation of hordes [1], quite apart from the fact that such masses can very easily fall a victim to a criminal minority, as recent history has clearly demonstrated. The masses do not hide their mediocrity and there is a real danger that a certain plainness is forced upon the society as a whole. This may result in all that is different, elevated, individual, meritorious and select, thus the most valuable qualities of all sections of the population, being trampled upon. It might even go so far that life would be governed by the motto "To be different is indecent".

The means recognised by socio-psychologists and sociologists to counteract the dangers of mass formation arising from rapid technical progress and greater prosperity and to give the increasing impersonalisation and asociality a positive turn, can only be realised if there is an adequate number of good houses and residential areas with schools, buildings for culture and recreation, sports grounds and other recreational facilities. It is only then that the individual and the small communities into which our crowded world is split up can be given a real chance – by being alone and joining purposefully in communal life – to promote human feeling towards fellow men and spontaneous creativity, which are now in danger of being lost.

Apart from the idea of "mass-society", great dangers attach to the manner in which this society is ultimately organised. For, in our efforts to achieve a new equilibrium, a social technique on a par with our present-day technology and scientific knowledge, we are faced with great difficulties. These difficulties are all the greater because allowance must be made all the time for new facts, which threaten to change the course and render the road ahead uncertain. It is clear that our world is rapidly moving from a period of "laisser faire, laisser aller" to an era in which planned thought and action are beginning to play an ever greater part. It is also clear that in recent decennia the masses have acquired very great power.

It is not clear, however, where the centre of gravity of our social

[1] Ortéga y Gasset: La rebelión de las masas, Madrid 1930.

21

organisation will lie. Will the control of the agents of production continue to be organised largely on a capitalistic basis, will it become more and more socialised or are we approaching the era of managers [1]? Whatever the trend may be, the individual and the society are constantly threatened by dangers. The freedom of the individual to express himself by taking the initiatives either alone or in concert with others, can be lost if it turns out that a planned society must of necessity be accompanied by a strangling bureaucracy.

The freedom of the consumer can be endangered by excessive power of production directed to profit-making. His interests can be crushed by excessive influence of power groups, representing specific group interests.

Rationalism can become a dangerous dogma and crowd out many valuable things in no way associated with the intellect. The wish to cherish these things, however, should not lead to failure to use the intellectual powers of man to attain guaranteed freedom in various spheres, as it is precisely mental indolence [2] which is likely to endanger the things we cherish most.

The enormous technical progress made, which is actually still gathering momentum, can be a blessing to mankind, provided an all-out effort is made quickly to achieve a controlled and balanced further development. It will be appreciated that the growth of technical skill is becoming increasingly dangerous as long as there is the slightest chance of this skill being directed to destruction instead of to building up a new society.

This constructive process will also be endangered unless an effort is made to develop a social technique which guarantees that the growing economic facilities are used to attain a higher standard of living for all.

The outbreak of a war is a possibility which we must constantly bear in mind. A substantial part of the world income must be spent on armaments and the like. Even now destruction by acts of war is a daily occurrence. All these things are due to the fact that up till now too many human potentialities have been spent on technological and scientific development and too little on the development of the moral powers inherent in man. This has resulted in a general disproportionality in the development of human capacities, so that in some respects man possesses a technical skill which has by far outgrown his moral power and which is accompanied by an inadequate insight into the workings of social forces. This condition of unbalance is also noticeable in human society proper, since the morality and the sound judgement necessary to solve the social and economic problems are not uniformly represented in all groups and classes. This unbalance constitutes a growing danger to the happiness and the pros-

[1] Burnham James: *The Managerial Revolution*, New York 1941.
[2] Karl Mannheim: *Man and Society in an Age of Reconstruction*, New York, London 1951.

perity of the individual in general, because interdependence increases as further progress is made in science and engineering.

The interdependence of the various countries becomes greater because almost any country exhibiting a positive economic development requires raw materials and finished products from numerous other countries and conversely must find export markets for its own products.

The progress in engineering likewise makes the individual more and more dependent on other individuals, each group dependent on other groups and each class dependent on other classes. A prolonged strike of the métro and other means of transport in Paris will not only affect practically the whole population of the French capital and such tourists as may be present in the city, but it will soon have a noticeable effect on others in France and abroad who have direct or indirect economic relations with Paris. There is no sense in building skyscrapers unless one can be reasonably certain that there will always be a supply of electric power to operate the lifts and other essential technical provisions and that the lift attendants will not continually go on strike.

All the dangers which beset the greater part of mankind every day and the misery which is its lot, the poor social organisation and the unbalance bearing down on it have been dramatically expressed by man himself in the manner in which he has built many of his cities and villages. Fortunately, there are also good examples of how it should be done, but even so there are still too many people on this earth who do not live in a habitable world.

War and occupation have taught the people of our western world that at many things which in everyday life we take for granted are not assessed their true value until we have to do without them. The great importance of a proper dwelling, of daily life in a properly laid-out neighbourhood and of many other things associated with building was perhaps not fully appreciated until we felt the impact of the substantial shortage of buildings – especially of dwellings – which resulted directly and indirectly from acts of war.

It was not until then that the people of the western countries started to realise that every human being is entitled to a roof over his head and that the activities to which we refer when we speak of building are of fundamental importance to the world of to-day.

Since the late war it has become evident that in some respects we are earnestly trying to accept the basic principles of a democratic world. We are beginning to realise that the condition of unbalance of the past, which is no longer compatible with our growing interdependence, constitutes in effect a source of real danger to all and that we should build a world which affords each individual a reasonable chance to live.

Now – fifteen years after the second world war – much has been repaired and newly built with an energy which cannot be praised enough and greater prosperity has been achieved in many countries. But throughout the world there is one sphere in which there is still a serious shortage, which endangers a balanced economic and social development. Even in the countries with the highest level of prosperity we cannot build enough to fulfil reasonable requirements. No statistics are needed to prove this. One need only take a walk through the overpopulated slums of New York, Chicago, Paris, Rome or in any other large city, make a journey through the rural districts of southern Italy or Georgia in the United States or try to rent a small flat at a reasonable price in any of the large cities. This situation is also clearly illustrated by the increasing traffic difficulties and parking problems in and around the centres of large cities.

It is true to say that in the post-war years we have not succeeded in working out and putting into practice the methods and means necessary to realise to an adequate extent what we consciously or subconsciously felt to be one of the greatest problems of reconstruction and improvement in the western part of the world, i.e. to give the people, in addition to food and clothing, a sufficient number of good houses and other essential buildings. It is becoming clearly evident how this failure has adversely affected the mental and physical health of the people. The great shortage of all kinds of buildings and especially the inability to make up for this shortage quickly are undermining the vitality and the chances of many.

In crowded houses, for example, the death rate of children is high. Slums form a breeding ground for criminality and asocial conditions. The development of family life is seriously hampered either by the absence of a private home or by having to live in a slum. It is alarming to note the high percentage of families in many countries who experience daily the serious drawbacks of a dwelling which has such serious defects that the fundamental conditions for life and home-making are endangered.

Crowded schools seriously lower the standard of education. Bad roads cause the number of deaths, injuries and material damage to rise beyond acceptable limits. The struggle against hunger is an insolvable problem without dams, irrigation systems, dikes and other works.

It would not be difficult to go on like this and to prove the extent to which the shortage of buildings affects almost every sphere of social, economic and cultural life. We are not threatened by the shortage of buildings alone. Psychologically speaking, we are also attacked in our older towns and villages by the combination of confusing remnants of centuries, which – with a few exceptions – have not retained sufficient practical or other value for the present, with a number of generally abominable, opportunistic, technical solutions of the last hundred years [1].

[1] *Richard Neutra: Survival through Design, New York 1957.*

24

This is all the more true since the demonic dynamics of modern transport – often taxing our senses to the limit – have been introduced into these unharmonious surroundings, which are no longer in any way compatible with our modern way of life. It is understandable that the formation of hordes is promoted by the excessively large cities, where everything is crowded and where human beings are packed in tenement houses, in overcrowded public transport and the like, in such a way that the individual is ultimately only satisfied if he is no different from anybody else.

There is a danger that war and revolution will be seen as the only way out by those who are compelled to live in the putrid atmosphere of the slum, the more so since the people there are becoming more and more aware of their poverty and their expectations in respect of a change for the better are sharply rising.

It is not surprising, therefore, that in an increasing number of countries the programme of the government or those of the political parties include such important items as promotion of house-building, redevelopment of old city centres, the building of schools, road-construction and the like.

But to give the world at once a new skeleton and a new face more is needed than building on the scale now possible and with the conventional methods.

Great national and international action will be necessary, directed towards achieving increased production and a higher standard of controlled quality. Such controlled quality must incorporate the important element of foresight. This foresight is needed to attain a habitable world according to the standards of the next generation.

Apart from the different means required to achieve this aim, there will be a demand for people capable of creating the proper atmosphere for a new approach in order to realise what practically all the people in the world are longing for, namely the replacement of destruction and the fear thereof by construction and the hope of a habitable world.

4   Towards a habitable world

man is formed by family life and school education | a dwelling of optimum quality a necessity | schools an integral part of our town planning |"builders" wanted | a milliard new dwellings alone must be built in this century | the world can afford this investment, provided national incomes continue to rise and armaments expenditure shows a relative decrease

The personality of man is formed in the first instance by the particular way of life with which he is confronted as a child in the home, which generally reflects all the characteristics of the society concerned. This way of life is strongly influenced by the space in which it develops: the dwelling, the street and the neighbourhood in which man spends his daily life, and the school, where the young people are for the greater part of the day in contact with others of the same age.

Good housing, *i.e.* well-planned and well-built dwellings, streets and neighbourhoods are of inestimable importance for the development of the young child. Slums could well be regarded as the "democratic" version of Hitler's concentration camps, because anyone doomed to live in a slum seldom emerges from it unharmed.

However, the fact that the development of man's personality is to a very large extent determined by the specific nature of the economic system, since the absolute law of self-preservation dictates the conditions under which he must live, does not mean that he should not strive in concert with others for certain political and economic changes.

The relationship between man and society is not static, because with his capacity to look ahead man can by education and experience prepare himself for the next social phase still hidden in the future.

In the development from infant to young adult, who sets out to make his contribution towards the society, there are, in addition to good health, two links of exceptional importance: family life and school education. These should moreover be closely tied up.

To achieve family life directed to the society of the future it will be necessary for greater attention to be given to the enormous responsibility which in this respect rests on the shoulders of the mothers and fathers throughout the world.

Family life cannot develop along sound lines unless a proper dwelling is available, where it is possible to be both alone and together, where life within the family can come to full development and a sound relationship

27

is promoted between the family and its individual members on the one hand and the society with all its possibilities on the other by the proper location of the dwelling in neighbourhood and town.

A good dwelling, according to the standards of the higher developed countries, should guarantee [1]:

A. HEALTH AND SECURITY
1. adequate protection against cold, damp and noise;
2. adequate ventilation, access of sun and light;
3. adequate facilities for personal hygiene;
4. adequate facilities for cleaning clothes and articles for domestic use;
5. supply of water for drinking and washing, discharge of faeces and waste water.

B. INDEPENDENCE
1. adequate separation of the individual rooms, etc. and of dwellings from each other;
2. adequate sound insulation.

C. FACILITIES
   adequate space for:
1. working: cooking, sewing, hobbies, study and doing special work;
2. rooms: sitting together, having meals together, recreation, receiving visitors;
3. sleeping: proper bedroom for parents, with adequate privacy; room for cradle and baby care; proper accommodation for the sick and for lying-in mothers; separate bedrooms for boys and girls;
4. storage: articles for daily use, a stock of foodstuffs, seasonal clothing and bed clothes.

D. CONTACT WITH SOCIAL LIFE
1. adequate accessibility: location along paved roads or paths, accessible for deliveries, transport of the sick, help from neighbours;
2. adequate facilities in the neighbourhood for the necessities of life, health care, education and practicing religion;
3. recreation and culture (so-called district provisions);
4. adequate differentiation in size and type of dwellings in the district, so that a harmonious society develops according to age and social structure;

[1] H. M. Buskens, Director-General of Housing and Building in the Netherlands in an address delivered at the Congress of the International Federation of Christian Trade Unions, Blankenberge, Belgium, 1957.

5. adequate orientation with respect to the community: general situation in neighbourhoods and areas, communication with work centres and town and village centres; communal buildings, parks and play-grounds;
6. adequate adaptation of the housing standard and "standing" of the neighbourhood to the occupations of the occupants.

More and more people are needed with a high standard of intelligence, because in developing countries the centre of gravity of human work is shifting from agriculture via industry to services, so that an increasing number of brain workers will be required[1].

People are wanted to distribute the arsenal of knowledge throughout the world, because a balanced distribution in this sphere is one of the basic requirements for a healthy society. For this reason we shall have to search among all sections of the population for the talented, so as to avoid wastage of this valuable raw material.

It will be easier to achieve this if we have good schools in the right place, *i.e.* in the centres of neighbourhood and town. These schools must form integral parts of our town planning, just as education forms an integral part of our lives, thus promoting a close co-operation between school and family. The schools should form an essential part of the space transformed by human hands, where order, beauty and science ensure that what the child sees daily is not in contrast with what it is told in preparation for its future life. In these schools the young people should in small groups learn to preserve their individuality and yet to prepare themselves by contact with a number of others in a team to play together, learn together, co-operate and live together.

Thus, in the family and in the school the young person is prepared for his further life and it should be borne in mind that this implies preparation both for his occupational task and for life outside his occupation. Both these aspects should be given attention, especially since there is every reason to believe that in the future the time spent on the occupational task will become shorter. Even now it will be necessary to make allowance both for the transition from handwork to mechanisation, which in many areas of the world and in many occupations is in full swing, and for the second industrial revolution, which will bring about automation and even shorter working hours.

Occupation and spare time activity can together form a basis for a healthy society even in an automised world.

To achieve this it is necessary to draw up exacting requirements for the dwelling and its surroundings, the school and its surroundings, the factory

[1] *Colin Clark: The Economics of 1960, London 1951.*

and the recreation facilities provided in and outside the dwelling, but especially for the integration of these elements of life in the town-plan.

Automised production and the associated short working hours need not present any difficulties in this respect, provided the travelling time to and from work does not become so long – as is the case in many large cities – that a considerable part of the spare time is spent "under way" in a tiring and costly manner.

A lot of spare time involves special requirements with regard to the accessibility from the home to the community centres, the sports grounds, the parks and any other buildings made suitable for recreational purposes.

To be able to achieve all this it will be necessary to do a lot of "building" and what we need therefore is "builders". These builders should be able to understand that such a complex problem can be solved only by an approach based on planning, in which the art of decision is supported by the knowledge of decision, the "decisionics". It is not surprising, therefore, that in recent decennia planning has more and more been introduced in our thinking and actions. If we accept planning in industry, realising that it just cannot function properly without it, it will be clear that this method is also indispensable in our efforts to create a habitable world, which is far more complex than an industrial concern.

There is, however, one main condition that must be fulfilled, namely that the individual must be afforded the greatest possible freedom. For a plan of social control in a human society it will be necessary to ascertain carefully to what extent individual freedom can be brought into agreement with the requirements of a properly functioning society in order that the new society we are in search of will furnish a new freedom, in which the independent responsibility of individual and group are integrated.

The effort to achieve a balanced development will be considerably easier if the scientific work is placed on a wide basis. In the past too much attention has been given to technical research, of which the direct importance is clearly obvious. Too little attention has been given to the social, psychological, biological and other problems, especially those directly related with human life in all its aspects.

This unbalance especially finds expression in the material environment we have created for ourselves. It should be realised, however, that our life and our material environment cannot be separated, but that they form a whole. Consequently, in our effort to create a better world we cannot develop a healthy dynamic trend in totally inadequate surroundings.

To achieve a habitable world a great deal of building will have to be done, both in the literal and in the figurative sense. With building in the literal sense we are also faced with great difficulties. The building capacity available in the world is limited, while the actual – for the greater part urgent – need of buildings is practically unlimited, although only a small part of this need finds expression in a concrete demand backed by capital.

"Builders" are wanted who can make the world habitable within the span of a few generations. Millions of people will have to co-operate and be prepared to make a sacrifice in order to save the world from destruction and hunger and themselves from being overrun by the frustrated masses, who are waiting in vain for the fulfilment of their expectation of an improved standard of living.

All available forces will, therefore, have to be mobilised to attain with the least possible delay a world habitable for everyone in the literal sense. This object cannot be achieved by an idealistic cry alone, however great the effect may be. It will have to be a matter of cool calculation to ascertain what this cry actually involves. This will reveal the basic condition which must be fulfilled before realisation can be attempted, namely that full constructive development can only be obtained after destruction has been forced as far as possible into the background.

There will be few people who will not agree that hunger and sickness must be combatted with all available means and that education, work and recreation should be given such attention as to ensure a reasonable chance for everyone to achieve individual development and to learn to live with others in harmony. If on the other hand it is realised that this can only be achieved when the whole of the world's population is reasonably housed and the available space has been transformed in such a way that sufficient arable land becomes available for a healthy world, many people will be inclined to say that the necessary means for this are lacking.

It is impossible to calculate accurately how much building must be done to attain a world habitable for everyone in the year 2000. The available statistical data are far too inadequate for this purpose and long-term prognoses involve too many uncertain factors, especially as regards the growth of the world population and the increase in prosperity. Accurate calculations are not necessary; it would be sufficient to acquire some insight into the order of magnitude involved.

Suitable starting points for an attempt to gain this insight would be an estimate of the world population in the years 2000 and 2050 and an estimate of the present state of world housing. This provides a basis for drawing up tables 5 and 6.

31

TABLE 5

WORLD POPULATION AND HOUSING

Years	World population in milliards	Size of family	Number of families in millions	Number of dwellings in millions	Number of persons per dwelling
1—1—1958	2.8	4.8	580	500	5.6
1—1—2000	5.6 *	4.5	1245	1100 (A)	5.1
1—1—2050	8.4 **	4.2	2000	1800	4.7

*It has been assumed that the further drop in the death rate will on an average be compensated by the drop in the birth rate and that the increase in the population in the period 1958-2000 will therefore, relatively speaking, be equal to that of the period 1950-1955 (see table 3).
**It has been assumed that in that period the population will on an average increase by 56 millions per year.

It can be safely assumed that a considerable part (ca. 40%) of the available dwellings are slum dwellings of the worst type, especially in south-east Asia (150 millions) and South America (30 millions), while in the rest of the world there are at least 20 million slum dwellings, which should disappear as quickly as possible.

Assuming the average life of a house in the future to be fifty years, the houses built after 1950 need not be replaced before the year 2000 (ca. 50 millions), while it can be further assumed that in addition a small part of the world housing stock (ca. 10%) will be reasonably fit for use in the year 2000.

On the strength of the foregoing it is possible to indicate the state of world housing in table 6.

TABLE 6

STATE OF WORLD HOUSING ON JANUARY 1, 1958

Quality of dwellings	Number of dwellings in millions
Should be replaced as quickly as possible	200
Do not fulfil reasonable requirements to be made in the year 2000 or should be replaced before then for other reasons.	200
Reasonable to good; need not be replaced before the year 2000.	100 (B)

It is now evident from tables 5 and 6 that in order to ensure reasonable housing for everyone in the year 2000 it will be necessary to build 1000 million dwellings in the present century, viz. 1100 million (A, table 5) less 100 million (B, table 6).

TABLE 7

ESTIMATED HOUSE-BUILDING IN 1957

Areas	Number of dwellings completed in millions
Europe, including Soviet Russia	4.3
North and South America	1.7
Rest of the world	2.0
Total:	8.0

To attain in the year 2000 a world housing stock of 1100 million dwellings of reasonable quality, it will be necessary to build in the forty-two years available roughly 25 million dwellings per year. Seeing that it will take a few decennia to attain a production of this size, it will be clear that in the second half production will have to be considerably greater than 25 million dwellings per year. This is especially necessary, because in the period 2000–2050 production will also have to be considerably greater than 25 million dwellings per year and consequently a higher rate of production must be attained at the end of the present century. In view of the enormous arrears production must be increased as quickly as possible and for this reason the relative increase in production in the first part of the period has been assumed to be higher than in the second part.

Such a production scheme is shown in table 8, from which it will be seen that in the last period production has risen to the level which will on an average be necessary during the following 50 years.

TABLE 8

PRODUCTION SCHEME HOUSE-BUILDING 1958-1999

Period	Average number of dwellings built per year in millions	Total number of dwellings in millions
1958 — 1969	approx. 12 (8—16)	140
1970 — 1979	21 (16—26)	210
1980 — 1989	30 (26—34)	300
1990 — 1999	35 (34—36)	350
1958 — 1999		1000

Assuming now that in the period 2000–2049 the life of a house will be put at 50 years and consequently the whole stock of dwellings available at the beginning of the year 2000 must be replaced and that to cover the increase in population the world stock of dwellings at the end of this period

TABLE 9

PRODUCTION OF DWELLINGS IN PERIOD 2000-2049 (IN MILLIONS)

	Replacement	Increase	Total
Built in period 2000 — 2049	1100	700	1800
Built per year	22	14	36

will have to be 1800 millions, it will be evident that during the whole of this period the average production will have to be 36 million dwellings per year.

A balanced development of our human society cannot be achieved by building dwellings alone. Numerous other types of buildings will be necessary, such as schools, hospitals, churches, factories, workshops, shops, etc.

In addition, considerable building activity will have to be displayed in the spheres of civil and hydraulic engineering for the construction of roads, ports, airfields, bridges, locks, dams, dikes, irrigation systems, etc. and for everything associated with the transport of gas, electricity and water and for discharging waste products. The total volume of building required can in terms of money be estimated at $2\frac{1}{2}$ times house-building.

Thus, again expressed in terms of money, the total volume of building realised in 1957 was $2\frac{1}{2} \times 8$ million dwellings = 20 million dwellings. It is estimated that this required 75 milliard dollars in all.

In 1999 the amount required for this will be roughly 300 milliard dollars, since the volume of building will have to be $4\frac{1}{2}$ times as great. It is true that the quality will have to fulfil more stringent requirements, but in view of possible rationalisation and the fact that, relatively speaking, more building will be done in areas where cost prices are low, it would seem that four times the amount of 1957 would be sufficient.

The total amount of the gross civil investments can be put at twice the figure of 300 milliards mentioned above, so that in 1999 these will require 600 milliards in all. Hence, the sum of the national incomes will

TABLE 10

GROSS INVESTMENTS EXPRESSED AS A PERCENTAGE OF THE NATIONAL INCOME

Category	Percentage
House-building	4
Other buildings	4
Civil and hydraulic engineering	2
Other gross investment	10
Total:	20

have to be 3000 milliards, assuming that the gross civil investments constitute at most 20 per cent of this sum.

What we are concerned with, therefore, is an increase in the sum of the national incomes of the world from 900 milliards in 1957 to 3000 milliards in 1999.

This means that this sum should on an average rise by 3 per cent. per year. Assuming that the capital coefficient (ratio of net investments to increase in national income) is high, *viz.* 4, seeing that considerable investments will be required for house-building, education, recreation and the like and a large proportion of the investments will not immediately have a noticeable effect on productivity, it follows that the net investments should amount to $4 \times 3\% = 12\%$ of the sum of the national incomes, which roughly corresponds to 20% gross investments.

The above estimates are shown in table 11.

TABLE 11

WORLD INCOME AND INVESTMENTS (IN MILLIARDS OF DOLLARS)

Period	Sum of national incomes	Total gross civil investments	Armaments	Gross investments in building and civil engineering	Total housebuilding
1957	900	150	80	75	30
1999	3000	600	?	300	120

In 1957 dwellings cost on an average $ 3750 each and for the end of the century this figure has been put at $ 3330, allowance having been made for a higher standard of housing comfort, lower cost prices due to rationalisation and a relatively much higher percentage of dwellings built in regions where cost prices are lowest due to low cost of labour, simple construction and special forms of organisation.

This average price for the whole world is only of arithmetical value in the case of very rough calculations such as the present.

Owing to differences in quality, level of costs, climate and the like the price of "low-cost housing", with which we are chiefly concerned here, ranges from 200 [1] to 2000 dollars each in the densely populated and poor tropical and sub-tropical regions, from 3000 to 5000 dollars each in Europe and from 8000 to 10,000 dollars each in the United States of America.

Making the world habitable for all before the end of the present century needs more than just a 3% increase in the total world income per year. It also necessitates a change in the geographical distribution of income.

Since the greater part of the population in the poor countries live on the borderline of minimum existence and because it is precisely in these

[1] *Minimum investment in case of intensive "aided self-help".*

countries that on an average the population there increases by 2% per annum, they can themselves just save – and thus invest – enough to keep the income per head of population about the same. In the rich countries, where the population increases on an average by 1% per year, it is possible to invest sufficiently to raise the level of prosperity even further.

Without international aid the distribution of income would develop as set out in table 12.

TABLE 12

DEVELOPMENT OF INCOME WITHOUT INTERNATIONAL AID

	Population in millions		Total income in milliards of $		Income per head in $	
	1.1.1958	1.1.2000	1957	1999 (without aid)	1957	1999 (without aid)
Rich countries (North America, Australia, New Zealand, Europe and U.S.S.R.)	830	1200	730	2620	880	2180
Poor countries (Latin America, Africa, Asia)	1970	4400	170	380	85	85
Total	2800	5600	900	3000		

Without international aid, therefore, the poor countries cannot make sufficient economic investments and certainly cannot do much to improve the social infrastructure. Moreover, the increasing tension in the international distribution of income would probably lead to disastrous results long before the end of this century.

As is already being done to an increasing extent, the rich countries would then have to develop a capital movement to the poor countries in such volume that at least relatively an equal rise in income would result. This clearly demonstrates the enormous difficulties caused by the rapid growth of the population in the underdeveloped countries.

The rich countries can effect this capital movement to the poor countries by public and private gifts and loans at a low rate of interest and moreover by loans on normal terms, as well as by foreign private investments.

The essential point is, however, that the rich countries should be prepared to make a sacrifice in order to improve the future income in the poor countries. The result of this will be that the growth of the income in the rich countries will be slowed down.

There are three possibilities to bring this about in the rich countries: by reducing consumption, by reducing investments for civil purposes or by reducing investments in armaments. The third possibility makes it possible not only to start the underdeveloped going, but also to meet many urgent requirements in the rich countries with a view to creating there also a habitable world for all.

In 1957 a sum of 230 milliard dollars in all (see table 11) was spent on civil investments and armaments. This represents more than 25 per cent of the sum of the net national incomes. Hence, if it were possible gradually to reduce the costs of armaments to $4\frac{1}{2}$ per cent of the world income, it would also be possible to an increasing extent to make available large sums of money for extra constructional activities in the countries concerned and in the underdeveloped countries.

A five-year plan would then roughly look as follows:

TABLE 13

Year	1 sum of national incomes* in milliards of $	2 Armaments expenditure expressed as per-centage of 1	3 Armaments expenditure 2 in milliards of $	4 Armaments expenditure at constant perc. of 9 in milliards of $	5 4—3 in milliards of $
1960	983	9.0	88	88	0
1961	1013	8.1	82	91	9
1962	1043	7.2	75	94	19
1963	1075	6.3	68	97	29
1964	1107	5.4	60	100	40
1965	1140	4.5	51	103	52
Total 1961 — '65			336	485	149

* Assuming an annual increase of 3% (1957: 900 milliard dollars).

If each country were proportionally to reduce its present armaments expenditure, an amount of nearly 150 milliard dollars would be available in five years time, which amount could be spent for a considerable part on an effort towards achieving a habitable world. This amount would be sufficient to revive hope, practical idealism and the like by a visible effect. This will be necessary if we want to call a halt to hunger and sickness and to open new perspectives for everyone, thereby providing a powerful stimulant for what we are really trying to achieve: increased productivity of the individual and of the population as a whole on behalf of our effort to build a world habitable for all.

*two questions | one answer: we must! | we must build |
greater forces to be mobilised | a practical ideal | stimu-
lating effect of visible achievement | a world problem*

There are, in principle, two main questions which must be answered.
Firstly, can we gradually eliminate the most active form of destruction:
war, the armaments associated with war, and revolution, without endanger-
ing our freedom, and, secondly, are we likely to use the means and forces
which become available for building up a healthy society in our own
country and in the underdeveloped countries, thus forcing destruction
even more into the background?

When we consider the first question we should fully realise that as
regards intensity a future world war may and probably will assume hitherto
unknown proportions.

Sorokin has worked out century index figures of war intensity. These
figures have been derived from the number of wars, weighed according
to the numbers of killed and wounded, the number of countries involved
and the percentage of soldiers with reference to the total population. He
arrives at the following picture:

TABLE 14

WAR INTENSITY

Century	12th	13th	14th	15th	16th	17th	18th	19th	20th*
Weighed index figures	18	24	60	100	180	500	370	120	3080

* *Up to 1940.*

There is no doubt that the intensity figure of the second world war would
be appreciably higher than 3080 and that a future world war, in which
the aggressor cannot defend himself and the victim can only undertake a
counter-attack, would produce a figure of an entirely different order of
magnitude. With these facts in front of us we cannot possibly resign our-

39

selves to this situation under the motto: "There is nothing we can do about it" or just be satisfied with some theory or other which holds that war is unavoidable and that consequently we are not responsible for it.

However important history may be in many respects, we shall have to turn our back on it as far as war is concerned. Instead, we shall have to turn our eye to the future and make every effort to avoid another total world war which would reduce the population so severely that a logarithmic scale would be needed to incorporate the war intensity figure of the present century in the same graph as those of the previous centuries.

This means, therefore, that the answer to the two questions can only be the following. It is not important whether we can or cannot, want to or do not want to; we simply must.

We should be prepared, however, to make our constructive efforts on the same scale and with the same thorough planning as we are accustomed to do for the preparations for and the act of destruction. It is quite safe to assume that, if we systematically replace destructive production by constructive production, there will certainly be no lack of marketing possibilities. The poverty and the want in the world are too great for that.

Even the argument that in a case like this we would – especially at first – have to supply a great deal without payment is not very important, as long as we spend less than we are now spending on destructive production.

Moreover, there will then be a good chance of creating a higher demand backed by capital for things which are of direct service to a healthy world.

Another important element in all this is whether the developed countries can help without disturbing the essential values of the assisted countries. This requires a great understanding and knowledge of the cultural situation in these countries, because otherwise it will be impossible properly to match the new with the old, which might lead to disruption. It is also important that the assisted country should realise that money is not a magic charm, but that it is essentially a matter of own achievement and that acquired liberties will not result in greater prosperity unless new relationships – acceptable to all parties concerned – are brought about.

Those responsible for giving technical assistance will therefore have to be thoroughly trained for the correct performance of their task.

At a meeting held in New Delhi in 1956 one of the organisations of the United Nations, the Unesco, accepted as plan 4 a proposal made by India to the effect that the evaluation of cultural values between East and West should be promoted; this can be of exceptional importance for the future development of world peace.

A better understanding of how the other lives or wants to live is not only necessary for bridging the gap between East and West, but valuable for everyone in his daily surroundings, in his town and country and in the part of the world in which he lives. This holds good, of course, if we want to promote that people everywhere should "live" together, *i.e.* live in a community in the true sense of the word.

Only if we can achieve this will it be possible to increase what we possess and to improve the way we use it, so as to give our society the foundation of the elevated standard of civilisation and culture which will lead to the victory of construction over destruction.

But this needs more than a great effort on the part of a very small minority composed of a few leading politicians, a number of leading intellectuals and a small group of idealists whose thinking rises above the everyday level.

Man will now soon have to make up his mind to put his assets to good use. Whereas formerly he could afford to be foolish because he was not in danger, now there are only two possibilities to choose from: the road of progress or the abyss.

The road of progress means the difficult way towards a world of the correct social and psychological dimensions. This road can never be successfully followed if our actions are confined to long discussions at international meetings with at best a sympathetic vague resolution or the provision of means absolutely inadequate for doing anything of practical value to solve the concrete and urgent problems with which we are faced. In this case not much more can happen than is already happening now, gladdening and valuable in itself, but not enough.

All that is done in the theoretical and idealistic spheres, such as the attempts to attain an international system of law, the promotion of human rights, moral rearmament, world federalism and the like are not given a fair chance, owing to the small scale on which matters are set up.

If we want to set greater forces in motion to achieve much greater action, we shall have to convince many, especially young people. It should be realised, however, that words will then not be sufficient, but that great deeds with a convincing effect will be essential.

The difficulty in recruiting sufficient supporters lies in the fact that reality is constantly in contradiction with the ideals cherished and that for many people it is difficult, when surrounded by so many things that are not as they should be, to be sure that they are on the right road.

And yet a moderate optimism is justified, because there are sufficient indications of a growing desire for a new and practical ideal, an ideal that can stimulate large sections of the population into taking action, whereby it becomes reality.

41

War and occupation have taught us that suddenly, as by a miracle, people can become united and together, irrespective of religion, conception of life, politics or colour, can achieve a close system of co-operation and action, but in that case there is almost invariably a common enemy to be conquered.

What we need is not a common effort which ultimately results in one human being destroying another or something belonging to him and finds satisfaction in doing so. On the contrary, what we should look for is something which enables one human being to build up something for the other in such a way that it is a source of satisfaction to both. This should be a constructive aim, which – in addition to providing the beneficial effect of an inspiring picture of the future – produces the enormous stimulating effect of visible achievement.

The post-war years have shown that for a short time it is sometimes possible to inspire a large number of people to take part in a joint action, such as clearing up or building up something. In the cities which were destroyed and are now being reconstructed there is even to-day some evidence of a common ideal, which joins people together and brings them happiness.

In a case like this we see a decisive victory of pure construction over destruction, whereby reconstruction in a wider sense becomes possible. These post-war years have made us realise how important building really is, not merely because in the more highly developed countries it is a source of livelihood for about 10 per cent of the population, but also because we cannot stage our life without a properly designed theatre in which it can be enacted.

If we seriously entertain the growing desire to follow the road of progress and to turn our backs to the threatening abyss, we shall have to build, we shall have to build more and better, and we shall have to convince others by building in a style worthy of mankind.

Within the span of a few generations we shall have to ensure that the whole world is reasonably "housed" and rendered "fertile" by technical projects to the extent that the material foundation for a habitable world is laid.

This involves a reorganisation of our production apparatus and substantial intellectual investments in building. This also means vast national and international action, for which great sacrifices will be necessary.

It means building in such a way that with the available means the highest possible value for human life is attained. It also means building in a style which convinces many people both rationally and emotionally, thus enlisting their co-operation.

The problem of purposefully building a habitable world must be seen as a world problem, closely associated with the world problems of hunger, sickness, war and revolution.

Building can be convincing, because it simultaneously produces:
- the stimulating effect of a hopeful future;
- the convincing power of a gradually growing visible achievement;
- the beneficial effect of constructive work;
- the favourable effect of steadily improving "housing" and greater "fertility".

The building of a habitable world for all should combine social justice and economic efficiency and can strike a new balance between freedom and responsibility, between work and happiness, between science and culture. The building of a habitable world for all is made possible by the gifts of nature, but it is a task which must be accomplished by man.

Part two: PROBLEMS AND METHODS

6   More and better building

*more efficient use of the existing building capacity with
a fair distribution | more by fewer obstructions | more by
more means | more but also better | optimum quality |
towards industrialisation of the building industry | the
principle: standardisation based on functional quality |
looking ahead | active planning | rational programming,
design and production | a play in many acts*

How can we, within the span of a few generations, raise the world building production from 8 million to 36 million dwellings per year and increase the production of other buildings to such an extent that a balanced –
geographically properly distributed – world building activity is created?
This is the great problem with which we find ourselves faced in our efforts
to create a habitable world for all.

Taking the present building capacity as a basis, it will be evident that first
everything possible must be done to build as much as possible with the means
now available. Not just because this in itself would provide an appreciably
higher yield from the expended means, but also because more efficient working methods are urgently required as a basis for the future, rapidly expanding building capacity in order to avoid considerable wastage.

On the whole it would be true to say that the intellectual investment
will be greater according as more must be obtained with the available material means and thus less is sacrificed per unit of product. The crux of the
matter is then as a rule to intensify the thinking which should precede the
action to such an extent that a higher degree of efficiency is attained in the
action proper.

Although greater efficiency in production means both "more" and
"better", it is understandable that the struggle waged in most sectors of
economic life in the western world during the last hundred years to achieve
greater efficiency was directed in the first place to obtaining a greater production per man-hour.

Greater production per man-hour was essential for the rapidly growing
concerns and industrial areas so as not to go under in the often hard struggle
of competition.

Greater production was made possible by mechanisation, whereby moreover the industrial worker was gradually relieved of the almost unbear-
able physical exertions originally demanded of him.

Greater production per man-hour was essential to ensure – either under
pressure from the growing power of the trade unions or not – a reasonable

existence for all and gradually to break through the poverty level by virtue of a mutually related, rising production and consumption.

In the building industry the effort to achieve greater production has resulted in greater attention being given to standardisation, prefabrication and mechanisation on the one hand and to improvement of working methods and sound organisation on the building site on the other.

The effort to attain greater production with the available means should coincide with the effort to achieve the fairest possible distribution of the available building capacity. This will cause building to have a balanced stimulating effect on housing, work, recreation and transport.

This is all the more important because invariably a limited production capacity is pitched against almost unlimited requirements and the demand backed by purchasing power is not always a reliable guide in this respect. It is not just a matter of making good progress at one particular point, but of advancing along the entire front. The object should be not only to improve the social infra-structure and thereby favourably to affect the whole of our society, but also to increase the economic strength on a number of essential points with the least possible delay.

If we want to achieve increased building production with the available means and a fair distribution of the building capacity over the various social sectors, it will be necessary to introduce a new approach in the building industry and also to effect important changes in the organisation of our society. It is not solely a matter of technical ingenuity and increased labour productivity. What we want is an overall, planned action, in which technico-economic, social, sociological, psychological and also political elements are harmoniously incorporated.

If we attempt to attain a practical gain by thinking first and acting afterwards, we shall encounter many difficulties. In many countries progress is seriously hampered by a wrong rent policy, by land speculation or by a permanently excessive or unstable rate of interest on capital. For a new approach it is also necessary to break through the technical rigidity which threatens as a result of incorrectly assigned responsibility. In many countries technical progress has become too dependent on a system of unnecessarily varying and out-of-date municipal building and housing regulations and on the arbitrary interpretation thereof. Another important factor as a basis for renewal is a greater continuity of work both for the individual concern and for the total building volume of a town, province or country.

Greater attention should also be devoted to improving human relations, teamwork, working conditions on the building site and thus to the overall mentality in and outside the trade.

It should be realised more and more that a greater volume of building is necessary to achieve a balanced development of our society and that this involves essential sacrifices. We should understand that road-building is not in the first place an instrument for contra-cyclical manipulation, but that without adequate road-building much human suffering and great material damage is caused daily by accidents, excessive wear and petrol consumption, loss of time, etc. We should also realise that the rent must not be regarded as an item to balance the family budget, so that indirectly the housing of the people is at the mercy of the wage policy, but as a payment for an indispensable service. The trade unions should understand that they ultimately rob themselves if they refuse to decrease technically out-of-date tariffs and compel their members not to lay more than 500 bricks per day. We should realise that in the long run an out-of-date building industry will dislocate the whole of social life and that from the social point of view a television set in a slum house is just as ridiculous as make-up on an unwashed face.

However, it will not be enough to attain greater production from the existing building capacity, especially if our object is to create a world habitable for all. A great deal more is needed for this, namely relatively more means for building and rising prosperity and thus relatively less expenditure on armaments and a retarding of other forms of prosperity, the latter at least as long as the required minimum level of habitability has not yet been attained. After reorganisation or adaptation of the production apparatus, this increasing prosperity and reduced expenditure will make a far greater production of buildings possible.

Continuous building production will only be possible by effective national and international long-term action to bridge the wide gap between the present with its limited and insufficiently distributed purchasing power for buildings and the future when, also as a result of this building activity, the world will have attained a state of sound and balanced development.

Large loans at low rates of interest and grants will be required for this, but also and especially great individual efforts.

In countries where serious shortage of capital goes hand in hand with a surplus of labour such an individual effort can effectively take the form of "aided self-help", provided care is taken to ensure adequate preparation and training.

Seeing that in industrially highly developed countries the initial period of "poverty" has now almost elapsed, it is realised everywhere that higher efficiency means both "more" and "better" and that our way of thinking should be directed not only to "maximum" results, but more especially to "optimum" results. When seen in this light, increased productivity should be the synthesis of "more" and "better", thus the synthesis of quantitative and qualitative aspects.

To realise this it is necessary that in industry, apart from the need to give constant attention to achieving greater production, the handling of quality problems should be subject to a rational industrial policy. It is not sufficient to display an uncontrolled effort and incidental activity with respect to such problems.

This policy should be directed to two components: the design quality and the production quality.

The design quality is what one wants to make and what is laid down in model, drawing or specification.

The production quality is what one actually makes, thus the extent to which the industrial products are in accordance with the design quality.

Improvement of quality does not always result in a rise in design quality. It can often be achieved by raising the production quality, which in some cases may even be accompanied by a lowering of the design quality.

Quality control is of great economic importance to the user. A rational choice of design quality and a guaranteed production quality afford him the best chance of buying articles which give him the best value for his money.

The rational choice of design quality can only be made on the strength of a carefully drawn up programme of requirements, based on the results of a functional study. In this way it is determined what function the industrial product concerned must fulfil for the category of users for whom it is intended.

As goods are usually produced for a market and thus for invisible customers, an attempt must be made to make them visible again. In former times this was simple. There was an interview with the customer at which his wishes were discussed and the goods were generally made "to measure". This is now no longer possible in the literal sense, but the purchaser can be made visible in an abstract sense by close study of the tastes, wishes and properties of the potential customers. We are not primarily concerned here with an analysis of what can be sold, but rather with determining the actual requirements, which the consumer often does not know himself, but which can be established with his assistance.

Quality control is also of great economic importance to the producer, because if he succeeds in combining increased production with better quality he can often supply a functional product of acceptable design with less waste and at a lower price. It will be appreciated that this will greatly improve his competitive position.

A clear example of the lack of a quality policy was demonstrated by the Japanese industry in the thirties, when it flooded the entire world with very cheap products, which, however, were often still too dear. Not just because the design quality was low – as allowance had been made for this in the low price–but usually because the production quality was so low that an excessive percentage of these mass-produced products was absolutely worthless. Japan has learned its lesson in this respect: since the second world war it has been paying special attention to the modern statistical methods of quality control, as is clearly evident from the goods now being supplied.

Quality consciousness can also be of great social importance, because it introduces a new element into mass-production which improves the direct relationship between man and his labour.

Quality control for industrial products cannot lead to significant results until a systematic overall quality policy has been developed, in which four phases can be distinguished:

(*a*) improving the sense of quality to create a suitable mentality for a conscious overall quality policy;

(*b*) The development of programmes of requirements based on functional studies in respect of industrial products in order to lay a foundation for economically justified decisions of the entrepreneur and for practical usefulness of the product;

(*c*) creating such design quality that as far as possible allowance can be made for the objective requirements of the programme and that, whilst foreseeing the requirements for rational production, a form is attained which ensures a harmonious whole;

(*d*) achieving a high production quality by realising in production, within acceptable limits, what is laid down in design and specifications.

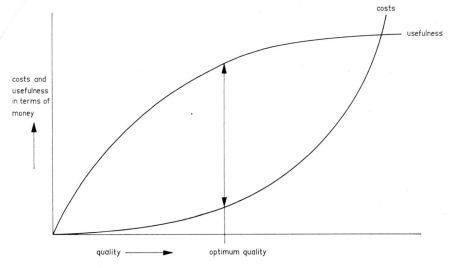

The aim of this overall quality policy must be to give the produced goods an optimum quality with which the differences between "usefulness" and "costs" has been raised to a maximum.

Usefulness and costs must be taken in the widest sense.

51

Seeing that in industry there is a noticeable trend towards speeding up mechanisation by introducing automation wherever possible and thus promoting in a revolutionary manner maximum production per man-hour, it is urgently necessary to draw attention to "conscious" quality. Very high investments would become worthless in a relatively short time if an effort were not made to give the article to be produced the human "measurement". This requires a thorough quality analysis, whereby it is determined what must be produced to make engineering serve the rapid development of a habitable world, thus creating a balanced prosperity for the benefit of all. Such prosperity cannot be based on the type of motivation research in which the producer abuses the weaknesses of the consumer to serve his own interests. On the contrary, engineering should be used for building up a society in which material and non-material aid is offered to the individual, the family, and the community as a whole with the object of removing imperfections of a conscious and subconscious nature. Motivation research can prove very useful indeed in the effort to achieve this "conscious" quality.

In the building industry also it is very necessary that close attention should be given to increasing production, but in addition it is necessary to introduce a new quality notion. When designing buildings the effort is too much directed to the unique and the associated aristocratic quality, while too little attention is given to series- and mass-produced articles with their democratic quality. The quality policy should be based on the latter and must, therefore, follow the development which has become evident in other branches of mass-production industry. The essential point is not solely the number of dwellings made available by new construction, but also building dwellings of such quality as to permit the housewife to run her household efficiently. We must constantly remind ourselves of the fact that in more than 500 million homes a large number of essential practical actions must be performed every day, which would require much less effort if efficiently built and equipped dwellings were available.

Conscious quality, characterised by correct dimensions and layout, by appropriate finish and the right choice of materials, has a very favourable effect on the usefulness of the building. The work of hundreds of thousands of doctors, nurses and others would be made considerably easier if the layout of hospitals were based on the frequency of contacts, so that it would not be necessary to cover 15 miles per person per day if 10 miles per person per day would suffice. In this respect quality is a very important element owing to the fact that, compared with other goods, a building has a very long economic life.

Quality control, however, should not be restricted to the programme of requirements, the design and production of the individual building, whereby its functional and aesthetic value is raised often at lower cost price, but should also and especially be directed to the totality of buildings. It is true to say that the healthy development of the society depends to a very large extent on the quality of our total constructed environment.

The endeavour to increase direct and indirect productivity, *i.e.* the "more" and "better", in the building industry has in many respects found expression in marked changes in design and production of individual buildings and in closer attention being given to their physical planning.

It would be wrong to assume that this development in the building industry could be accelerated only by raising the number of horse power per worker and making specific technical changes in the production process. In certain cases they may well be a logical result of another approach, but they can never produce the desired development. To achieve what is necessary in the building industry both quantitatively and qualitatively it will be essential – considering the rapidly growing world population and existing arrears – to accept the fundamental principle inseparably bound up with rational industrial production. This fundamental principle is standardisation based on conscious, thus functional quality.

The architect Neutra puts it as follows:

"Standardisation and a functional concept of what a thing is or rather how it ought to perform are unavoidable in an industrialised world. They alone have proved that such a world, no matter what its drawbacks, must not perish in fakery and confusion, and in the obliteration of quality per se."[1]

Mannheim, the sociologist, says on this point:

"It is quite easy to live in a standardised house, possess a standardised wireless, and drive a standardised car without becoming intellectually standardised as well."[2]

But the architect Walter Gropius[3] rightly says:

"Die Existenz von Standardprodukten kennzeichnet immer dem Hochstand einer Zivilisation, eine Qualitätsauslese und Abscheidung des Wesentlichen und Überpersönlichen vom Persönlichen und Zufälligen. Es ist heute notwendiger denn je, die grundlegende Bedeutung des Begriffes "Standard" tief genug zu fassen als einen kulturellen Ehrentitel – und sich gegen die seichte, reiszerische Propaganda zu wenden, die wahllos jedes industrielle Massenprodukt zum Standardprodukt erhebt."

It is clear that standardisation can only be accepted if it enables our optimum knowledge and skill to be realised and not if by restriction of types it

[1] *Richard Neutra: Survival through Design, New York 1954.*
[2] *Karl Mannheim: Man and Society in an Age of Reconstruction, New York 1951.*
[3] *Walter Gropius: Architekt, Frankfurt/M, Hamburg 1956.*

standardisation

is merely confined to standardisation of what can be produced and sold with the least difficulty.

It is remarkable that standardisation is accepted without question by everyone when it concerns motor-cars, radios, refrigerators, washing machines and many other industrial products, but rarely when it is applied to dwellings, schools or other buildings. There appears to be no objection to certain standard elements such as doors, kitchens and the like, but for the rest there is a trend whenever possible to make a new design for each individual case. This causes an enormous waste of labour in the architects offices, in industry and with the contractor, because each time a constructional detail is made slightly different, while the lay-outs exhibit excessive variation without any technical, sociological or cultural reasons being evident. Apart from this variation, however, the waste is also due to the fact that as regards design a considerable part of the work is of necessity of average (or

functional quality

lower!) quality. This among other things results in waste of labour and excessive maintenance costs, which could be avoided with carefully thought-out standardisation.

With standardisation each problem, even the smallest, can be given careful attention by experts, because their findings can be used for a large number of cases. Moreover, the architect and his staff are at present so overloaded by all this detail work that often they have not sufficient time to devote their attention to one of the really important elements of their profession, *viz.* the transformation of material things into cultural and spiritual values.

It is remarkable to note how many people oppose standardisation, using as an argument the increasing monotony of the new residential districts. It is quite true that new residential areas can be somewhat boring or monotonous, but this is almost invariably a question of monotony without there

55

being any question of systematically applied standardisation. It is in fact a monotony of slight variance. What we need is standardisation without monotony and not monotony without standardisation.

monotony of slight variance

Standardisation should be fully accepted, because without it no optimum achievement as regards number and quality can be attained. In any case it is good to realise that a human being can lead his life quite well in a standard dwelling, but that he can hardly do so without a dwelling.

As long as the building capacity is too small to meet requirements we shall be faced everywhere with the difficult task of preserving a correct equilibrium between quantity and quality within the scope provided by the means available.

Conscious quality need not necessarily lead to "better and thus more expensive" building and it certainly does not imply expensive hardware and a marble entrance in a house inadequately protected against extraneous noise. What it does mean is the need to give careful consideration to qualitative and quantitative elements and to weigh actual requirements against economic feasibility.

What it amounts to is a conscious increase in the intrinsic value of what is being produced.

It should be appreciated that the importance of quality is greater according as the economic life of the product is longer. A bad paper serviette is a source of annoyance only once, but a bad house can adversely affect a family for a period of fifty years.

It is, therefore, precisely in the building industry that quality plays an important part. It determines the efficiency of a building, which must serve its purpose so many years, and in some cases it also determines its cultural value. Added to this there is the fact that the conscious effort to achieve quality improvement can often lead to rationalisation, which also has a favourable effect on production costs.

Generally speaking, it is not correct to say that improvement of quality must result in increased production costs. Quality improvement can, in effect, be accompanied by a reduction of costs and may often lead to a reduction of operating costs.

The problem with which we are faced is to find a systematic, industrial approach to building on such a scale and in such a way that optimum results are obtained, backed by the conviction that in terms of an existence worthy of mankind it is a matter of "to be or not to be". When speaking of an existence worthy of mankind we are not just using a loose phrase. What we mean by it is an existence directed to the preservation of mental and physical health, the development of the human personality and the perfectioning of the natural and artificial environment, which can be regarded as the theatre in which the play is presented.

Another object is to rebuild our cities in such a way that they no longer have a harmful or destructive influence on life, but instead afford man a space to live fully matched to and integrated with all his widely divergent requirements. This space should facilitate a maximum of desired contact between people – so important for the society – by a minimum of traffic.

Its form should reflect and improve our culture, because the designs possess a high index of value for life, furthered by a substantial sense of social responsibility. It is clear, therefore, that we shall have to find a new approach if through industrialisation we want to build more and better and . . . . . . make our building effort worthy of mankind.

It has become evident from the foregoing that more and better building on the scale necessary to attain a world habitable for all within a few generations requires planned and systematic work based on thorough standardisation based in turn on functional quality. This quality should not only be of a technical character, but should especially make allowance for the various aspects of the user, the builder and the spectator.

Building is to a large extent a question of looking ahead. One builds for the future. Admittedly, one can only partly foresee the future, but by working out a reliable technique for making prognoses it is possible to limit the

industrialisation

uncertainties which the future conceals. Thus it is possible to arrive at more reliable decisions, to promote sound planning and to ensure proper estimates in all phases of building. This should ultimately lead to the crystallisation of a number of plans.

They should be plans for the overall development in a given sphere, in which building plays an important part, because a given development is preceded, accompanied and followed by building. It is especially important, therefore, to regard building as an integral part of the desired overall development and to strive for balanced progress. For this evolution it is necessary that the available space should be adapted, for which physical planning is an essential requirement. The world population is growing rapidly and the space necessary to accommodate all the people can only be created by making optimum use of such space as is available and avoiding unnecessary waste of natural resources.

The overall development plans and the physical planning can form the basis for the plans and the programmes for actual building and for commencing the battle against shortages.

It is imperative that all these plans should be made on the strength of active planning. It should not be a flight into a mass of paper to escape reality, but a systematic preparation for a sound action to achieve optimum results. On paper certain mistakes can be avoided beforehand, while large frames are set out within which full rein can be given to personal initiative and a conscious effort made to ensure the greatest possible individual freedom.

Before coming to the design and the production of the building a number of fundamental decisions must be taken, of which the most important one is certainly the choice of the quality standard in connection with the quantitative aspects which find expression in number, volume and costs. It is quite certain, however, that to ensure the greatest possible usefulness for the users it is necessary to pursue a functional controlled quality. There is every reason to believe that the formalistic approach is rapidly on the way out now that everywhere the importance of the practical features of the building for man and society is gradually being understood.

Hence, the starting point for every building should be a programme of requirements based on functional studies, whereby the objective quality of the future building is ensured.

It is the task of the building industry to solve the technico–economic problem involved in the realisation of the programme of requirements with all the means available to a rapidly developing building technique, making effective use of standardisation, quality and dimension control in production and design.

As designer, the architect has the task not only of moulding all the objective factors into a single unit, but also, in creating this unity, of adding a number of subjective factors.

The subjective factors which influence quality originate, inter alia, from the creative capacity of the designer, irrespective of whether he is the architect or the consultant for constructions. They manifest themselves in the constructional and spatial solutions of given conditions, in a choice between alternatives, in form, in colour and in the cultural significance of the design.

The distinction between objective and subjective factors does not imply that they exert their influence independently of each other. On the contrary, they are closely associated. A building can be qualified as good, if the architect has succeeded in combining all these factors into one.

The functional, technical, economic and aesthetic qualities of the building are not determined solely by the quality of programme and design, but also by the production quality. In this connection it will be necessary to establish equilibrium between speed and finish. An optimum achievement can only be attained here if due allowance has been made for production requirements in the programme and in the design and an efficient or-

construire c'est prévoir

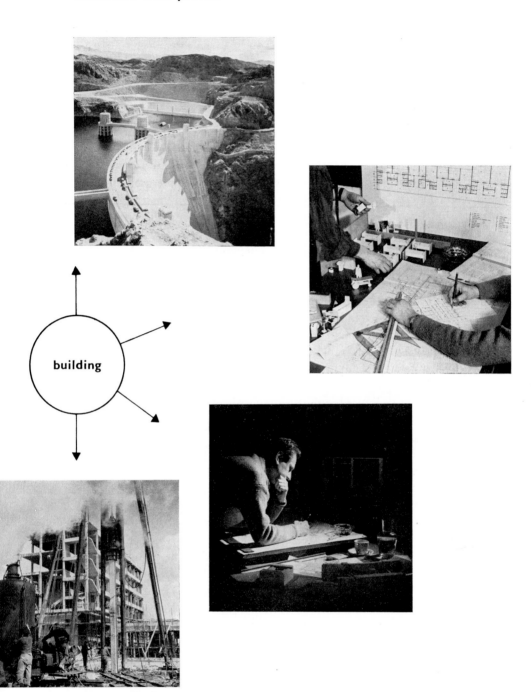

better building is better living

ganisation and lay-out of the building site, based on sound human relations, has been established.

The greatest possible effect can be derived from a building if it is properly used and also properly kept clean and maintained. Expert management and a reasonable rent constitute the basic requirements for this, as well as for the ultimate elimination of the building when it is old.

Looking ahead, making plans, working out programmes, designing, erecting and managing buildings – a series of closely associated activities. The quality of any action is dependent on the quality of the preceding action and also determines that of the next.

Building is a play in many acts and with an even greater number of scenes and a constantly changing cast. When reviewing the steps which must be taken prior to the realisation of a building, the decisions which must be taken and the problems involved, as is done on the following pages, we realise two things. In the first place we realise that any attempt to fuse together the desiderata, the knowledge and the skill of so many people will not have the slightest chance of success unless full attention is given to the teamwork of the "actors".

In the second place it becomes clear that the further discussion in the following chapters of such subjects as looking ahead, planning, programming, etc., cannot possibly be exhaustive.

7   Construire c'est prévoir

human action directed to the future / man wants to control the future / growing power / many uncertainties / the descriptive statistics / facts more important than opinions / the probability theory / describing more than is observed / the stochastic statistics / discovering and controlling influences / the decisionics / the most favourable policy

1. EXPECTATIONS OF THE FUTURE

An essential element of all human action is that it is directed to the future. This may be the very near future, such as buying a loaf of bread for the next meal or putting up an umbrella when it starts to rain. It may also be the distant future, such as studying for a profession or taking out an insurance to cover funeral expenses. The element of future is invariably implied, either consciously or subconsciously, in any action performed or any decision taken in the present. It is not surprising, therefore, that throughout the centuries man has contemplated the future and, on the strength of beliefs, conceptions or theories, has entertained expectations of the future or has ventured to foretell the future.

For many centuries the western world has allowed itself to be guided by the conception of history as a divine plan, which, however, relates to the final round of history; the great final struggle on the day of judgement, rather than to the gradual evolution of things. In the course of time various ideas have been developed regarding the latter, of which Marx and Spengler represented two typical schools. Marx introduced the idea of evolution and progression, while Spengler recreated the old cyclic conception in his "Untergang des Abendlandes" in a grand historical picture.

Apart from the final conception of the divine plan and the cyclic conception, which essentially and unavoidably implies the cycle: birth, growth, rise, crisis, descent, collapse and decay, there also developed a more active expectation of the future. In this a more or less important place has been reserved for human responsibility and human intervention, irrespective of whether this is within the scope of the final religious, the cyclic or the evolutionary conception of the future. It is becoming more and more evident that for the future much will depend on the way man meets the challenge of the present.[1]

It is not to be wondered at that man resists the idea of a future which he

[1] *Prof. Fred. L. Polak: De toekomst is verleden tijd, Utrecht 1955.*

63

cannot influence in any way, especially if he considers his growing power in many spheres, such as technical science, economics, psychology and the like. In the practice of agriculture and industry he sees the art of forecasting being performed with increasing success, while he is constantly faced with proofs that his actions can be directed to part or full control of things to come. The prognosis which does not materialise also plays a very important part, if an action is thereby brought about which prevents catastrophe.

Once it is realised that all human action affects the more or less distant future, it will not be difficult to understand how important it is to gain some insight into what can be expected from the future. A better insight in this respect will improve our possibilities of "looking ahead" and gives our action a better chance of success, because it can as far as possible be consciously directed along the lines foreseen. This is especially important if these actions involve considerable interests, e.g. important investments which in order to be economically justified must have a large useful effect over a long period of time. A typical example of this is the creation of a building, which usually involves large investments and has a long economic life, whereby a static element is introduced in the dynamics of our life. Hence it is impossible to build without looking ahead and it also impossible to build in a manner worthy of mankind without acquiring the greatest possible insight into the expected future development.

For this reason it is necessary that also on behalf of building the technique of forecasting should be developed and applied in a responsible manner. Every effort will have to be made to give building a new scientific, i.e. a more accurate and more reliable "foundation" based on previous experience.

This does not imply that as regards volume and quality building for the future will be determined by scientific prognoses alone. In the first place the technique of forecasting has its limits. In the second place the realisation of building plans is in the hands of people, which means that in addition to scientific preparation some influence will be exercised by the intuitive imagination of, for example, the designer. It is the combination of these two elements which determines the ultimate results. These results can, therefore, surpass the calculations of the scientist.

The prognoses regarding quantities can be in the form of extrapolated time series, as used to predict the population of a given area, but they can also lead – and this applies also to qualities – to the acceptance of constant values, whereby on the strength of what is now known effective standardisation can be achieved for given future periods.

If, in building, the information regarding future use is inadequate, it will only be possible to cope with this factor of uncertainty by stipulating as a requirement the temporary, flexible or transportable nature.

It is not solely because a building has a long economic life and involves large investments that we should know as much as possible about the future, but also because there is usually a considerable dependency between each individual building and a number of other buildings. A decision to build a given number of houses somewhere at the same time involves the decision to build, for example, one or more schools, a number of shops, a community centre, etc., and to lay on streets with sewers and supply systems for gas, water and electricity.

Hence, in many cases it is no longer possible for a single person or a number of persons to decide whether something is to be built, also for the simple reason that once the building has been put up many people are obliged to look at it every day. For this reason it is necessary to combine a certain community influence with the building initiatives of the individual. It will be clear that this may result in a serious form of obstruction to the individual who is better able to see into the future than those who have adapted themselves to a slowly operating official machine and there is a decided risk that sometimes the cure will be worse than the complaint.

What, how, how much, where and when we build demands from the community and the individual a series of decisions for the future, which usually implies the making of the best choice from a number of alternatives. It will be appreciated that in most cases such a decision cannot be taken on the basis of a preformed opinion or by philosophising on the subject with others. Precisely because one should learn to live with the uncertain factors which are essential for knowing the future it is necessary to call in the aid of cool calculation, to get a maximum of knowledge about these uncertainties.

The long life of a building, the high investments involved and the marked influence which it has on the community are all reasons to introduce very systematically the principle of "look before you leap" and to utilise the latest methods now in full development. These new methods will put an end to too much guessing and via mathematics will lead to "decisionics". Often the mathematical, statistical methods are used for this purpose, which have been developed via a series of discoveries and which have led from describing to deciding.

2. FROM DESCRIBING AND ANALYSING THE PAST TO THE DECISIONS FOR THE FUTURE.[1]

The first discovery which was consciously or subconsciously made was that facts are more important than opinions. It is remarkable that many people in practical life – and this certainly also applies to everything concerned with building – have not yet come to this first and probably most fundamental stage of statistical thinking.

[1] A.R. van der Burg: Van beschrijving tot beslissing, Rotterdam 1954.

The factual description of a large number of phenomena resulted in a new insight being obtained, *i.e.* that multiples can only be grasped mentally if they are reduced to a single unit, thus arriving at the average or the discovery of the singular.

When studying reality one is struck by the great variety of things, even if they are things of one kind, such as the height of women, the time required to perform a specific job, the maintenance costs of houses of the same type, the number of motor cars passing per unit of time, the time required to build a house, etc. It is not until one has become familiar with seeing the unity of things, *i.e.* the average, that one starts to wonder about the variety, which now assumes an entirely different significance than with the first discovery of reality. The studying of deviations led to a new important discovery, *i.e.* variation as an essential characteristic of a specific category of things.

If one wants to study systematically the reality of the present, this is usually done to increase one's insight to such an extent that it becomes possible to compare different situations in order to predict new situations. It is then often necessary that the given reality should be divorced from those elements which disturb the possibility of comparison. In this connection it it often found that the magnitudes examined exhibit excessive variety, because they are influenced by factors which are irrelevant in the investigation concerned. If it is desired to compare the cost price per bed in different hospitals, an efficient comparison of a number of hospitals of which some have and others have not a nurses' wing, cannot be made without deducting the costs of the nurses' wing in the one case or adding these costs in the other. In this way converted figures are obtained, in which irrelevant sources of variation have as far as possible been eliminated. These are called standard ratios. They fluctuate less than the original figures from which they have been derived. The great significance of the standard ratios lies in this "semi-invariance". In practice these standard ratios can be used for two important ends:

(a) They can be used to make comparisons between two or more cases in which a number of disturbing factors are eliminated, such as a comparison of the productivity of brick-laying in different regions, in which, for example, the differences in the size of the bricks, the type of the building, etc., are eliminated by expressing everything in "working units".

(b) The standard ratios can under certain conditions be so strongly invariant that they can be used for prognoses and for testing the value of certain plans. If an architect produces a calculation for the building of an infant school, it can be ascertained with the aid of the standard ratios whether the price of this school is reasonable

as compared with that of other schools of the same type. In this case allowance must not only be made for changes in building prices, if any, by correcting the standard ratios, but in addition it should be borne in mind that a higher price does not always imply that a given design, considering the quality to be expected, is too expensive.

Standard ratios can be fixed points of rest, where otherwise everything is different and changing. If applied with intelligence, they can be very useful.

The same applies to the so-called index figures, which might be called standard ratios changing in time. They are referred to a basic year, which is usually put at 100, and as a rule relate to, for example, the costs of a worker's dwelling, a specific selection of building materials or something similar of a constant composition.

We have learnt from experience that certain phenomena are related with each other. In physics we soon familiarised ourselves with Boyle's law, which says that the pressure of a rarified gas at equal temperatures is inversely proportional to its volume. For purely theoretical purposes such laws are quite adequate.

The difficulties start, however, when we are not concerned with a perfect laboratory case, in which only a single condition varies and the other influences can be kept constant, and if, moreover, we do not want to come to a more or less vague conclusion, but wish to quantify the relationship between the results and the influencing factors. It then appears that the relationship between things is imperfect, e.g. the relationship between the building costs of a dwelling and the size of the dwelling expressed in square or cubic feet. In many of these cases it is still possible to arrive at a definite conclusion by means of a statistical analysis, although it must be admitted that this conclusion is of an entirely different nature than Boyle's law referred to above.

Let us assume that we wish to investigate the relationship between a set of conditions A, B and C on the one hand and the result R on the other. The application of the correlation method led to the discovery of the imperfect relationship and it became possible:

(a) to express the degree of relationship between each of these conditions and the result R in the form of a coefficient, the so-called correlation coefficient;

(b) to represent the nature of the relationship by a so-called regression formula of, for instance, the following form

$$R = \alpha A + \beta B + \gamma C$$

where R is the result and A, B, and C, the numerical values of the conditions which to a large extent determine the result and α, β and γ can be determined numerically with the aid of statistical analysis. The relationship expressed by such a formula is not a complete relationship, because the result R derived from the formula is not the real result obtained under these conditions, but an average of results which can be expected under these conditions. The degree to which calculation and reality are in agreement is expressed by the correlation coefficient.

The statistical subjects discussed here all belong to the sphere of descriptive statistics. They furnish a characteristic description of reality, such as becomes apparent from observations, *e.g.* the number of rooms per dwelling in a given town district.

Thanks to a fortunate encounter with a special branch of mathematics, the probability theory, it is possible in modern statistics to describe more than is observed. The significance of this theory lies in the fact that in reality situations occur which bear an unmistakable resemblance to abstract models from the theory of probability, in the same way as the joiner identifies the top of a table with a mathematical rectangle.

Any layman knows that the so-called games of chance, such as roulette or tossing a coin, answer to the model of the laws of probability. These laws will never furnish any information about a specific throw or move, but only about the results of a number of throws or moves as a group, *e.g.* that when tossing a coin a thousand times heads and tails will come up about the same number of times.

Naturally, the value of the probability theory does not lie in its application to games of chance, but in its application in a large number of technical, economic and other problems. Nowadays, not a single telephone exchange is built without an extensive use of the probability theory being made with respect to duration of calls and waiting times. What would we do in present-day hydraulic engineering if the probability theory did not enable us to say something definite about water levels. There are still numerous other problems connected with building which could be effectively solved with the probability theory.

Through this theory we have discovered the part played by chance in the many practical problems with which we are faced. Originally its significance was restricted to those cases in which pure chance phenomena occur, which is seldom the case in practice. The combination of statistics and the probability theory resulted in the full application of the statistical method in so-called stochastic statistics.

The statisticians, however, made an important new discovery, namely that it could even be very instructive and useful in a given situation to establish that the laws of probability were not applicable. This may sound a bit strange, because it would seem that very little could be done in such a situation. Yet, it is not difficult to see that the opposite is true if it is realised what chance actually is. Phenomena which occur by chance are those which cannot be explained from any assignable cause. This means that if the laws of chance are not or not wholly applicable, it must be possible to find a cause somewhere.

This is the fundamental idea underlying stochastic statistics and which enabled it to assume such great proportions. This can be illustrated with a single example. In a factory a product is manufactured in series. A specific property of this product, *e.g.* its length, is essential. If all the production conditions remain the same, there is no reason to assume that the articles produced to-day will have a greater length than those produced yesterday, or that one out of ten will be longer. Yet the articles will differ in length, as is always the case. When measuring the length of consecutive articles a chance series will be found to which only the laws of chance can be applied. If a change in the production conditions occurs to the extent that the length of the product is systematically affected, the series of lengths will no longer be a chance series. Conversely, it may be concluded from such a series that something must have changed in the production conditions and that, therefore, there must be a cause for the behaviour not conforming to the laws of chance.

This reasoning forms the basis for statistical quality control. The production is inspected by measuring one or more properties of the product at regular times. As long as the data constitute a chance series everything is proceeding according to plan. As soon as it appears, however, that the series is no longer a chance series, it must be assumed that the production conditions have changed, *i.e.* that something has gone wrong somewhere. The person in charge receives a signal that some action must be taken. In the first place the trouble must, of course, be located (to which end information can be obtained from the statistical analysis) and in the second place measures must be taken to remove or neutralise the cause of the trouble. This complex of measures to keep the production conditions constant as far as possible is called quality control.

The constant search for non-chance elements in an observed group of events with a view to getting to know something about the factors which influence this group is, in effect, the same as the passionate search of the professional gambler for a system which will enable him to break the bank. Hence, stochastic statistics might derisively be called the sport of discovering systems in the great gamble of life.

The union between statistics and the probability theory has also had other fortunate consequences. One of these is the discovery of the value of taking samples, which has appreciably improved our insight into reality without involving any undue costs. The results obtained with sampling are not only applicable to the persons or things contained in the sample, but also – subject to a calculable margin of uncertainty – to the entire group of persons or things out of which the sample is taken. Hence, with the aid of a sample we can describe more than we have observed. Provided systematic errors are avoided in the sampling technique and the unavoidable sampling errors are made sufficiently small by taking a sample of the correct size, sampling can be called the discovery of justified generalisation. When seen in this light it is also understandable that statistics is sometimes defined as the science which from a series of particular findings arrives at a general conclusion or, to put it differently, the science which by gaining knowledge regarding a number of individuals acquires insight into the species.

During the last few decades fairly extensive techniques have been developed to ascertain which factors give rise to changes in the species and to what extent they change, often in very complicated situations. In practice this means the discovery of influences for the better and for the worse, both qualitatively and quantitatively. This makes it possible to convert the problem of, for example, irregular production or fluctuating harvests into the problem of controlling the factors causing these fluctuating results.

With a continuous production of standard steel windows – to take a very simple example – samples may reveal that a significant dimensional deviation occurs between the series, which is caused by incorrect adjustment of the sawing machine used to cut the structural steel. Hence, an improvement can be achieved and such undesirable mutations within the type avoided by inspecting and correcting the adjustment of the sawing machine at regular intervals.

This is not the place to give a detailed account of the techniques used for tracing causes. On the other hand it may be of interest to mention an important economic aspect of this type of investigation. Thanks to the statistical methods it is possible to carry out these investigations under normal operating conditions, thus without experiments on a laboratory scale. This makes the investigations much cheaper, since apart from saving the time of the investigator there is practically no interference with the normal routine of the process.

However, the most important result of these investigations is that, as far as industry is concerned, they produce results which enable the production process to be fully controlled, also in cases in which apparently uncontrollable circumstances are encountered, such as those originating from natural raw materials. The quality improvements and savings which have been effected in the relatively small section of industry where statistical methods have so far been applied, have already made a substantial contribution towards the general rise in prosperity.

It will be evident from what has been discussed so far that statistics has gradually developed from the passive stage of objective description to the active stage of analysis and interpretation. This enables the statistician to furnish the management with such information as they require to increase their insight into all kinds of problems.

What until recently the statistician could not do, except in a number of simple cases, was to solve these problems in such a way that the decision as to what action to take could automatically be derived from conclusions of the statistician. For a number of years, however, a new development has been in progress, which in England and the U.S.A. is known as operations research[1] and which in the Netherlands is also indicated as " decisionics" because the Dutch are of opinion that this term best represents the essential point of the matter. The object of decisionics is to carry out such investigations that it will be possible by objective and preferably quantative analysis to draw up the most favourable policy for the situation in question.

A considerable number of problems, of which three examples will be given below, could be suitably solved by applying these rapidly developing methods. It should, however, be realised that the research work necessary for this requires time and that quick decisions can therefore only be made by intuition. This constitutes another reason for taking out sufficient time for preparation when making large-scale investments such as are necessary for the construction of buildings.

(a) A firm has a shortage of warehouse space and wants to build a new warehouse. How large should this warehouse be? To take this decision it is necessary to determine the optimum size of stocks. A concern holding stocks of raw materials and/or spare parts will endeavour to maintain a stock large enough to reduce the risk of production being impaired by lack of raw material to a minimum, but yet small enough to avoid unnecessary capital investment. In this case, therefore, there are two kinds of costs. On the one hand a cost results from maintaining stocks, which manifest itself chiefly in the form of loss of interest, loss by deterioration of quality and cost of storage, while on the other hand there is the risk of lack of production, which is also a cost. By incorporating these various costs in a formula it is possible to determine the optimum stock, *i. e.* the

---

[1] *During the war the assistance of scientists from non-military circles was enlisted in Britain, since it was realised that a number of difficult strategical and tactical military problems could not be satisfactorily solved on the basis of intuition and experience of military persons alone. This initiative proved very successful and an official team was set up to do this research work. In this connection the term "Operations Research" was used, which referred to military operations. After the war a large number of O.R. workers returned to industry in England where they started to apply the research methods evolved during the war years to industrial and transport problems. American industry did not follow Britain's example until 1952 and in the last few years West-European industry, even if only to a limited extent, also makes use of operations research.*

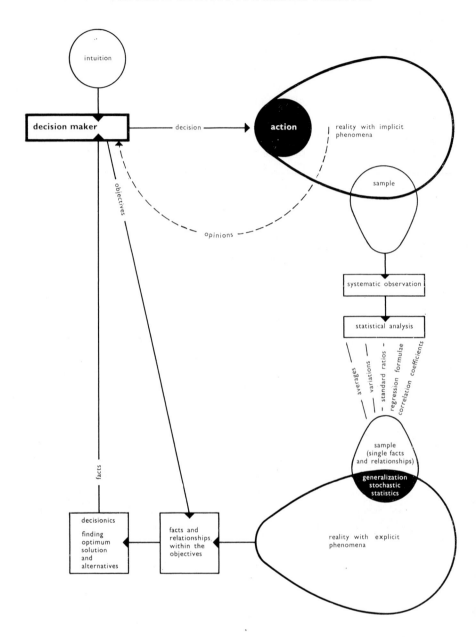

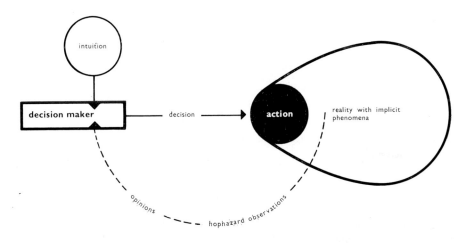

stock for which the sum of all these costs is as low as possible.

(b) What should the distance between tram stops be? A short distance involves higher operating costs and more loss of time for the passengers. A long distance means longer walking times to the tram stop. By means of a statistical study the magnitude of these losses can be determined as a function of the distance, from which the distance involving a minimum of social costs can be derived.

(c) Where should petrol pumps be placed? The oil company will want the pumps at points where sales will reach a maximum. The essential point, therefore, is to relate sales to all the location factors, such as density of traffic, composition of traffic, distances to other petrol pumps and to towns, etc. This is a fairly complicated study, but once it has been made it is indeed possible to determine the most favourable points to place the pumps.

This list of examples could easily be extended by a few hundred more, but the three examples given above are sufficient to present a picture of the numerous possibilities presented by decisionics. They illustrate that a very large number of problems, which were formerly solved exclusively on the strength of intuition, can now be worked out rationally. This does not imply that intuition can now be entirely discarded, because it will always remain the main factor in laying down a policy. However, if it should be possible in the case of important decisions, on which the future development often depends to replace the intuition of the management partly by the reason of decisionics, noticeable results could be obtained. It will be

73

clear that decisionics can be very usefully employed in the sphere of building in the interest of the individuals and the society.

Table 15 contains the most important decisions to be taken in the field of planning and building.

TABLE 15

PHASES AND DECISIONS IN PLANNING AND BUILDING

A   FROM PREPLANNING TO BASIC DECISION

Basic data		Decisions
General development plan; available space	1.1	Physical planning (national, regional and town plans)
Building capacity; allocation to a number of important sectors; operating budgets	1.2	Building programmes (house-building, school-building, factory-building, road-building, etc.)

B   FROM BASIC DECISION TO BUILDING IN USE

Future development: financing possibilities; list of available space; management data	2.1	Basic programma of the building
Analysis of functions; synthesis of functions	2.2	Programme of requirements
Architectural conception of the programme of requirements; provisional estimate of building costs and operating costs	2.3	Provisional design
Technical properties of materials, type of construction and installation; final estimate of costs; funds available; specification and drawings; tender; contract	2.4	Final design for production
Labour analysis; planning of production; costing calculation	2.5	Production of the building
Definitive operating account; plants for cleaning and maintenance	2.6	Management of the building in use

8   Building is planning

spontaneous co-ordination or conscious planning / building programmes part of a general development policy / the design of development / battle against shortages / breaking through the vicious circle / the physical planning / careful use of the available space / changing functions of cities / lacking knowledge / need for traffic research / the social-economic planning of building / continuity of building / basic data for planning building activity

If we want to make the world habitable for everyone within the span of a few generations, this means that, among other things, we must make a conscious effort to establish a more balanced and a better material foundation. Building plays a fundamental part in this respect, because by adaptation of the available space a more efficient theatre is created in which the play of life can be properly staged. More than anything else, however, we need a well-written play, capable producers, talented actors, with or without prompters, stage critics and a large responsive audience, who in due course will start to take part in the play.

Building forms an integral part of the development we are striving for and cannot be divorced from this overall development. Building aims at adapting existing space to the growing requirements and consequently allowance must be made in every respect for the available space and the quality thereof. In building it is necessary to give constant attention to the social desiderata and the economic possibilities, while a serious effort must be made all the time to extend these possibilities and to match them with requirements.

Building requires foresight, because it is a task performed for the future, both quantitatively and qualitatively. We have seen how, by using new scientific methods, it is possible to replace guesswork by decisions based on facts, in which as far as possible allowance is made for the uncertainties of the future. These activities should result in:

(a) the design of development, in which the most important material aspects of the desired development are laid down, due allowance being made for the essential non-material aspects;

(b) physical planning, in which the available land is allocated with optimum effect to housing, work, recreation and transport;

(c) the social-economic planning of building, whereby social requirements and economic possibilities are brought together as realistically as possible and the facilities to build are increased as much as possible within the scope of the overall development and the available space, such in view of the practically unlimited needs.

Before going deeper into these various plans, a few remarks on planning in general will not be out of place.

In this increasingly more complicated world of ours we can no longer depend solely on accidental discoveries made with trial-and-error methods or on inventions which improve matters in one specific respect. We have to make allowance for everything associated therewith in other spheres and we should fully appreciate the need for multi-dimensional planning.

It is remarkable how many people have an aversion to planning, although they use this method themselves, for example, in their work or when they go on a journey. Even a lot of housewives do their work according to a predetermined plan and it is not unusual to find a planning board in their kitchen. We consider it an accepted thing that the railways plan their services and that there should be no discrepancy between their plan and reality.

The aversion to planning which some people have is quite understandable, however, when such planning interferes with personal freedom. It must be admitted that this kind of planning indeed involves a definite risk and we must therefore endeavour to combine planning and freedom as far as possible. However, it will often be impossible to grant the individual so much freedom that it would damage the real interests of the community as a whole. It will be clear that planning invariably involves the difficult task of serving collective and individual interests alike.

If the plan is to be a framework within which individual creations and actions must take place, it should not be too detailed. A town plan for instance should not be detailed to the extent that the architecture of district or street is laid down beforehand.

If planning is intended as effective preparation for certain actions, such as planning on the building site, the plan should contain sufficient accurate details that it can serve as an instruction for the performance of such actions, which can then be carried out according to plan instead of being improvised.

In every community there is a spontaneous co-ordination of functions based on tradition. This can certainly be effective in a stable community, in which certain working methods have been tried out over a considerable period of time, but during the last three hundred years it has proved useless as a means to protect a developing community against unbalanced growth and to make it direct its efforts towards combating want and increasing prosperity. The growth of the population, the great number of inventions, the growing number of hitherto unknown requirements, the use of untried new techniques, the acceleration of the changes themselves, all these circumstances render trial-and-error methods and spontaneous co-ordination totally inadequate. It is not surprising, therefore, that the lack of conscious planning led to conditions conducive to social conflicts, a situation of conflicting aims, a great deal of duplication and a minimum of collective order.

Under the present circumstances every industry, every institution and every sphere needs a plan of activity and a plan of operations. The more efficient these plans are, the better they will serve their purpose as a guide for those responsible for management and decisions.

Even organisations which themselves indulge in a maximum of scientific planning behind their own doors tend to offer a strong resistance to the more extensive type of co-ordination: community planning. One might well ask whether this scepticism and hostility are justified. This is indeed the case if a plan degenerates to something which denies the reality of life and is made to escape the responsibility for the action itself. It then becomes a substitute for reality.

We cannot, however, condemn plans just because there are bad planners. Planners who make paper plans, which acquire a life of their own, do not make sufficient allowance for the object in view and are misused for aesthetic, political and commercial ends.

Any planning set up as a framework for a specific activity can be split up into four phases:

(a) The phase in which by description and analysis a basis of standard ratios and other factual data relating to the actual situation are provided.

(b) The phase of prognosis and decisionics, in which a survey is given of the expected future requirements with the associated social and economic possibilities.

(c) The phase in which the creative element starts to play a part and the actual plan, although based on the first two phases via the creative talents, is worked out.

(d) The phase which consists in convincing the community and making the necessary preparations for the action proper.

There is no doubt that the lack of a scientific basis for the second phase, the lack of creativity in the third phase and neglect of the fourth phase have often discredited many plans as well as the notion of planning.

1. THE DESIGN OF DEVELOPMENT

The planning of development aims at achieving optimum use of the available direct and indirect means. The provision of labour and capital, raw materials and semi-manufactured products, tools and machines should be co-ordinated in such a way that these means will be available in the correct proportion, at the right time and in the right way.

Much can be achieved in this respect by adopting a general development policy, of which the building programmes of the region concerned form an integral part. It is especially important that the social-economic planning of building should not be seen separate from the overall development, because on the one hand certain building activities must provide an essential basis for this development, while on the other the further development will result in considerable building activities. The overall development of a region is preceded, accompanied and followed by building activities.

The improvement of the social infra-structure, which is a primary condition for a further economic development, can be furthered appreciably by building.

In the general development policy Tinbergen[1] distinguishes four principal aims:

(a) to create the general conditions favourable for development;

(b) to aquaint the government itself, the business community and the general public with the potentialities and advantages of development;

(c) to make a number of investments, usually of the "basic" type;

(d) to take measures designed to facilitate and to stimulate private activity and investment.

Many countries, especially the underdeveloped countries, suffer from fundamental weaknesses, such as structural unemployment, lack of capital or land, a fluctuating trade balance, or a shortage of highly qualified engineers and skilled labour, which seriously hamper any effort to achieve a balanced development. In the struggle against these fundamental weaknesses the creation of conditions generally favourable for development and the making of a number of investments of the "basic" type are phases. They are essential to make a given region habitable for all. In this respect it is not only necessary that the overall development, but in some cases even a world-wide conception should be made to prevail over the direct interests of a given project in that region.

A justified minimum housing standard in the widest sense, as well as adequate transport facilities for people and goods, must be ensured everywhere with the least possible delay. Power and water must be available in sufficient quantities and the available land will have to be adapted to the growing requirements of mankind by reclamation or irrigation. These investments may not always appear to be justified from the point of view of the actual conditions prevailing in a given region, but they may well be justified within the framework of the political and economic development of the world as a whole.

To be able to conduct a development policy it is necessary to have at least a certain minimum of skill in making reliable prognoses on the strength of specific data, of estimating technique when such data are lacking, of

[1] Jan Tinbergen: The Design of Development, Baltimore 1958.

talent to achieve flexibility by drawing up alternative plans and the like, but it is also essential - if the programming is not to result in a set of lifeless paper plans - to make a serious practical effort to remove certain "shortage" obstacles.

This applies especially when making fundamental investments, which includes the greater part of building and civil engineering. These investments will not always yield a short-term return to the extent that the investor can speak of making "easy money". Hence, the government is responsible for the overall development of a region, but also for a large part of the realisation of fundamental buildings.

Yet, it is quite certain that a region cannot be made habitable by the government authorities alone. Industry, the community, the individual, builders and occupants alike will have to put their shoulders to the wheel to eliminate the shortage factors.

Consequently, it will be necessary to promote, within the framework of the planned development, the initiative and the interest of the individual in the private sector by programming, information, encouragement and demonstration, by national or international financing facilities and, if necessary, by taking protective measures, furnishing grants or providing tax facilities.

In this way an atmosphere can be created in which constructional works with favourable and unfavourable capital coefficient are realised in such proportion that a balanced short- and long-term development is greatly promoted.

Provided relatively adequate means are available, development planning is largely a technical matter. These conditions will not be created, however, as long as we are satisfied with a form of planning in which everything is reduced to the minimum; we must aim at optimum activity. Armed with the planning data, it will in that case be necessary to wage a continuous battle against shortages. Here also, continuous and sound collaboration between government and industry is essential.

In all these shortage problems one invariably encounters one of the fundamental aspects of the economy of a country, namely the problem of capital intensity. Practically all the underdeveloped countries suffer from a serious lack of capital, which appreciably retards the highly essential fundamental investments.

In the public sector the maximum of a country's investments is determined by the sum of:

(a) government surpluses after deduction of current expenditure;
(b) national loans;
(c) permissible deficit financing;
(d) grants and loans from other countries.

A similar limit can be determined for private and public investments together.

If a country is to achieve optimum investments, both the government and industry will have to restrict current expenditure to a minimum, while the people will have to save as much as possible, voluntarily or compulsory, directly or indirectly. The great difficulty is, however, that saving is out of the question until incomes are so high that the people are not obliged to spend all of it on essential consumer goods. Hence, the first thing to be done is to break through this fatal vicious circle. In the effort to achieve economic equilibrium and stability it will be necessary, therefore, to make a justifiable use of "deficit financing", while moreover an attempt must be made to obtain maximum aid in the form of grants and loans from other countries or from international funds.

In connection with all this it is good to remember that during the first fifty years of this century it proved possible to spend roughly 2500 billion dollars on war and armaments. This amounts to more than 1000 dollars per head of the world population in 1950. As soon as we discover the secret of defending human rights in a more constructive manner it will probably appear that for this also certain forms of "deficit financing", which were so commonly applied in times of war economy, can be applied on a somewhat wider scale than is now considered acceptable.

There is no sense in increasing investments unless an adequate number of skilled workers and other essential means of production are available. If optimum long- and short-term investments are to be achieved, it will be necessary to choose those techniques which for scarce capital give the highest yield from the social and economic points of view. Moreover, it is necessary to ensure the most favourable distribution of investments over the public and private sectors to achieve optimum investments, while the greatest possible benefit should be derived from the powers of individual initiative.

Scarcity of good buildings, backward building technique and inadequate building capacity are some of the fundamental weaknesses of many countries.

According as the tension between available investment capacity and the need of investment becomes greater, the greater will be the significance of the right decision with respect to the practical investment policy to be adopted. The essential point is to make the best choice between two or more possibilities.

As the structure of our society becomes more complicated, the more susceptible the social organisation will be to incorrect decisions. What was formerly an almost imperceptible damage can now mean the end of a development policy or the end of a concern. Generally speaking, the manag-

82

ers are consequently taking on greater responsibility when making their decisions.

In view of the enormous sums which will have to be invested in building and for other purposes on behalf of world development it is of the greatest importance that for important decisions use should be made of the developing operations research technique, *i.e.* decisionics, to ensure with greater certainty that invariably the best choice is made.

Hence, it requires a certain technical skill to carry out development and investment policies, while a certain minimum of statistical material must be available. An effort should be made to pass from opinions to facts with the least possible delay, even though at first it should be necessary to work with rough figures.

From the macro-economic point of view data regarding the size of the population and the expected increase during the period under review, as well as the size of the active part of the population and the trend of productivity, are important. All this should be seen against the background of the sources of prosperity, *i.e.* the available land, capital and skilled labour, and worked up into a planned development of national income and expenditure (private consumption and investment and public expenditure), import and export trade, importation of capital and total national capital.

To be able to follow this development closely it is necessary to have reliable statistics of production, trade, prices, government finance, income and distribution of incomes. The micro-economic programming fills in this macro-economic framework with information regarding branches of industry or important concerns, if necessary, regionally classified.

It should be clear, however, that it is impossible to delay the development of a given region until a sufficient amount of information is available. On the other hand it will then be essential to work with reliable estimates, if necessary, based on samples. Moreover, it may be useful in certain cases to focus statistical attention on essential elements or regions and to obtain in part a better basis of facts than would be possible at short notice for the whole of the project.

2. PHYSICAL PLANNING

We have seen in the foregoing that the overall development of a given region is preceded, accompanied and followed by building. If building is to be worthy of mankind, it implies physical planning, in which a conscious effort is made to achieve the best use of the available land in the interests of the individual, the family and the community.

Physical planning involves the co-ordination of human activities in time and space on the basis of known facts in respect of place, work and people.

It is a conscious effort to integrate collectively all those activities for which the earth is regarded as a building site, a source, a foundation and a stage.

When realising at least to some extent the consequences which the expected doubling of the world population in the next 42 years will have and taking into account that in the same period much that is now backward must be eliminated or developed, it will be clear that very careful use will have to be made of the available space. In this respect we shall have to be much more careful than in the past when we lived too much with the idea that our planet was infinitely great, while we often struggled with nature as if it were one of our greatest enemies. Fortunately, we are now beginning to realise more and more how important it is to render the rich resources hidden in the available space useful to mankind and to develop an efficient process for controlling nature by integration of nature, engineering and culture.

In the old cities and their environs we find factories and workshops everywhere, which obstruct organic growth and promote traffic chaos, while the daily entry and exodus of often hundreds of thousands of people living in the suburbs merely emphasises the inadequacy of the present situation and frequently robs people of their valuable spare time. Chaos and slums have crystallised in many old town quarters. We are now faced with the immense task of transforming much of what we possess as a result of our building activities in the last few centuries in such a way that it acquires a higher "living value" and of doubling the "living capacity" of our constructed environs during the next 42 years.

The past has taught us that we cannot leave the adaptation of space to the initiative of individuals working independently of each other. For this the power of the individual is inadequate. In effect he can only allow himself to be guided by his own individual interests if he is to survive in the struggle for life. Even then he is often incapable of clearly defining his interests in our rapidly changing complicated world. This, of course, does not imply a condemnation of property as such, but it does imply a condemnation of the nineteenth century tendency to regard property as the ultimate end when settling matters which can drastically affect the fate of cities and of the community.

The image presented to us by the mirror of history – if we care to look in it – tells us no lies in this respect. History does not only tell us of chaotic cities in our century resulting from individualistic uncoordinated expansion and from the retarding effect of land speculation on the desired development. Great misery was created in England after the middle ages when communal land fell into the hands of landowners, whereby whole villages were robbed of their means of livelihood, resulting in a growing roaming proletariat living in conditions which are hard to imagine now. Something similar

84

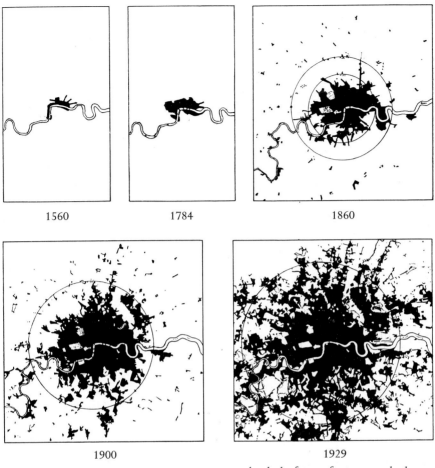

1560   1784   1860

1900   1929

hundreds of years of spontaneous development

should be taken into account that the growing world population will for a considerable part have to be accommodated in cities. The possible and essential mechanisation in agrarian production will have as a result that there will be a relatively smaller need for labour in agriculture, horticulture and cattle-breeding. There is no objection at all to a growth of the urban population as such. There has never been a civilisation without cities.

It may be true that cities are formed for a number of reasons (market place, around a stronghold, for strategic purposes, the will of a despot, etc.), but the fact that since the earliest civilisations cities have invariably been centres of culture undoubtedly indicates that the city fulfils very real human needs. These needs can be satisfied by a city, because it offers so many possibilities. Throughout the ages the city has made distribution of labour and a great variety of contacts possible. These activities can be per-

87

formed without any great loss of time (limited surface area) and in relatively great safety.

In our present society these arguments are no longer the same. The safety of the city is no longer a factor to be reckoned with. Instead of affording protection the city is now a selected and concentrated target for enemies from outside, while as regards safety certain large cities are gradually presenting a very unfavourable situation owing to bad housing and an increasing number of asocial inhabitants.

The argument of a city having so many aspects, however, is just as valid to-day as it was before, but the objection to our present-day cities is, of course, that in practice the effectiveness of these many aspects is not such as we should demand on the strength of the aims of our present-day society. For many real requirements of human life our present-day cities offer no or too few possibilities. Our cities bear the stamp of a one-sided emphasis on the direct interests of the production process. They offer practically no playing facilities for the children. But children will play all the same and in our cities, where they have very little opportunity to do so, this means a source of annoyance to the grown-ups. The result is that the children are constantly being reprimanded. It is not surprising, therefore, that the young people in our cities, when they find their normal healthy urge for activity curtailed, suddenly exhibit a tendency to express this urge in a less normal, a less healthy and a less innocent way.

Easily accessible recreation facilities are an essential requirement for young people and adults alike. And what exactly is the position as regards facilities for establishing contacts? Despite all the technical progress, transport has become such a problem and involves so much waiting time that in practice very few of the potential life-enriching contacts can be realised. Thomas Moore complained that in his time "the sheep ate man". Now it very much looks as if man is being forced out of the picture by motor-cars.

The task of our planners should, therefore, be to create the spatial accommodation for the varied requirements of man and society. It is a problem of space and time. A limited amount of space must be made suitable for the requirements of man, which are gradually becoming more differentiated, while functional integration should give the overall results optimum value.

On the one hand care must be taken that as a result of bad spatial accommodation the individual does not go under in a world of masses and technical perfection, while on the other hand a sound collectivity must be ensured. For all this it is necessary to look as far as possible into the future in order to limit the effect of uncertain factors hidden therein.

Physical planning of a given region requires simultaneous activity in a large number of spheres, of which – leaving military interests out of consideration – the most important are:

88

Population (climate, hygiene, etc.), agriculture (soil and water, reclamation), forestry, mining, industry (location, etc.), recreation (protection of areas, wild life preservation, scenic and historic monuments), traffic (waterways, railways, roads and airfields).

The task of town-planning is threefold:

(*a*) redevelopment of existing towns and villages
(*b*) expansion of existing towns and villages
(*c*) building of new towns and villages.

Physical planning cannot come to full development until a number of practical difficulties have been cleared up and a number of fundamental problems have been solved to the extent that sound decisions can be made.

Technically and administratively, for example, it is as a rule very difficult to make plans for a sufficiently large area that can be regarded as a spatial unit, such as a whole country, a suitable part of that country or an area including a number of countries. The result is that all kinds of separate plans for villages and towns are made, which as regards their mutual relationship and with respect to the area to which they belong are not or insufficiently matched.

In town-planning there is the great difficulty of town boundaries, which either make it necessary to resort to amputated plans or lead to an enormous loss of time.

Other important difficulties are the absence in many countries of practical expropriation legislation and the absence of price control facilities in respect of the land. In both cases the development of physical plans becomes too dependent on individual interests and sound planning will generally prove an impossibility.

Other difficulties are the time factor and the matching of the various plans. It will be clear that physical planning should provide for conditions prevailing in from thirty to fifty years time. Our general social-economic development plans are made for periods of at most ten years, while planning in the building industry usually covers periods from one year to at most ten years. It is not a simple task to match all these plans, which are drawn up by different authorities. Yet, this matter will have to be given very careful attention, because otherwise large parts of our cities will be partially habitable all the time. Owing to the facilities for housing, work and recreation not being created in a balanced way in regard to time and space, traffic will increase appreciably, because the people will not feel at home in the unfinished district or cannot find employment within reasonable travelling distance in view of the inefficient transport facilities.

Sound decisions regarding fundamental problems of housing, work, recreation and transport often can not be made because scientific research lags behind practical building, so that the trial-and-error method reigns supreme and a systematic scientific approach will only be adopted in isolated cases. Everything depends too much on opinions and too little on facts. It is quite amazing that throughout the world there are scarcely any research funds of any importance for this type of work, which involves essential interests of every human being.

For the redevelopment of existing old cities and villages it will invariably be necessary to take important decisions regarding the demolition of old districts and buildings, the filling up of canals and the like. The question arises here whether it would not be better to keep the very best and preserve it for the future by restoration and maintenance rather than obstructing urban life by hanging on to a lot of old unpractical buildings of which the aesthetic, cultural and touristic value is hard to determine and which will be impossible to keep up as prosperity rises and consequently handwork becomes scarcer and wages go up.

To avoid having to take quick and wrong decisions, it is essential that a series of alternative plans should be drawn up for each old city centre at an early stage and that an appropriate comparison of costs, advantages and disadvantages be made. When these preliminary studies have been made it will be possible to make a proper choice from a sufficient number of alternatives and thus to arrive at an optimum solution.

The expansion of existing cities and villages immediately raises a number of fundamental problems. What is the ideal size of a neighbourhood? The socio-psychological research which is required to solve these problems is still in its infancy.

The conventional, generally formalistic, approach must be abandoned and should be replaced by a systematic and functional approach, which from description leads via analysis to synthesis and to a number of alternatives, of which the essential elements can be laid down in sociometric models.

The size of the town is an even more complicated problem, but its solution can be greatly facilitated by a better knowledge of the size and the required functions of the city centre, the residential areas, working districts and recreation districts. This also requires functional studies at the earliest possible stage. Some say that a city of a million inhabitants is already too large, while others say that two millions is the limit, but meanwhile the cities are growing ominously and it is realised that many new towns will have to be built. However, the knowledge required to create new towns according to a sound and clearly outlined plan is lacking. The work performed with the new towns in England may be regarded as a good beginning of a new phase in this sphere.

With all these studies and decisions it is not enough to aim at a higher standard of life; it is also necessary constantly to compile a survey of costs and proceeds of the alternative possibilities in order to be able to reach the right decisions. These surveys should be as complete as possible and drawn up with an eye to the future. Much damage occurs in the present, because in the past we failed to make a systematic study of the costs and proceeds involved in our decisions and consciously or unconsciously left specific important matters out of consideration. Examples in this respect are the lack of recreation grounds, air pollution (smog in London), the problems of transport, refuse disposal and the enormous expenditure which will have to be incurred to demolish after years have elapsed (fewer years all the time) buildings which have become inefficient.

As working hours are shortened and greater efforts are made to ensure adaptation of asocial people there will be a great need for all types of recreation. Our knowledge of the need for recreation facilities is inadequate. We know that in existing towns there is usually a great shortage of such facilities and it is evident that in many new plans serious attempts are made to improve this situation. It is doubtful, however, whether we have found the right yardstick. Hence, it is necessary to establish the actual requirements in this respect by functional analyses, taking into account the expected future developments, and to determine a number of standard ratios. This means that different interests must be weighed one against the other and the weighing of such interests is purely a matter of economics.

In this case also an effort must be made to ensure that the marginal effectiveness of the various possibilities is proportional to the sacrifices made. It should be realised, however, that the weighing of such interests cannot be allowed to depend solely on the demand of those operating on the market. The point is to conduct a long-term and not a short-term economic policy. In our short-sighted society a short-term economic policy will never result in a spontaneous demand (backed by capital) for playgrounds and in the long run the lack of such provisions can lead to an alarming number of frustrated young people, who are incapable of making good use of the knowledge and capital invested by former generations. This amounts to negative investment. Allowance will have to be made for this in economically justified planology. It will have to furnish us with the techniques to achieve the so very desirable optimum range of aspects.

This problem is also encountered in our present-day traffic and this is certainly the greatest source of anxiety for our urban authorities. In effect, our towns owe their existence to the efforts made to achieve a maximum of contacts with a minimum of traffic. If we are not careful, our towns will become places where a maximum of traffic is realised with a minimum of contacts.

To meet the demands of the steadily increasing traffic we make very costly provisions, sacrifice numerous other things and as a rule we do not hesitate to demolish a building of irreplaceable value if it stands in the way of the motorist. We quickly find, however, that with all our demolishing and building we have not solved anything and that owing to the higher density of traffic the chaos has become greater than ever before. It is a sobering thought that in many cities the modern buses on some routes are just as slow or even slower than the horse-drawn trams of fifty years ago; that in Montreal the waiting times of motor lorries represent a loss of thirty million dollars per year; that with all our special provisions and the shortening of working hours people lose more and more time in travelling to and from their work. Unfortunately, the only reaction often still is "to pull down more buildings".

Fortunately, there are also hopeful signs, which indicate that efforts are being made to find more efficient solutions. There is the effort to obtain structurally balanced neigbourhoods by building in such a way that the dwellings are not directly along the main road, the more radical effort to create satellite towns, the building of by-pass roads to take the through traffic round the towns. The clever attempts to organise the traffic in the actual town centres in the best possible way are also of great importance, however poor the results may appear to be at first sight.

Despite the admiration which these attempts certainly deserve, we must ask ourselves whether they are adequate for our purposes. Are we not inclined to regard this overwhelming growth of traffic as something quite unavoidable? Is not our factual knowledge perhaps too slight for us to make a large-scale attempt to match the communication requirements of our society with all those other requirements which our cities must fulfil?

The greater part of the traffic research carried out hitherto has been on too small a scale. Often the authorities confine themselves to carrying out from time to time a traffic census in the form of a physical count of the number of cars, pedestrians, bicycles, etc. passing a given point.

But we must know more. If we want to make real headway, we must have basic data regarding who and what is transported, wherefrom, whereto and why. It is not until this information is available that we can properly ascertain how we should plan our cities, whilst preserving the greatest possible individual freedom of choice. This is necessary if we want to preserve the towns as powerful centres of our society, i.e. as places where a maximum of contacts can be realised with a minimum of traffic.

If a careful analysis is made of the internal transport system of a large concern, we are no longer surprised to find that the results obtained are generally different from what even the best informed manager would have expected. It then appears that the nature, the number and the duration of the contacts deviate appreciably from the views – ostensibly based on sound reasoning – held on the subject. If this holds good for the communications pattern of a single industrial concern, it will be appreciated that it will apply to an even greater extent to that of an urban agglomeration.

Very little research has been done in this direction and yet this type of research is highly essential. In particular, insight should be acquired into

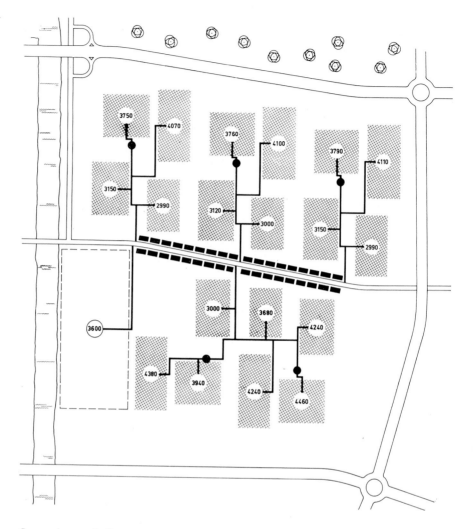

Contacts between dwelling units and shopping area in an urban area of 40.000 inhabitants. The figures represent the distance from the dwelling units to the nearest block of local shops, from there along the other shops and back to the dwelling units. For the traditional lay-out the average distance is 3669 m. For the concentrated lay-out the average distance is 2550 m.

the motives of transport. Since people do not react in the same way everywhere, a number of investigations must be carried out in various places and at various times.

The choice between collective and individual transport will also be an important factor in this connection, because it is not realised sufficiently how great the sacrifices are which the enormous growth of individual transport demands. Individual transport means that far more roads must be built and

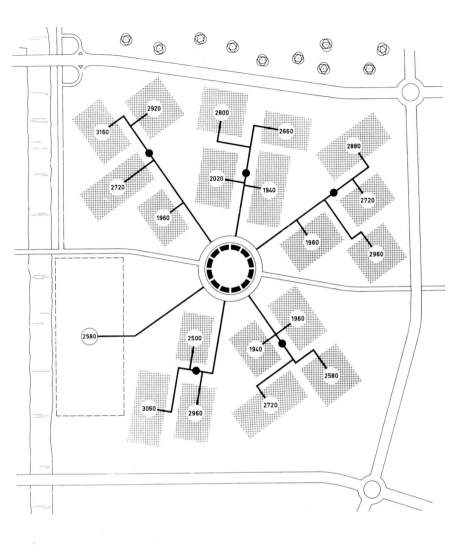

far more energy used than in the case of collective transport. This is clearly evident from Table 16.

Furthermore, a study must be made of times of both the transport and the waiting involved. The results of such investigations will provide a better chance of achieving optimum grouping.

Naturally, transport is not the only aspect of this grouping and there are other problems which also require our attention. An important point which

TABLE 16

THE CONSEQUENCES OF COLLECTIVE AND INDIVIDUAL TRANSPORT

Type of vehicle	Required length* (m)	Total road area required (m²)	Number of passengers per vehicle	Road area per passenger (m²)	Average energy consumption per passenger**
Tram	25	55	100	0.55	32
Bus	21	52.5	70	0.75	87
Passenger car	14.5	23.2	1.7	13.7	450

will influence our decision is whether it will be possible to build multi-storey residential buildings which as regards rent and comfort can compete with the single-family house in the open market.

It must be admitted that at the present time increased prosperity leads to suburbanisation, resulting in vast areas of low houses, involving transport of few people over great distances, relatively large land requirements at the expense of a really liberal distribution of scenic landscape and everything else that is required for social recreation. In the U.S.A. alone 1.1 million acres of open land are lost per year in this way. In this respect many problems could be simplified by multi-storey building, which would be attractive from both the economic and the human points of view. The answer to the question

* Length of vehicle + braking distance
** Kcal/km.

whether we can eliminate the drawbacks of the large cities by introducing a more controlled, decentralised structure, causing less solitude and fewer traffic problems, is a closely associated aspect.

The same applies to the problematics of new towns, *i.e.* the question as to when it becomes desirable to create new towns. Fortunately, the greater transport and communication facilities provide a higher degree of freedom in this respect. An industrial area need no longer be in the immediate vicinity of the power source, *e.g.* coal mines, but can just as well or better be located in a centre of (world) transport. A case in point is the Netherlands steel industry at IJmuiden. The Netherlands has neither ore nor sufficient coal, yet, the favourable location and transport facilities with respect to Sweden, Spain, England and the Ruhr makes it possible to produce steel for the world market at competitive prices.

The possibilities of decentralised use of power will probably become even greater (electric power from nuclear power stations). For large concerns it will also be easier to build new establishments separate from the old. Hitherto, the objection to this has generally been the practical impossibility of achieving the desired uniformity in the daily management of affairs. There is every reason to believe that automation is bringing about a drastic change in this respect. The use of long-distance telephone facilities will enable the administrative data of establishments throughout the continent to be instantly processed by an electronic data processing centre.[1]

It will be appreciated that the scope of this book does not permit a detailed discussion of the problems involved, but even so it will be clear that the problems which we must give our planners to solve are quite considerable. Fortunately, the town-planning of recent decennia clearly exhibits a tendency towards improvement. Planners and town-planners, however, are rightly of opinion that there is as yet no reason for complacency. Planology must be further developed, but we must guard against planocracy. The task of our planners should be of an advisory and not of a dictating nature. It is their task to advise the authorities and to give them insight into the merits of possible alternatives. The ultimate result is not solely determined by the quality of the plan, but also by the extent to which those interested in the execution of the plan are co-operative or obstructive.

Consequently, it is an essential condition that the interests involved in the proper execution of the plans should be made clear to the lower public authorities and to the public as a whole.

We should also guard against planocracy in the sense that in the event of a change in conditions the plan does not have a retarding effect instead of

---

[1] *This progress of cybernetics is not just wishful thinking. An American concern with ten establishments throughout the United States has already made considerable progress in this respect. In addition, the large American telephone companies are busily engaged in developing further possibilities.*

stimulating a better development. The plan should be flexible and lay down the purpose for which the land is to be used in broad outline and no more. The ultimate realisation of social development will largely have to be achieved in a decentralised manner, thus leaving room for fresh initiatives.

Finally, we should guard against planocracy in the sense that the planner replaces the town-planning architect. The planner studies optimum land use, naturally with due observance of the town-planning aspects. The planner works chiefly in two dimensions. As Saarinen has stressed all along, town-planning is essentially three-dimensional and cannot be laid down in advance once and for all.

The architect should be in a position to weigh a building against the atmosphere of what has already been built, which can never be accurately predicted, let alone sensed. For this he needs a certain degree of freedom. A really live town cannot possibly be the product of a single master brain. In practice, the towns forced into a two-dimensional strait-jacket beforehand usually breathe a very dismal atmosphere.

Without planning we shall be faced with chaos. It would amount to failure to appreciate the dynamics of our society if we were to assume that we could perfect our town-planning to the extent that any tension between the project realised and actual development would be entirely ruled out. The perfect prognosis is feasible only in a society which we cannot and do not want to accept now: a society without progress and without hope of a better future.

On the other hand our planning knowledge and skill should be increased to the extent that the tension between realised projects and future practice, so essential for the progress of our human existence, does not become so great that the essential constant adaptation would surpass the boundaries of human ingenuity.

3. THE SOCIAL-ECONOMIC PLANNING OF BUILDING

It is true that "a living nation builds for its future" but it is equally true that a nation must build to keep alive in the future. For a balanced development policy which aims at making the world habitable it is necessary that a substantial part of the investment capacity should be made available for building.

In view of the enormous shortage of dwellings and many other essential buildings careful attention must be given to the distribution of the available building capacity, so that the improvement of physical and mental health can be accompanied by an increase in employment and by an increase in productivity. Careful planning of the building activity is an essential requirement and should be the basis for combating certain shortages. Hence, it is necessary to resort to active planning aiming at optimum results.

In this respect it should be realised, however, that optimum building activity cannot be achieved unless sufficient continuity is ensured. If in the future the demand for building should continue to be either too small or too great, as was the case in many countries in the past, there is no doubt that too little will be built at too high a price. It is not sufficient, therefore, to wait and see how the buying power for buildings will develop, but on the contrary it will be necessary for the benefit of the overall development policy and in particular to ensure a continuous building production that the appropriate provisions are made in the economic system to ensure capital formation and a sound distribution of investment capacity, while the great differences in interest on capital should be substantially reduced.

Continuity of building on an acceptable level is often threatened by fluctuating economic conditions, when building is regarded as a supplementary source of employment or as a means of retarding overall investments.

This will lead to a fundamental situation of unbalance in the building industry with the danger that good workers will transfer to other branches of industry and building will become too risky to warrant large investments in the production apparatus.

In the long run a wrong rent policy can also prove disastrous for the continuity of building. The most natural basis for housing, *viz.* the reasonable rent paid for the important service rendered by the dwelling, is then seriously weakened and with it the basis of sound financing of justified maintenance and new construction. When the rent level is too low the wrong economic sluice is opened and the purchasing power will find its way too soon to other goods and services, thus causing unbalanced spending, which as a rule cannot be entirely rectified.

During a recovery period after a war or in the first phase of development in a given region it may be necessary, however, to bridge a difficult period by introducing rent subsidies or building premiums.

It is essential, however, that the rents should be raised to a reasonable level as soon as prosperity increases and the real income permits and certainly before the changed way of life makes it impossible.

If it is desired to develop the social-economic planning with respect to building, a certain amount of statistical information must be available. For the sake of clarity a diagram [1] of such information is given below:

[1] *This diagram has been taken from the report of the Working Party on Housing and Building Statistics, Paper No. 24, June 2, 1958. Economic Commission for Europe, Housing Committee.*

STATISTICAL SERIES FOR BUILDING.

I. Occupation series of dwellings

1. Pre-war:
   number of existing dwellings and of family households [1]
2. Post-war:
   (*a*) number of dwellings cross-classified according to number of occupants and number of rooms [2]
   (*b*) number of inhabitants and number of family households
   (*c*) number of existing dwellings and rooms
3. Population data (pre-war and post-war years)

II. Activity in the housing sector

1. Dwelling construction expressed quantitatively:
   (*a*) dwellings completed (total), classified according to:
      (*i*) class of builders (public authorities, housing associations, private persons)
      (*ii*) size (number of rooms, floor space, volume)
      (*iii*) structure (dwellings in houses and dwellings in blocks of flats)
      (*iv*) character of building activity (new construction, repairs, etc.) (addition to dwelling stock only)
   (*b*) dwellings under construction
2. Rent (index)

III. Activity in the building sector

1. Volume of building:
   (*a*) residential building (and dwellings therein)
   (*b*) non-residential buildings
2. Value of building, etc., work done (investments):
   (*a*) residential buildings
   (*b*) non-residential buildings
   (*c*) civil engineering
3. Production index

IV Manpower and wages

1. Employment and hours worked:
   (*a*) in housing
   (*b*) in non-residential building/with details of qualification
   (*c*) in civil engineering

[1] *For a year as near as possible to 1939, but not earlier than 1930.*
[2] *Or, for countries for which such information is not available, the number of family households cross-classified according to number of rooms and persons per family household.*

100

2. Unemployment [1]
3. Wages

V. Building materials

1. Consumption
   (*a*) cement
   (*b*) bricks
   (*c*) roofing materials   supplemented by data on other
   (*d*) glass   materials or on different qualities
   (*e*) wood for building   of materials listed
   (*f*) steel for building
2. Prices (index of consumer prices or wholesale   same details as
   prices) for the same materials as under 1   for consumption

VI. Index of building costs

   (*a*) residential building
   (*b*) non-residential building
   (*c*) civil engineering work

Even the collection of the data necessary for the statistical series given in this diagram requires an advanced stage of administrative development. Hence, the social-economic planning with respect to the building industry in the underdeveloped countries cannot as a rule be based on such perfect statistical data, while also in many so-called developed countries building statistics are not sufficiently far advanced.

In the case of those countries which have an adequate administrative apparatus it is strongly recommended to pay careful attention to this statistical activity, and it would be a considerable advantage to have this work done centrally in an institute or a ministry. It is important that this work is placed in the hands of good professional statisticians, especially because increasing use is being made of samples (which is likely to reduce the costs involved) and because sound generalisation and drawing the correct conclusions from statistical data requires expert knowledge.

This also applies in the case of underdeveloped countries and it is encouraging that the U.N.O., the World Bank, etc. are more and more calling upon statisticians and econometrists of world reputation for drawing up a development policy for underdeveloped countries.

Social-economic planning has three closely associated tasks:

(*a*) drawing up programmes, which can to a certain extent be regarded as a task description;
(*b*) the battle against shortages affecting realisation;
(*c*) observation and analysis of realisations.

[1] *Indices of earnings or, if not available, of wage rates.*

The distribution of the total available capacity over the different sectors of building should be effected on the basis of sub-programmes for the most important spheres, such as house-building, school-building, public health buildings, factory-building, road-construction, etc. These sub-programmes could be drawn up to cover a period of one or more years.

Insofar as the decision lies with the government authorities the planning can be regarded as the preparatory stage for production, as has been done in some countries in social house-building, road-construction, etc. The preparatory work is then exclusively dependent on the efficient performance of government organisations, while the execution of the set programme depends on the method of working of the builders with the normal windfalls and disappointments, for which allowance should be made in the planning.

Insofar as the results depend on private initiative, as is largely the case in commercial building in many countries, the planning can be a reservation of the total building capacity for the expected initiatives or the sum of appropriate allocations. This requires a good statistical apparatus, which draws attention in an early stage to plans in preparation and the development thereof and which makes it possible to activate plans where necessary.

9   Building is programming

the initial idea | a study and a decision to build | the basic programme | the programme of requirements | the quality factors | the functional analysis | the functional synthesis | the general functional study | the application | the individual functional study

Building does not start with the laying of the first brick, nor with the excavation work for the foundations. Building starts long beforehand with an initial idea, a study and a decision to build.

The initial idea to erect a building must be immediately followed by a study to establish facts and to make prognoses, resulting in an ultimate decision arrived at by decisionics as discussed in the foregoing.

The question to be decided is whether to build or not and, if the answer is in the affirmative, to what extent.

In some cases it is certainly right from the start that building must be resorted to because of an earlier decision *e.g.* to start production of a new article, for which the building of a new factory is an essential requirement. In other cases the final decision to build cannot be taken until the building costs or the operating costs of the building are known. In many cases, however, it will have to be decided each time after one or more stages of preparation whether it is worth while to start the next stage of preparation.

These preparations are indispensable. They are necessary for laying down the requirements which the building should fulfil. The critical examination resulting from that first decision and the drawing up of the requirements in the so-called programme of requirements are the responsibility of the principal.

The principal is not always fully aware of his responsibilities in this resort. As a rule he is inexperienced as far as building is concerned and he feels uncomfortable about the whole business. This is not surprising, because generally he only acts the part of principal of a building project once or a few times in his life. In practice, it often happens that the building is already being talked about and all kinds of sketches are on the table before a number of important decisions have been seriously considered. The architect is then obviously regarded as someone who will tackle the job and who will design a building that will fulfil all the future requirements which will become evident in practice, without it having been explained to him beforehand what exactly is required. In addition, it is usually also

GENERAL CHART

FROM INITIATIVE TO PROGRAMME OF REQUIREMENTS

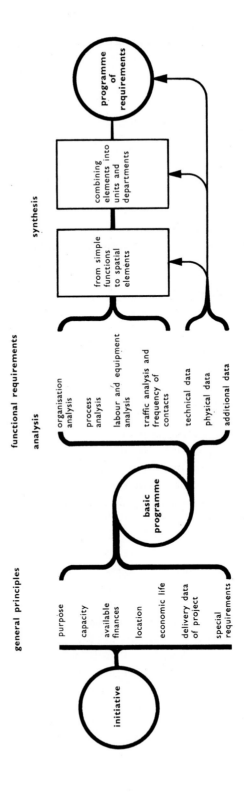

general principles

purpose
capacity
available finances
location
economic life
delivery data of project
special requirements

initiative

basic programme

functional requirements

analysis

organisation analysis
process analysis
labour and equipment analysis
traffic analysis and frequency of contacts
technical data
physical data
additional data

synthesis

from simple functions to spatial elements

combining elements into units and departments

programme of requirements

expected that the building will not cost too much. Such a procedure must undoubtedly lead to difficulties. By laborious questioning the architect must persuade the principal to appreciate fully the consequences of his wishes and yet ultimately arrive at an acceptable programme. Sometimes, however, it appears in the provisional design stage that the design does not fully represent the real intentions of the principal and it also occurs sometimes that during the production or after completion of the building the principal discovers that the architect has failed to bridge by intuition the gaps in the information furnished.

This state of affairs involves a waste of time and money for the principal, but also has a disturbing effect on the relationship between principal and architect.

In many countries the tasks and obligations of the architect, which hitherto were chiefly determined by usage, have become more clearly outlined or else usage has acquired a more compulsory character. Strangely enough, the obligation of the principal to furnish the architect with a sound programme of requirements has not been sufficiently regulated, although it is more or less taken for granted that he should do so. On the other hand, there is nothing that compels the architect to ask for such a programme of requirements before accepting the order. It is most desirable that this matter should be properly regulated, not only in the interests of the parties directly concerned and to avoid disputes between them, but also in the interests of society as a whole, which can only benefit if the programme ensures an optimum of the investments made.

It is in the interests of both the principal and the architect that the latter should not start designing too soon, but first ascertain what decisions must be taken, what information should be available and what other experts should be called in if the principal cannot take care of this himself owing to lack of time, experience or knowledge.

If the task is handled systematically, the first thing to be done is to draw up a basic programme in which the general principles are laid down regarding purpose, capacity, location, target delivery date, etc. (see general chart).

The second stage starts with the composition of the programme of requirements, which is the final stage of the preparations for the design.

In this stage the actual requirements resulting from the decisions laid down in the basic programme are systematically worked out. It is then necessary to ascertain what rooms, etc. are required, the approximate dimensions of these rooms and any further requirements they must fulfil in connection with the use to which they will be put (*e.g.* floor load, wall finish, air conditioning, etc.).

To be able to formulate these requirements the processes which must take place in the building must be analysed to determine their spatial consequences, which means that functional studies must be made. In some cases it will be necessary to call in experts on widely divergent subjects. The works engineer will have specific ideas about the location of the machines, the advertising man is interested in the best way to display the goods, the cinema manager wants to be able to disperse the audience after the performance in the quickest possible way, the chemist is concerned with the equipment of the laboratory, the man in charge of the store has certain ideas about the method of storage.

It will not always be possible to fulfil all the various wishes within the given range of possibilities. The building ultimately realised is invariably the outcome of a number of compromises which by careful weighing and checking have been raised to optimum value via functional studies. It is desirable, therefore, that the principal takes care of the necessary co-ordination. With large building projects it is advisable that a small team, called a programme committee, works out the programme of requirements under his direction. The composition of such a team depends on the nature of the building to be erected. Usually one of its members will be an architect who watches the constructional aspects of the requirements.

The team should generally also include a functional adviser who is trained in handling the problematics of a programme. When it is necessary to make a choice from alternative solutions, it is the responsibility of the principal – having heard the opinions of all parties concerned – to take a decision. Naturally, it is essential that information regarding the costs of alternative solutions should be available during these consultations.

The question as to the extent to which the programme of requirements should be detailed is difficult to answer in a general sense. In some cases a brief description of the requirements will suffice, while in others it will be necessary to incorporate detailed diagrams regarding the location and the lay-out of the various units of space. Sometimes it may be sufficient to state the objects to be placed in a unit stating also the amount of working space required, while in other cases it is preferable to state merely the overall dimensions of the unit.

The nature of the building, the regulations of the authorities and the mentality and experience of the architect are also factors that can play a part here.

Programme changes during the design phase or even during erection will not always be avoidable, even with the most thorough preparation. Thorough preparation, however, can ensure that these changes will be restricted to those which are strictly essential.

108

The quality of the basic programme and of the programme of requirements determines to a large extent the quality of the building. The functional qualities of the building can be greatly enhanced by carefully weighing the desiderata against the possibilities and taking into account the results of studies or the experience of others when drawing up the programme of requirements.

Table 17 presents a survey of the most important quality factors that determine the objective quality of the building. The information has been classified in seven main points and has been obtained by analysing and checking a number of technical, sociological, physiological and psychological aspects. It enables an accurate description of the required rooms to be compiled. On the strength of this information the principal can present the architect with his accurately defined wishes and requirements.

TABLE 17

QUALITY FACTORS OF THE PROGRAMME OF REQUIREMENTS

Aspects \ Programme	Technical aspects	Sociological aspects
	Physiological-psychological aspects	
1. *Rooms:*		
Number	Centralisation and decentralisation, direct contact	Organisational unit, avoiding conflicting situations, social status
Dimensions:		
	Arrangement of equipment and/or inventory; space for process and circulation	Joy derived from work Social status
2. *Constructional requirements:*		
(a) construction	Floor load, loads on walls and ceiling, minimum column spacing	Feeling of safety
(b) finish	Strength, maintenance, dirt deposits, reflection, ventilation	Good working conditions, view, sun access
3. *Physico-technical requirements:* Interior air conditions:		
temperature, humidity, purity, velocity	Requirements originating from process and materials. Labour output	Joy derived from work, comfort

continued on next page

109

TABLE 17 CONTINUED

QUALITY FACTORS OF THE PROGRAMME OF REQUIREMENTS

Aspects \\ Programme	Technical aspects _Physiological-psychological aspects_	Sociological aspects
Lighting: artificial lighting, daylight sun protection	Lighting of the room and light for carrying out the process	Joy derived from work
Noise nuisance, vibration	Fatigue, deadening noise of process	Mental and nervous load
4. _Provisions:_ Outlets for gas, water, compressed air, electric power, etc., communication systems, fire protection, refuse disposal	Requirements for process	Personal hygiene
5. _Requirements for access and departure:_ Location: each room with respect to other rooms	Contacts, flow of goods, process flow, internal transport, organisation, supervision	Avoiding conflicting situations, social status
each room with respect to street	Access roads, parking facilities	Contact with outside world (view, sun access); status of process to be accommodated
Constructional consequences: number and dimensions of entrances, facilities for means of transport	Requirements of process and materials	
6. _Internal and external flexibility:_ Internal: adaptation possibilities	Adaptation to changed circumstances and changed process	
External: possibilities of expansion	Correction of errors in prognosis. Growth	
7. _Additional requirements of the principal_		

General principles to be considered in drawing up a basic programme include:

1. purpose
2. capacity
3. amount to be invested
4. location
5. economic life
6. target delivery date of building
7. possibilities of expansion, flexibility, transportability.

The *purpose* of the building should be described in such a way that a rough impression can be gained of the consequences for the building and a basis is provided for a subsequent more detailed description.

To determine the *capacity* it will usually be necessary to calculate or at least estimate as closely as possible the requirements and/or marketing possibilities. The questions to be answered in this connection would concern, for example, the number of pupils to be accommodated in a school with a given curriculum and the educational method to be adopted in the school, the number of beds to be provided in a given hospital to be able to serve a specific region in a certain way, the capacity of a filling station along a certain highway, the marketing possibilities of a given article, etc.

To answer questions regarding the *amount to be invested* or the maximum permissible operating costs it will also be necessary to make calculations or estimates that can partly be derived from the purpose and the capacity. Allowance will have to be made for information regarding, for example, the acceptable nursing charges in the case of a hospital or regarding the contributions or grants from third parties in the case of a sports hall or a theatre.

It is not always necessary or desirable to assume a fixed sum for the realisation of a building. It will often be sufficient to indicate the limits between which this sum may lie. This applies particularly if further details regarding the permissible capital investments cannot be furnished until a later phase of preparation.

The *location* may be fixed beforehand, for example, if it is desired to build a shop in the centre of a town and only a single site is available. If there is a choice, the pros and cons of the different possibilities will have to be weighed.

The points to be considered would then be, for example, the availability of labour in a given area, transport facilities (public means of transport, waterways, etc.), the price of land, building restrictions applicable to a certain site, nuisance caused by industries established in the vicinity (*e.g.*water pollution), nuisance caused to others by the establishment to be erected, representative aspects of the location, etc.

111

The determination of the *economic life* of the building is especially important in connection with the operating costs but can also affect the design and construction of the building. Often there is a tendency to construct a building in such a way that the technical life substantially exceeds the economic life without there being any rational grounds for this.

The fixing of the *target delivery date* of the building is often passed over lightly. This date, however, can be of essential importance. This is the case, for example, with a building for an exhibition which is held for a limited period only, with a hotel which must be open to the public before the holiday season starts, with a factory which must put its products on the market before a competitor takes the lead.

When fixing the target date care must be taken that the architect and the contractors are given sufficient time to prepare and execute their work properly. Hence, it will be necessary to ensure efficient general planning of the preparatory work, particularly with a view to avoiding unnecessary loss of time in taking the decisions essential for smooth progress.

The possibilities of *expansion*, *flexibility* and *transportability* must be included in the survey right from the start. If these subjects are left too late, this can lead to serious damage later. A concern which could increase its sales but finds it impossible to do so because its machine shop cannot be expanded, whilst the likely increase in sales is not such that it would justify erection of a new building elsewhere, will suffer a loss. A business office which can only introduce mechanisation by adapting the building at considerable expense will likewise suffer a loss.

It is not an easy matter for the principal to furnish the answers to all these queries, which moreover may be dependent on each other to a large extent. As is evident from the foregoing, we are especially concerned in this phase with problems of an economic or industrial-economic nature or other questions which can only be answered with expert knowledge and training. The principal will, therefore, often have to call in experts or institutes specialising in certain subjects. The preparation stage of building starts with the initial decision to build; arguments are collected to support this decision, and these arguments can, if necessary, be revised in the course of the preparation phase.

The basic programme being completed and accepted, the second and final stage of preparation starts with the gathering of data for the programme of requirements.

In the programme a distinction is made between functional requirements (concerning space elements, space units, transport) and supplementary requirements (concerning lighting, protection against heat and cold, installations, etc.). The functional requirements result from a functional analysis, followed by a functional synthesis.

The functional analysis comprises, in the main, five steps:

1. The purpose of the building to be erected is taken as a basis to derive the functions to be fulfilled and thus the actions to be performed in it.
2. The process which must take place in the building is established by efficient arrangement of consecutive and/or parallel process elements.
3. The logical arrangement of the process elements is checked against a chart of the organisation to be accommodated in the building (and vice versa).
4. The requirements in respect of manpower, machines, installations and equipment are determined for each process element individually.
5. The nature, volume and frequency of the traffic and transport involved between the various process elements are determined.

We shall now take a closer look at these five steps of the functional analysis with reference to specific examples.

The functional analysis commences with a description of the activities that will take place and of the people, materials, machines, furniture and the like which will be involved therein. The information from the basic programme – chiefly the description of the purpose – will have to serve as a basis for this function description, but in addition supplementary information will be required, which, if necessary, must be acquired by study.

EXAMPLE 1

ORGANISATION CHART

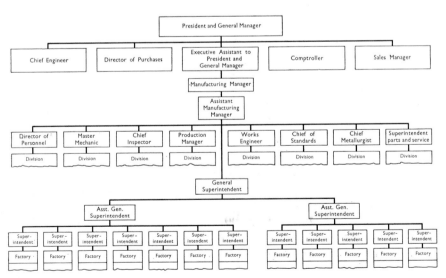

113

When composing the description, reference must be made first of all to an organisation chart of the works, which will illustrate the hierarchy and the differentiation of the organisation, but not the size and the importance of specific production departmens for instance (example 1).

The manner in which the description should be set out depends on the type of building and the nature of the process which will take place in that building.

It will usually be practical to represent this process in the form of a chart which is called a process chart.

In the case of factories for which the description can be arranged in the chronological order of the operations, this chart can generally be derived from the operations process chart, which shows the operations and the flow of the goods produced, and from which in turn a rough idea of the organic units or departments, as well as the necessary inventory articles for these departments, can be derived (example 2).

In the case of a business office where there is generally no question of production of a given number of products, but of processes, the process chart can be put in the form of a detailed organisation chart.

When describing the functions of a cinema the chronological order of the various events can be maintained and laid down diagrammatically.

In the case of a dwelling – in which a large number of processes occur simultaneously – it would be practical to bundle, describe and represent diagrammatically a number of associated functions together *e.g.* purchasing, preparing and cooking food, meals and washing up.

Generally speaking, it is incorrect to make a classification according to the rooms, etc. in which the various functions should be performed. In that case the rooms are fixed prematurely and would be used as a starting point instead of being derived from the functions.

The next step in the functional analysis is to lay down information regarding contacts, traffic or transports. This information determines the location of the rooms to be created, both with respect to each other and with respect to the street, and will have certain consequences in regard to the amount of space required (requirements relating to the capacity of circulation space, the width of corridors and the like when using certain means of transport, number and types of entrances ,etc.).

By observing or analysing comparable processes an insight should be obtained into these requirements. It will depend on the nature of the apparatus to be accommodated whether the traffic of people or the transport of goods or materials will prevail (*e.g.* in an office this will be the traffic of people, in a factory the transport of raw materials, semi-manufactured products, etc.) (example 3).

EXAMPLE 2
OPERATIONS PROCESS CHART

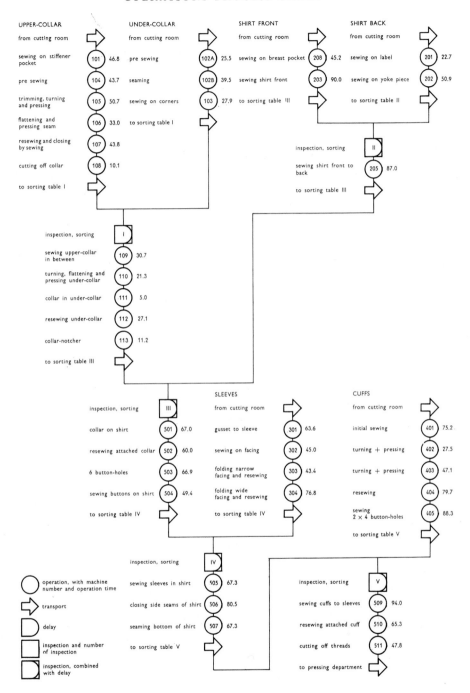

UPPER-COLLAR

from cutting room

sewing on stiffener pocket	101	46.8
pre sewing	104	43.7
trimming, turning and pressing	105	50.7
flattening and pressing seam	106	33.0
resewing and closing by sewing	107	43.8
cutting off collar	108	10.1

to sorting table I

UNDER-COLLAR

from cutting room

pre sewing	102A	25.5
seaming	102B	39.5
sewing on corners	103	27.9

to sorting table I

SHIRT FRONT

from cutting room

sewing on breast pocket	208	45.2
sewing shirt front	203	90.0

to sorting table III

inspection, sorting II

sewing shirt front to back 205 87.0

to sorting table III

SHIRT BACK

from cutting room

sewing on label	201	22.7
sewing on yoke piece	202	50.9

to sorting table II

---

inspection, sorting I

sewing upper-collar in between	109	30.7
turning, flattening and pressing under-collar	110	21.3
collar in under-collar	111	5.0
resewing under-collar	112	27.1
collar-notcher	113	11.2

to sorting table III

---

inspection, sorting III

collar on shirt	501	67.0
resewing attached collar	502	60.0
6 button-holes	503	66.9
sewing buttons on shirt	504	49.4

to sorting table IV

SLEEVES

from cutting room

gusset to sleeve	301	63.6
sewing on facing	302	45.0
folding narrow facing and resewing	303	43.4
folding wide facing and resewing	304	76.8

to sorting table IV

CUFFS

from cutting room

initial sewing	401	75.2
turning + pressing	402	27.5
turning + pressing	403	47.1
resewing	404	79.7
sewing 2 × 4 button-holes	405	88.3

to sorting table V

○	operation, with machine number and operation time
⇨	transport
⊃	delay
□	inspection and number of inspection
⊐	inspection, combined with delay

inspection, sorting IV

sewing sleeves in shirt	505	67.3
closing side seams of shirt	506	80.5
seaming bottom of shirt	507	67.3

to sorting table V

inspection, sorting V

sewing cuffs to sleeves	509	94.0
resewing attached cuff	510	65.3
cutting off threads	511	47.8

to pressing department

115

EXAMPLE 3

TRAFFIC CHART

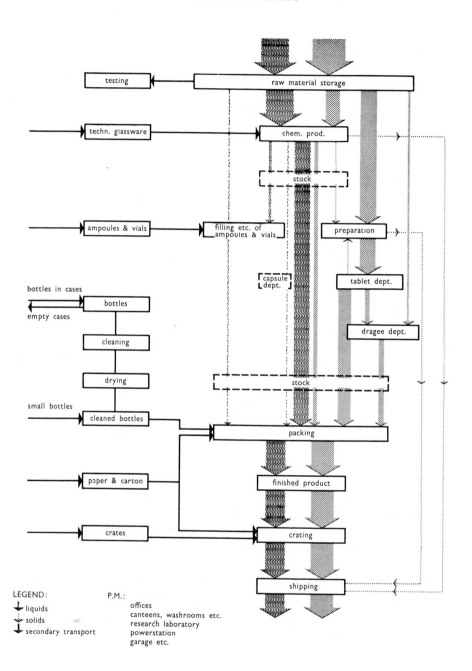

EXAMPLE 4

CONTACT AND FREQUENCY CHART

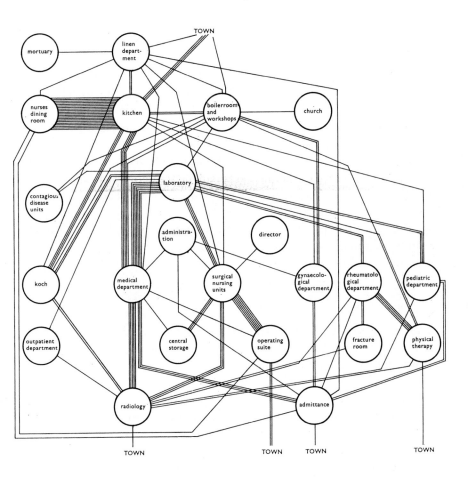

When determining the requirements resulting from the movement of people, problems will be encountered such as: which persons or groups of persons have regular contact with each other and which of them have regular contact with the public; how many people should be able to enter or leave the building within a given time; what is the frequency of the food transports? Such information can be laid down in traffic and contact diagrams. Sometimes it may be sufficient to incorporate in these diagrams simple indications regarding the frequency of the contacts (e.g. intensive or little contact) and the numbers of persons (e.g. many, few or none (example 4).

In other cases it will be necessary to ascertain an accurately described volume (e.g. number of times that a contact occurs, number of persons that should be able to use a certain entrance within a given period of time.

117

The same applies, in principle, to the movement of goods, raw materials, semi-manufactured products, etc., and the resulting requirements with respect to the capacity of circulation space, means of transport required, etc. The problems encountered here are for example: in which phase of a production process should a certain raw material become available, in what quantities and during what period of time?

Here again, the information can be laid down in the simple form of a contact diagram indicating the organic units between which contacts occur, but also in the form of a transport diagram indicating also the quantities of materials to be transported so that an insight is obtained into the volume of the various contacts or of the goods.

Before this transport diagram is made up it will generally be necessary to have, in addition to a contact diagram, a transport analysis in which the entire production process including intermediate phases, such as inspection, intermediate storage and the like, is analysed and in which per phase the quantities of materials which become or must be available at a certain place and at a given time are indicated.

The functional analysis provides as a rule a survey of the functions to be fulfilled, of the manpower and the machines involved, of their mutual association and of the traffic and transport resulting therefrom.

The time has now come to start on the functional synthesis with a view to determining the spatial consequences of the functions.

The following can be distinguished:

(a) working out the spatial elements (e.g. space required for a typist with desk and chair);

(b) combining elements into units (e.g. rooms, workshops, etc.);

(c) arranging units with a view to achieving optimum contacts;

(d) combining units into departments.

These operations present a number of problems.

When determining the spatial consequences, allowance must be made for the space which the worker requires for the operations to be performed, the space occupied by machines, furniture, stocks, etc. and the appropriate circulation space around the machine, the piece of furniture or the means of transport.

Often uniform elements are involved, which are repeated in a given building or a series of buildings so that it will suffice to determine the spatial consequences of a single element. For example, a typist sitting at a typing desk with a typewriter, a housewife sitting or standing in front of a drainboard, a worker working at a drilling machine (example 5).

These elements can later be combined into units, a room, a shop, etc., and arranged in accordance with transport requirements (example 6).

EXAMPLE 5

FROM SIMPLE FUNCTIONS TO SPATIAL ELEMENTS

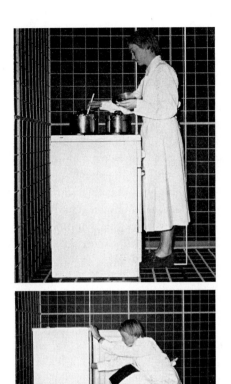

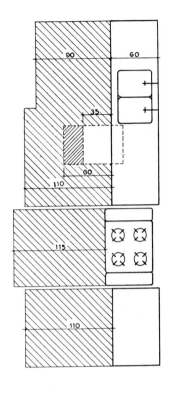

The size of the various units of space, etc. must be fixed; to this end the following aspects must be taken into account:

(a) what are the spatial consequences of each function?

(b) what functions can be combined in a single space without interference occurring and without the combination being in conflict with the requirements as regards location, ventilation, regulations of the labour inspection, etc.?

The possibility of combining elements to units of space are limited by various factors such as:

(a) psychological factors (too little space, too much space, feeling cramped or feeling lost in space);

119

(*b*) climatological factors (cold, warm, too damp, draught);

(*c*) economic factors (inefficient space, too expensive);

(*d*) labour-technical factors (space requirements not matching the production process);

(*e*) organisational factors (not readily surveyable, too large, too small);

(*f*) technical factors (constructionally impossible to realise);

(*g*) aesthetic factors (disharmonious space, bare, cold. businesslike, romantic, beautiful, ugly).

The importance of the various factors is in turn determined by the nature of the functions. Psychological and aesthetic factors for example will weigh more heavily in a dwelling than in a factory. In a factory, however, the economic, labour-technical and organisational factors may be of paramount importance.

If these units can be regarded, both organisationally and as regards contacts, as units of a still larger unit, they can, if necessary, be combined into departments. Such larger units might take the form of floors or wings (example 7).

Finally, the supplementary requirements must be fixed, taking into account for each unit of space the function or functions performed therein. These may relate to floor finish, air-conditioning, telephone, calling or public address systems, etc.

EXAMPLE 6

COMBINING ELEMENTS INTO UNITS IN A HOSPITAL NURSING
DEPARTMENT

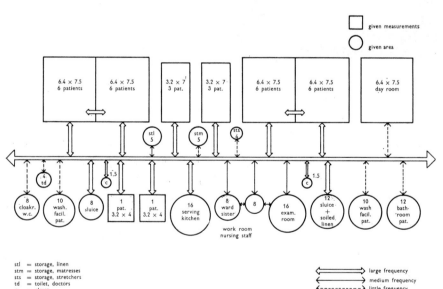

stl = storage, linen
stm = storage, matresses
sts = storage, stretchers
td = toilet, doctors
c = closet

The work involved in compiling a programme of requirements in its most extensive form results in:

(a) a list of units of space and inventory required, stating all relevant data (length, width, height, temperature, required ventilation capacity, etc.);

(b) a functional diagram, indicating:
   - the individual units of space, each of them with the floor area required, the location of the inventory articles with their work and circulation space;
   - the exact location of each unit with respect to each other and to the street, showing also the units formed into departments: lay-out (see example 8).

Moreover, the programme of requirements must be checked for its possibilities of realisation and against the economic requirements laid down in the basic programme. Hence, a report representing the programme of requirements is supplemented by:

EXAMPLE 7

COMBINING UNITS INTO DEPARTMENTS IN A TOWN-HALL

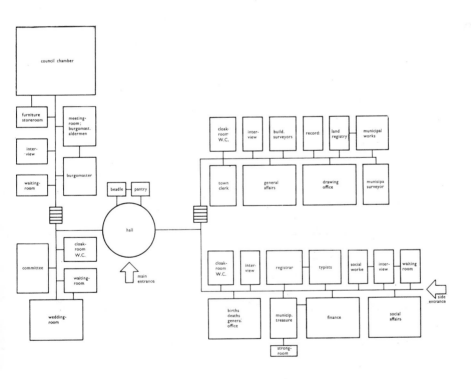

(c) a provisional estimate of the total capital investment and the investment per functional unity (*e.g.* per seat in a theatre or restaurant, per bed in a hotel or hospital, etc.);

(d) an estimate of the account of the future operation in the building in use (including all costs of this building).

EXAMPLE 8

LAY-OUT OF AN ENVELOPE FACTORY

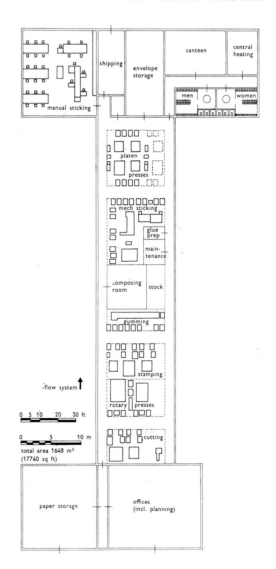

Since the composition of the programme of requirements has an overriding influence on the quality of the building, it is an important problem how the architect should obtain a programme of requirements incorporating for a given purpose the objective quality factors which determine the value of the future building or part thereof for the principal. A complete prior analysis of the quality factors for each individual building may be considered an impossibility in view of the extensive study this would require.

Although each building has its individual characteristics, it is a fortunate circumstance that buildings which have a lot in common or contain many similar elements can nevertheless be grouped together. The buildings which belong to a definite category serve the same purpose and are of the same type, e.g. a primary school, a policlinic, a one-family house for an agricultural worker, etc. Hence, the commonly occurring buildings can be divided into a number of essentially different types of buildings.

It is also possible to distinguish typical departments which occur in varying numbers in certain types of buildings combined in some way or other with other departments, such as kitchen, nursing unit, gymnasium, canteen, etc. There are also other typical units of space, such as waiting room, cloakroom, single hotel bedrooms, etc.

To ensure that a sound programme of requirements can be drawn up for each individual building with a minimum of costs and loss of time, a general functional study should be made for each regularly recurring type of building, making the greatest possible use of available information on typical departments or typical units of space occurring therein.

This general functional study should result in an operating scheme of the institution functioning in this type of building, e.g. a nursing home for old people, and in a schematic programme of requirements of the type of building concerned.

When the practical preparation for a given building is taken in hand, it is an easy matter to bring the available general functional study to the appropriate stage for the particular building. This study can be called an applied general functional study in which allowance can be made for the special circumstances of the individual case in question. The result can be a complete programme of requirements.

If it appears during the practical preparation that no general functional studies are available, one of three things can be done.

The building can be built without functional planning, in which case the risks involved should be weighed against the often imaginary gain in time and minor costs of the functional study.

Other parties interested can be approached with a view to carrying out a joint functional study and subsequently taking in hand the practical preparation of the individual building, in which case the time required for the preparations will be considerably longer. This method can be adopted in practice only if the building in question is one which is not too rare. However, if the building is one which seldom occurs or for which collaboration with others cannot be considered, the only remaining possibility is to make an individual functional study.

Functional research and the need for extensive teamwork in this type of research will not be discussed in this chapter.

When Bouwcentrum was faced with the task of making functional studies for types of buildings intended for the care of old people, the first thing done was to draw up a typology of old people, which is illustrated in Table 18.

Then general functional studies were carried out concerning the special types of buildings that correspond with this typology. The same systematic method has been followed in numerous other fields, such as dwellings, hospitals, town-halls, sport halls, hotels, etc.

TABLE 18

TYPOLOGY OF OLD PEOPLE WITH THE APPROPRIATE FORMS OF HOUSING, GENERAL CARE AND NURSING [1]

fit	requiring (general care or nursing)					
or	relativ-ely fit	infirm				
tempo-		physically			mentally	
rarily infirm		capable of being nursed at home	not capable of being nursed at home		asocial	mental-ly de-ficient	insane
			not re-quiring special medical care	requir-ing special medical care			
dwellings	homes with or without auxiliary dwellings	nursing homes	hospi-tals	special homes	nursing estab-lish-ments	mental hospi-tals

[1] *Taken from Report by Friesland Foundation for Social Case-Work.*

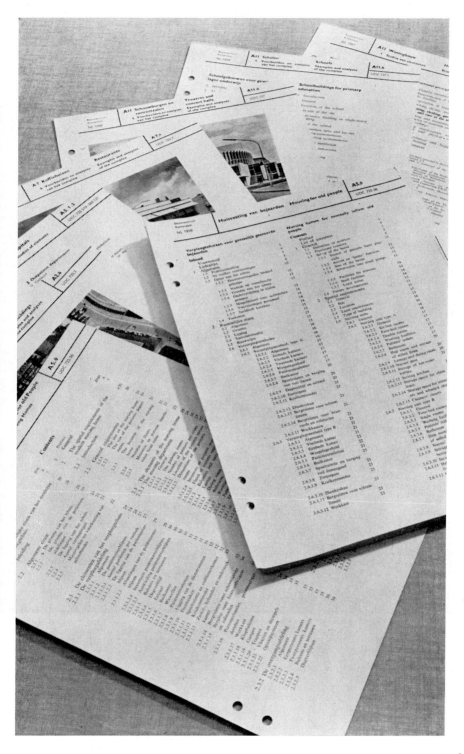

the "aristocratic" quality / the optimum quality / the optimum number of types / the physical requirements / finish of walls, ceiling and floor / grouping of space and building units / the load-bearing structure / the choice of building materials / the technical and functional life of buildings / minimisation of the "all-in" costs / the industrial designer / forms and aspects of forms / the task of the architect / the fine arts / the objective and subjective qualities of the design

1. TOWARDS OPTIMUM QUALITY

The specific phase of design commences after systematic preparations on small and large scale by physical planning, drawing up national and town building programmes and compiling the programme of requirements for the building or the group of buildings in question. This phase is not reached suddenly. Sometimes it is more or less consciously introduced by choosing the location of the building and by the specific work involved in drawing up the programme of requirements, especially the functional synthesis. It is at this point that the architect familiarises himself with the project so as to be able to contribute his share to the design. In this stage of the design, which should often be accompanied by a check analysis – to watch over the programme of requirements – and during which it is essential constantly to bear in mind the possibilities of rational production, the architect is faced with a difficult task. He must unite the knowledge and the products of many in a single building and the result should be more than just the sum of individual effective units of space and even more than a collection of such units joined together in the most rational manner.

Armed with his imagination, his powers of conception and his personal taste, his task is to create an harmonious and useful building and to give it a subjective quality, whilst observing the essential objective quality elements laid down in the programme of requirements and, in addition, those which are necessary to ensure rational production.

It is understandable that the artist-architect tends to regard each design as a completely new and unique problem. He does not think along functional lines like the lay-out engineer, but rather along formalistic lines in terms of mass, form, rhythm, proportion, accentuation, light and dark and other aspects of form and space.

If certain essential functional requirements stand in the way of his spontaneous conception of form, he will sometimes try to have his own way at the expense of the objective quality of the building, basing his

127

arguments on what he considers higher interests, which need not always be justified. In doing so he creates the impression that he wants to cover up his incapacity to control the complicated problem by an escape from reality.

He will sometimes want to design everything himself, every constructional detail, each building element and each piece of furniture, because nothing fully satisfies him in his concentrated urge to execute his unique task. He then aims at a singular "aristocratic" quality of the building according to a design with maximum subjective qualities.

It will be evident that, if at the same time he succeeds in satisfying the prescribed objective requirements, the resulting building will be a success in every respect.

In practice, however, this strong urge towards originality will generally lead to disappointment, although it cannot be denied that this prototype building has often resulted in surprising developments in architecture and building technique and has sometimes led to the rapid introduction of new materials in practical building. However, progress can be achieved far more efficiently by systematic experimental building without encountering serious difficulties as is the case now. The methods now adopted in many countries lead to an unwarranted and tiring diversity and to results which are often functionally and technically inadequate.

Many experienced architects, therefore, have departed from these methods and for practical reasons they have introduced a certain amount of standardisation in their own offices. Architects of great reputation indulge in a certain amount of a repetition even in outward appearance of the building as a whole or important elements thereof. The experienced architect has realised that it is simply impossible to treat each building project as a unique problem and to create in each case an original piece of art. He is beginning to see the project as a combination of a number of smaller problems, for which successful solutions found either by himself or by others can be used. He is beginning to display an increasing interest in industrial design, involving a repetitive industrial aspect instead of the singular achievement of the craftsman.

Theoretically speaking, anything that must be designed will have an infinite number of different properties, but in practice the number of properties that can be influenced by dimensioning, choice of raw materials and production methods is not infinitely great, but nevertheless quite considerable.

Assuming that by a thorough functional study it is established what requirements a chair must fulfil in a given situation, the result could be symbolically represented by a point in the n-dimensional space, where n represents the number of properties included in the study. Since no two people have the same physical build the design of a chair can only be ideal for one specific "owner". Symbolically, each situation has a different point in the n-dimensional space. Hence, the situation itself is unique.

In the case of a given steel structure it will follow from the strength calculations that an I-section girder with a resistance moment of 230 cm³ will be required. In another case the span or the load might be somewhat different and the resistance moment of the girder would have to be, for example, 238 cm³. It is highly improbable that for two different structures the required resistance moments would be exactly the same.

It need hardly be pointed out that in the case of clothing the situation of any consumer is unique. Even if we disregard all the differences with respect to fashion and taste, it will be necessary that – to ensure an ideal fit – a large number of measurements should be matched to the corresponding physical measurements of the wearer. In anthropometrical investigations carried out in 1947 under the direction of J. Sittig [1] on behalf of the

[1] J. Sittig, Consulting Statistician, Bouwcentrum, Rotterdam.

standardisation of sizes for ready-made women's clothing in the Netherlands, it was found that among the 5,000 women whose measurements were taken no two women were the same when taking as few as four physical measurements.

The requirements on which a building must be based are particularly complicated and consequently unique in each individual case.

The desire to treat each building project as a unique problem and the fact that each set of requirements is unique have a retarding effect on the industrialisation of building.

Practically all the old industries are more or less borne down by the tradition of the "made-to-measure" technique. This is not surprising, because a few centuries ago all material needs of man were largely satisfied to measure. The product was made by the craftsman for an individual customer and thus allowance could be made for all the specific requirements of that customer.

The fulfilment of human needs to-day is more and more being effected on the ready-made pattern, involving production for the unknown customer, whose specific requirements are not known to the producer.

It will be clear that as the level of prosperity rises the ready-made goods will have to fulfil more and more stringent quality requirements.

In building also there is an increasing tendency to design without knowing the ultimate users of the product (houses, schools, hospitals, etc.) and the fact, therefore, that each set of requirements is unique no longer constitutes a decisive argument to regard each design as a unique problem.

An additional factor is that the building materials and elements industry is rapidly developing, which promotes a strong tendency towards standardisation. The same applies to the installations and the equipment used in the building. If the architect wants to be practical, he must allow for all this. Moreover, he is swamped with brochures containing illustrations and descriptions of all kinds of finished and semi-finished products, which cannot fail to influence him to some extent.

Most of the factories concerned find themselves in a difficult position. They certainly appreciate the advantages of efficient mass-production, but they are often still inclined to make what the architect designs himself, although this invariably involves a noticeable or unnoticeable price increase. The result is that a confusing variety of all kinds of products is brought on the market, while the factories do not supply products of optimum quality owing to lack of specialisation and type restriction, usually accentuated by a limited home market. Often as a result of competition, the building industry finds itself in the unpleasant position of having to produce "made-to-measure" and "ready-made" products at the same time, thus making rational mass-production impossible.

Prosperity, ready-made products and mass-production are so closely associated that is is hardly necessary to argue about the desirability of mass production, because division of work, specialisation and mass production have undoubtedly resulted in an enormous increase in labour productivity. Moreover, the production of consumer goods is now so enormous, so varied and of such high quality as could not have been dreamt of two or three hundred years ago. All this has been possible despite the fact that, both as regards intensity and volume, human effort has been substantially reduced. It is due to the industrial development outlined above that it is now possible for workers in the industrialised countries to acquire consumer goods which make their life more agreeable than would have been possible for kings and emperors in the middle ages, while these same workers also have the spare time to enjoy these goods.

There is, of course, a reverse side to this picture. The advantage of "made-to-measure" is that allowance can be made for the individual requirements. This is only partially so with the "ready-made" article and seeing that each situation is unique as regards its specific requirements, this will unavoidably give rise to tension, which can only be neutralised by a sound compromise between what is desirable on the consumption side and what is possible on the production side. To find this compromise is the task of those responsible for rational standardisation.

If, in production, allowance were to be made for the exact character of the individual requirements, it would be necessary to abandon any form of mass production and give each article different properties. It will be clear that this is impossible. A question which then immediately presents itself is: if it is impossible to produce for all the points in the n-dimensional space for which there is a need, to which point or points should the design of the article in question be adapted?

What has happened in practice in recent decennia is that a system of standardisation has been adopted, *i.e.* for some articles a single type (corresponding to one point in the n-dimensional property space) has been established as a normal commercially available article and for other products more than one type.

Since for each article a single type (or a limited number of types) has been selected from an infinite number of possibilities, we are concerned here with a problem involving a choice or a decision.

If we ask ourselves how these decisions were taken, the answer must be: generally unsystematically and irrationally. These decisions were based, for example, on prevailing customs in the trade, but without taking into account that such customs might no longer be rational.

Reverting to the example of structural steel referred to earlier, who would dare to say that the I-section girders now manufactured with resistance moments of $19.5 - 34.2 - 54.2 - 81.9 - 117 - 161 - 214 - 278$ cm³, etc. constitute a rational series? Who would dare to say that the packing of cement in 50-kg bags is the best solution to this decisionic problem? Is it really true that the packing of oranges in boxes of 40 kg (dating back to the time when there was practically no female personnel in the greengrocer's shops) is the best method? Is it right that a woman who wants to buy a dress can only choose from a range in which a greater waist measurement automatically implies a greater length?

Yet, we have a problem here which is of great importance socially. Incorrect standardisation results in too many or too few types being manufactured and distributed and – what is worse perhaps – in the manufacture of wrong and irrational types. Such incorrect standardisation has a very damaging effect owing to waste of material and labour or because the needs of the people are not fulfilled to the extent that would be possible with the present state of techniques. The use of inadequate size systems for clothing, for example, results on the one hand in people being less well dressed than would otherwise be possible and on the other hand in enormous sums of money having to be spent annually on alterations to ready-made garments, even in a small country like the Netherlands. The worst of this type of loss is that is is generally not noticed and, if it is noticed at all, that it is considered unavoidable.

The basic idea of the solution should be to achieve such standardisation that the total costs of satisfying the requirements in a given sphere (the concern in industrial standardisation and society in national and international standardisation) are reduced to a minimum. To be able to calculate this it is necessary to know on the one hand the production and distribution costs in relation to the quantity and the quality of the standardised types, while on the other hand it should be possible to express the extent to which the requirements are not properly fulfilled as an element of cost.
The latter is done by introducing the loss-function.

Let us imagine the n-dimensional property space, in which an individual demand situation is represented by a single point.

If the types of articles manufactured do not exactly match the demand and can, therefore, be symbolically represented by a series of points in the n-dimensional space, none of which coincides with the demand point, the consumer will have to be satisfied with a non-ideal fulfilment of his needs and will consequently suffer a loss, which can be expressed by adding a cost figure to each point of the n-dimensional space. At one point only, *viz.* the point representing the demand in the given case, the value of this cost function is zero. To illustrate this we will take a very simple case, in which the number of dimensions in the property space has been reduced to one. The question is: "What should be the length of a bed for a man 1.75 m tall?"

Let us assume that by experiments we have established that the ideal length of the bed for this type of man solely depends on his height and that this length is 1.90 m (measured in a given way). This can be put differently by saying that the optimum fit is + 15 cm, which has the advantage that at the same time a solution is provided for men with a height other than 1.75 m. It will be clear that losses would occur if this man were given a bed of the wrong length. These losses differ according to whether the bed is too short or too long and it can generally be said that the losses are greater according as the distance to the optimum point is greater.

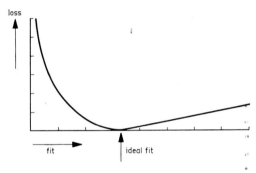

example of a loss function

As regards the nature of the losses, a bed that is too small will result in less comfortable sleep, while it will hardly be possible to sleep at all in a bed which is much too small. Hence, the damage is in the form of loss of health. If on the other hand the bed is too long, the damage is purely of an economic nature. In the first place the bed is more expensive than necessary (waste of material and labour), the sheets and blankets must be larger than necessary, and last but not least larger beds mean larger bedrooms and thus larger building volume than would be necessary for the ideal fulfilment of actual requirements.

In this case the determination of the optimum type, if only one type is to be manufactured, amounts to shifting the frequency distribution of the requirement in relation to the loss function until a situation is found in which the total loss on account of a bad fit is reduced to a minimum. Since the problem is one-dimensional, the shift is controlled by only a single parameter (*a*).

Let

x = the variable in question (the man's height)

$f(x)$ = the frequency of x (height of the potential users)

$L(x/a)$ = the loss function

The problem is then to reduce the magnitude

$$E = \int L(x/a) f(x)\, dx$$

to a minimum with respect to a.

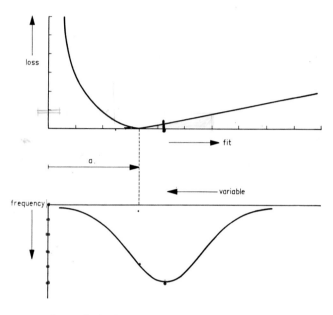

choice if one type is to be standardised

It follows that to match the size of the type to be manufactured to the average height of the users will generally not result in an optimum solution, because the loss function is not symmetrical. If a bed which is 20 cm too short will cause greater loss than a bed which is 20 cm too long, the type to be manufactured will have to be matched to a human height greater than the average height.

Similar calculations can also be made for more than one type and it is possible to arrive at a minimum loss due to failure to satisfy the requirements of the unique demand for any number of types. This loss will be less according as the number of types is greater. It is also possible to calculate the extra costs of production and distribution resulting from the additional types produced. These extra costs are higher according as the number of types produced is greater. The sum of the two types of costs represents the total extra costs which ultimately result from the variations in the demand. The point where this total cost curve shows a minimum represents the optimum number of types to be standardised from the social point of view.

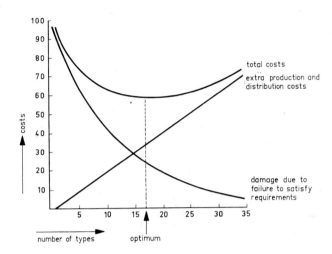

the optimum number of types

The amount of study necessary to achieve optimum standardisation must not be underestimated. It requires a thorough functional study to ascertain the demand situation, insight into the production and distribution costs of the product and a study of the damage due to failure to satisfy requirements. The last-mentioned point especially will generally be a problem that cannot be solved at short notice, because this damage can—especially in the sphere of the consumer—often be of a moral or aesthetic character. It is to be expected, therefore, that quick results can be obtained especially in the sphere of industrial standardisation, because the problems here are generally less imponderable.

This does not alter the fact that in our opinion also in the sphere of general standardisation an effort to achieve rational standardisation will be useful (and has already proved useful).

Even if it should be impossible to carry out the whole calculation, an attempt in that direction will furnish so much information regarding the functional requirements to be fulfilled by the product and its cost structure that a more rational fulfilment of the demand is achieved, even if the mathematical optimum standardisation cannot yet be realised.

The application of the above general theory [1] can raise standardisation

[1] *developed by J. Sittig, Consulting Statistician, Bouwcentrum, Rotterdam.*

from the sphere of a tug of war between interested parties to the level of a science.

The need for thorough industrialisation of building is now generally appreciated, because it is realised that without this the building industry will never be able to meet the growing requirements.

This far-reaching industrialisation can only properly take its course if every effort is made to achieve rational standardisation or, if this is not possible all at once, to effect a sound restriction of types. This alone can lead to the essential development of prefabrication aiming at optimum quality.

The result of this is that the architect will have to utilise standardised elements to an increasing extent, if he does not actually co-operate in designing fully standardised houses, schools and the like.

The architect will have the difficult but fascinating task of composing in such a way as to avoid monotony and to ensure that the personal touch and the objective qualities are preserved. In this connection it should be realised that in many cases uniformity can create a greater feeling of comfort than unnecessary, irresponsible and tiring variety. This variety is not found in nature, nor has it been handed down to us as an absolute necessity by former harmonious human societies.

The architect will have to be prepared to co-operate in and to promote the development of a far-reaching standardisation of dimensions. He can thereby render valuable assistance in the struggle against the still far too prevalent excessive variety, which in all the stages of planning, design and production has a cost-raising effect and constitutes a serious obstacle to achieving optimum quality.

The development of standardisation of dimensions cannot be undertaken haphazardly – and without the necessary co-ordination – in the supplying industries or in individual architect's offices, but should be based on a planned approach and on close collaboration on the strength of a common line of thought and work programme.

Without this co-ordination, standardisation and type restriction can never lead to rational assembly, because standardisation would then be based on different series of dimensions. The only possibility would then be the production of large series of fully standardised buildings. There are only a few types of buildings for which this could be considered and in many countries there is insufficient demand even for these buildings.

The object of so-called modular co-ordination, however, is to create a sound basis for standardisation and type restriction of elements for the erection and equipping of buildings and to achieve, by providing interchangeability, a combination of rational production of elements and maximum freedom of action for the architect. Modular co-ordination aims at bringing the dimensions of all elements under a common denominator, the module.

The European Productivity Agency in Paris is doing very valuable work in this respect, not only with a view to developing a practical and sound system of modular co-ordination, but especially with a view to securing international agreement.

In the international study of modular co-ordination the module of 10 cm (4 inches in the Anglo-Saxon countries) has been chosen as the common denominator. Hence, the dimensions of modular components are multiples of this module. By the modular dimension of an element is understood the dimension of that element plus the thickness of the joint based on the tolerance.

Since it is not yet known in the manufacturing stage what the adjoining materials will be, all dimensions are related to the module grid. This comprises three series of parallel planes together defining any number of 10 cm (4 in.) cubes. Modulation of any component or of any assembly is always based implicitly or explicitly upon the module grid. The module grid is the practical means of relating industrial production to individual design.

The practical application of the modular theory is governed by three main rules [1]:

(a) Every component should keep its station on the module grid.
(b) Only fastenings, weatherings and trim may cross grid lines between components.
(c) A modular joint is made within the clearance between two components.

The application of the rules to the design of building is a matter of architectural skill; provided he knows the rules, an architect can apply them flexibly.

An important aspect in the development of a practical system of modular co-ordination is the fixing of the optimum tolerances for manufacture and erection. They should be determined on the basis of observations and statistical analysis.

Modular co-ordination may not degenerate into a more or less abstract toying with dimensions, but must be based – as should be the case with all standardisation – on the "human measure". It is not a matter of engineering technique, but a method of human engineering.

2. DESIGN AND BUILDING ENGINEERING

Armed with a programme of requirements and sometimes assisted by technical experts, the architect is faced with the task of designing the

[1] *The Modular Quarterly 1958/3.*

building and thus realising technically (and aesthetically) what is required functionally and what is desirable for rational production. In working out the design the architect should strive for optimum quality. It is then that he enters the sphere of building engineering and he will be confronted with numerous technical, economic and industrial-economic requirements and possibilities.

Considering the many conditions which each individual solution must fulfil, it will be clear that optimum quality of buildings can only be achieved with a systematic and continuous growth of knowledge and experience. This involves sound planning of research work, experimental building, analysis of results, constant efforts to preserve the useful effect of this work for the future by rational standardisation with a view to avoiding the constant recurrence of difficult problems and cumbersome detail work, so that gradually a sound basis for efficient prefabrication is obtained.

Instead of jumping from one thing to another, a constant effort must be made to search for sound technical principles, which are not abandoned until it has been ascertained from analysed facts obtained by research and experimental building that there are better principles. It is only after the trial and error methods have been replaced by a systematic, planned approach that confrontation of the functional requirements with the technico-economic possibilities can efficiently lead to optimum results.

The effort to impart the desired objective qualities to the design resutls in a number of design phases, which partly take place consecutively and partly overlap each other:

– Translation into terms of engineering of the functional requirements to be fulfilled by each individual space and by the walls, ceiling and floor thereof.

– Arrangement of the individual walled-in and other space units in the building to be such that:
  (a) the desired lay-out of the space units and departments with respect to each other is achieved;
  (b) allowance is made for the daylighting and sun-access requirements;
  (c) technical and rational solutions are feasible for internal transport of people, goods, gas, water, electric power, etc.

– Design of a load-bearing structure and of the appropriate technico-functional main elements of the building, such as foundations, floors, walls and roof. In this connection due attention must be given to strength, rigidity and safety, but in addition allowance must be made for the requirements in respect of free spans, flexibility and facilities for expansion.

– The choice of building materials, prefabricated building elements and components for main structure and finish, installations and further equipment.

Numerous sound compromises will have to be found to adapt the functional requirements to what is technically and economically possible and desirable. In this connection some general problems are encountered, that are of fundamental importance for the technico-economic conception of building.

– The effort to achieve a better balance between the technical and the functional life of buildings.
– Working out integral costing studies, in which an attempt should be made to minimise the all-in costs.

In compiling the programme of requirements it was seen that a building consists of a number of space units each of which is multi-conditioned. When working out the design it will become evident that these space units cannot be developed independently of each other. On the one hand the lay-out determines certain conditions for the functional arrangement of the space units, while on the other hand the technical realisation will involve a certain amount of interdependence, at least if very expensive solutions are to be avoided. For example, a number of space units should have the same storey height and the same permissible floor load; only a limited number of rooms can be given a favourable location as regards sun-access, sound-insulation, heating and ventilation will to some extent have to be mutually adapted, etc.

2.1 *The space unit and its walls, ceiling and floor*

(*a*) *The physical requirements* The physical requirements to be fulfilled by a space unit relate to "climate" in the widest sense. This does not solely include the factors affecting the heat balance of the human body and capable of being perceived with the senses which register the sensations of heat and cold, but also the physical phenomena perceived with other senses, especially hearing, sight and smell. In answering the question how these requirements can be fulfilled, attention must be given first of all to the possibility of using – for the object in view – the favourable properties of the natural climate and excluding as far as possible the unfavourable influences. Since the natural climate is rarely constant, it will be necessary to introduce a means to adapt the indoor climate to requirements. In its simplest form this means to adapt the indoor climate could consist of moveable windows and curtains and in its most perfect form of a complete year-round air-conditioning installation.

As the demand for technical civilisation and prosperity in tropical regions rises, the problem of conditioning the indoor climate by cooling will gradually become more and more important. Whereas it is generally recognised that in cool climates the heating of walled-in space is an essential requirement and that, in effect, the western civilisation owes its existence largely to the possibility of heating living and work space, it is not so generally appreciated that the same applies with respect to cooling in hot climates. The considerably increased activity displayed by the population of the tropical regions will have a stimulating effect on the efforts made to find efficient solutions, while it is undoubtedly true that the application of cooling installations in the tropics will lead to a sharp rise in production and prosperity in these regions. Probably new cooling methods will be applied involving no moving parts and yet having a high efficiency. In any case an effort will be made to lower the high capital investments for cooling installations.

In the future, electric power will be used more and more for air-conditioning purposes, including heating, partly because with rising prosperity electric power becomes relatively cheaper and partly because it will be possible to raise the practical efficiency by application of the heat pump, electrical or thermal accumulation, radiation heating, continuous heating and better insulation.

With respect to acoustics and lighting also it is essential in the first instance to make use of the favourable influences of the natural climate and exclude the unfavourable influences. The exclusion of all extraneous noise and all daylight is rarely satisfactory in practice. In the sphere of sound-insulation recent investigations have revealed that it is feasible to achieve good insulation with lightweight constructions, but at the same time it has been proved at least to some extent that in practice there are certain limits beyond which one cannot go without taking special measures.

Hence, it will be necessary for the time being – quite apart from economic considerations – to make the requirements for sound-insulation less stringent than would be desirable or necessary from the functional point of view. It is interesting to note the more or less successful efforts made to create silence, in principle, by receiving the disturbing noise, amplifying it and transmitting it in counter-phase to the observer, so that the noise is cancelled out as it were.

Modern light sources with a high efficiency and/or a high light output, such as the high-power fluorescent tube, the development of light sources based on the principle of electro-luminiscence, the application of high frequency alternating current for fluorescent tubes, Xenon gas-discharge lamps with very high light current, etc. enable the lighting engineer to fulfil the necessary requirements and to create special effects.

(b) *Finish of walls, ceiling and floor*   Each space unit, irrespective of whether it is a bathroom, a factory workshop, a church or a shop, is confined by the surfaces of walls, floor and ceiling. These are the surfaces with which the occupant is concerned in the first instance and not with the construction. The requirements which such surfaces would have to fulfil can be divided into three categories, *viz.* the resistance to mechanical influences, the resistance to chemical and physical influences and the other requirements, which, *inter alia*, are concerned with comfort, aspect, reflection of sound and light, etc. Dependent on the purpose for which the space unit is used and other factors, greater importance will be attached to some of the requirements mentioned than to others and the choice of finish will be directed especially to what is considered essential.

The boundaries of the space units are more and more being used for technico-functional purposes. By the application of sound-absorbing materials the ceiling, for example, is used to an increasing extent to absorb the inconvenient low frequencies and to reflect the high frequencies, which are important from the point of view of speech intelligibility.

A second important aspect characterising modern ceiling finishes is concerned with lighting technique. Following the example set in the United States, the "luminous ceiling" is now receiving considerable attention also in Europe. With this lighting system, which enables a high light intensity to be achieved without the inconvenience of glare and contrast, a large part of the ceiling consists of transparent material.

In the case of floors an effort is being made to achieve such properties as non-slipperiness, resilience, resistance to wear and freedom from dusting, which greatly enhance the functional value of the space unit in question. As regards floor-finishing materials it would appear that the factory-made floor finishes in the form of tiles, slabs and strip replace more and more the seamless type of floor placed *in situ*. The most important advantages which the factory-made floor materials have over the seamless type are the greater constancy of quality, the smaller chance of failure in laying and the fact that the floor is ready for use a short time after laying. As a rule, repairs are easier and in any case simpler.

Exterior walls have developed from elements of simple composition, which must at once fulfil a number of technical functions (supporting, sound and heat insulation, weather screening), into elements of complex composition, in which a separate technical provision has been made for each specific function.

Walls, floors and ceilings are more and more being constructed in the form of hollow spaces to accommodate readily accessible supply and discharge pipeline systems.

Floors, walls and ceilings should be so designed as to avoid an expensive finish involving a lot of hand work. There are still too many buildings that give the impression of having been erected according to industrialised building methods, but where on closer inspection it becomes evident that the high degree of finish has been obtained by high-grade and expensive hand work.

An important step in the direction of industrialised building is achieved when the boundaries of the space units are made of prefabricated, assembled elements and the unavoidable joints are accepted. It will be clear that this requires a high standard of dimension control both in the rough building operations on site and in the finishing with elements supplied by the industry.

2.2 Grouping of space units: from micro- to macro-structure

After an initial technical evaluation has been made of the requirements to be fulfilled by the individual space units, these units should be efficiently grouped together.

bungalow

When grouped together the space elements form a building unit, of which the dwelling is the most obvious example. In the dwelling the space units are grouped in such a way that an efficient totality with boundaries and partitions is created and the architectural translation of the functional requirements begins to take shape. The simplest form is the detached house e.g. the bungalow.

row of terrace houses

Lack of space on the one hand and the requirements of functional town planning and design on the other make it necessary to join the individual building units into a block of dwellings. The simplest example is the row of terrace houses, i.e. a number of building units placed end to end.

142

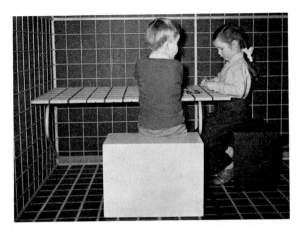

*space element
and building unit*

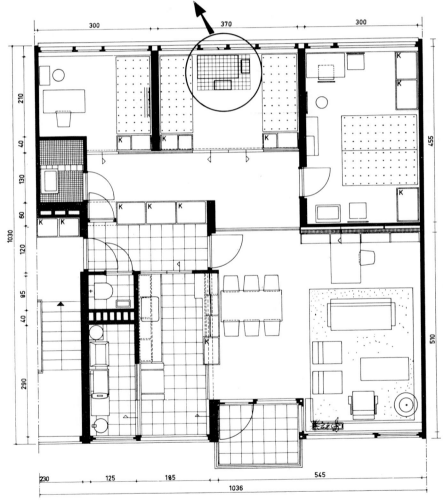

143

Vertical expansion produces gallery flats. Provisions must be made for the vertical transport of people, goods and services.

gallery flats

By grouping the building units in pairs, one above the other, a block of flats is obtained, with chiefly vertical transport within the block.

block of flats

A building unit with reception and bedrooms on different floors is a two storey single-family house.

two-storey single-family house

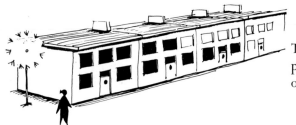

This can be of the detached type or placed in a row of a limited number of houses, *e.g.* terrace houses.

two-storey terrace houses

144

Vertical expansion will then produce the maisonnette type of dwelling.

maisonnette type

Grouping the individual building units round a vertical shaft and placing, for example, twelve storeys one on top of the other results in a tower flat.

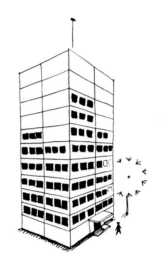

tower flat

Placing the gallery blocks back to back produces the corridor type.

corridor type

145

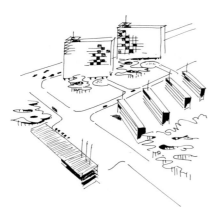

The search for a macro-structure of walled-in and other space of optimum quality, in which the rational aspect plays an important part, requires the skill of creating unity within the totality on the part of the architect-townplanner, as well as the specialised knowledge of the various experts, especially in the sphere of transport and in the sphere of organisation of building operations.

neighbourhood

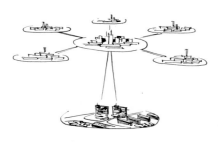

town plus satellites

The object should be to organise the building masses in such a way that a harmonious whole is achieved with rational connections between the elements, with vegetation, public buildings such as schools, churches, hospitals, offices and workshops. Neighbourhood, town and town plus satellites constitute qualitatively one and the same problem. The difference lies in the order of magnitude.

2.3 *Development of the load-bearing structure*

The next phase is to design a load-bearing structure in such a way that the building units can be located in the horizontal and vertical planes.

The old building method involving interior and exterior bearing walls imposed considerable limitations on the design and, throughout the life of the building as a whole, also on the practical efficiency with respect to its use. This would not necessarily be a serious disadvantage if the life of the building were short or if the requirements to be fulfilled by the building remained the same for a considerable length of time.

Practical experience has shown, however, that neither the one nor the other occurs very often and consequently the old, inflexible building method has left us with a large number of unpractical buildings. From the technical point of view they will last many decennia, but any change in the spatial lay-out of such buildings will prove a very costly affair.

It is not surprising, therefore, that a constant effort is made to achieve greater freedom in the spatial sense by developing load-bearing structures

146

which provide spatial flexibility within the building. By a technico-functional separation of the bearing structure and the building units the latter can be adapted to new requirements as soon as they are out-of-date without the bearing structure having to be modified.

This struggle of man to achieve greater freedom in the spatial sense is reflected in the development of building engineering.

In the case of the load-bearing walls the spatial freedom can only be achieved in a single direction, because our technical skill is limited. It is only possible to create a freedom limited by load-bearing interior walls.

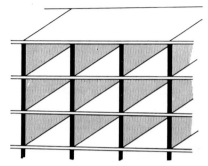

load-bearing walls

The effort to create horizontal freedom in two directions resulted in the load-bearing framework with inter-column walling. In this case the spatial freedom is no longer limited by load-bearing walls but by load-bearing columns.

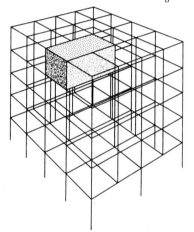

load bearing framework

Formerly, this framework could be technically realised by limited means only, *i.e.* the reinforced concrete frame poured *in situ* or the pre-fabricated steel and/or concrete frame. The development of the mushroom floor with curtain walls, providing great horizontal freedom in two directions, proved a step in the right direction.

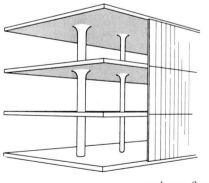

mushroom floor

147

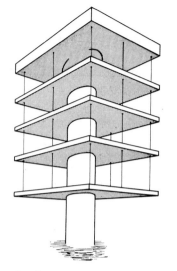

suspended floor

Another building method which presents interesting possibilities is the suspended floor method, involving a concrete core made with moving formwork or otherwise and an overhanging mushroom-shaped roof, from which the floors are suspended with cables.

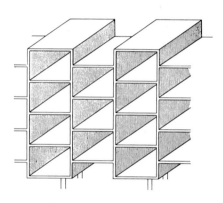

ox-frame

Lately "space-structures" have been developed *viz.* the so-called box-frames which create a unity of space and structure. These offer interesting technico-economic possibilities, but to a certain extent lead to limitations as regards spatial freedom.

Numerous constructional solutions are available for freespanning – without columns – large space units at ground-floor level for factory buildings and the like. In this respect important progress has been made with concrete, steel and wood as construction materials.

It is interesting to note how in the last fifty years reinforced concrete as a material of construction has developed from a substitute for the traditional method of stacking to a material with its own range of applications, such as mushroom floors and shell roofs.

148

Prestressing has made it possible to remove to some extent one of the disadvantages of concrete, *viz.* its own weight, so that larger and more slender spans can be made. The struggle against weight is also waged on another front, namely by the application of lightweight aggregates or by incorporating hollow space in the concrete.

It will be possible to achieve greater productivity by far-reaching pre-fabrication and the application of standardised formwork for concrete poured *in situ*. With prefabricated elements, constructional continuity can be maintained by means of modern glueing techniques.

The development of our oldest building material, *viz.* wood, has long been obstructed by the traditions of centuries, which determined the range of applications. A turning point in the history of wood was reached with the development of a computable tensile joint between two wooden parts and of new materials for making such joints. The range of applications of wood has been widened appreciably by the advent of the modern synthetic resins, which enabled high-grade glued joints to be made and made it possible to press wood shavings into sheets with exceptionally good properties.

The use of steel is promoted by the development of various grades of steel of optimum functional quality, such as high-grade steel for prestressing and steel with good welding properties, as well as by the introduction of new types of structural steel. Another promising feature is the combination of concrete and rolled steel girders (the so-called "Verbundbauweise"), whereby the properties of these two materials have been very successfully combined. In the future the application of the novel method of joining steel parts by glueing instead of welding or riveting will probably assume considerable proportions.

As a result of extensive research, a new approach is also noticeable with respect to brick as a building material. Special attention has been given to size and weight of the bricks, as well as to the composition of the mortar.

Perforated bricks have been introduced and the characteristic features of their application are lower weight, lower consumption of materials and better physical properties for building. Moreover, an effort is being made to eliminate from the process the use of mortar containing a lot of water and requiring a long curing time. Trials with bricks joined by glueing have produced satisfactory results.

High-grade bricks and mortars have been developed in Switzerland. Practical experience has shown that, if expertly applied, these materials can be used for erection of residential buildings up to eighteen storeys high. The load-bearing brickwork is then not reinforced, not even on the ground floor.

Plastics and light metals, such as aluminium and magnesium, which are

concrete

brick

150

timber

steel

151

still in an early stage of development, are regarded with considerable optimism in the search for new lightweight building materials.

In furthering building activity in newly developing countries due attention will have to be given to the application of locally available raw materials, such as bamboo, rushes, stabilised earth, volcanic rock, etc., in connection with the limited economic facilities.

One of the most fundamental problems encountered with building constructions is the method of calculation [1].

The calculation methods are characterised by the so-called safety coefficient – of arbitrary magnitude – whereby the assumed average material strength is divided to obtain what is termed the permissible strength.

It is certainly a moot point whether this approach is correct. In the case of most materials the collapse of a structure occurs in the plastic range, while the conventional calculation methods are based on the elastic deformation according to Hooke's law.

The collapse of a building depends on many sources of weakness, which can combine in many ways. Weakness may be due to:
– an alteration in the properties adopted by the engineer, who has chosen, as the strength of the construction materials, a mean value out of a range of more or less variable values; or
– applied forces whose magnitude it is impossible to predict accurately during the life span of the building.

Both these factors have a chance distribution. Hence, it seems advisable to base the methods of calculating the degree of safety on theories of probability. The problem consists in maintaining the probability of failure below a permissible limit, for the particular type of structure.

To enable this method of calculation to be applied generally and systematically, sufficient statistic material should be available. In order to attain optimum quality of structures full attention must be devoted to the further development of this theory. Great economic interests are at stake.

2.4 *The choice of building materials, etc.*

Both economic and technical factors are involved in the choice of building materials and prefabricated elements for main structure and finish, as well as in the choice of installations and equipment. Even if the choice could be made solely on the strength of technical considerations, the designer would still be faced with a task that would be difficult to bring to an entirely satisfactory conclusion. The wide range of possibilities and the rapid development of new discoveries on the one hand and the absence of objective data on the other make it very difficult to come to an optimum choice.

[1] *Prof. Torroja: Superimposed loads and safety factors, C.I.B. Bulletin 1958/1-2, Bouwcentrum, Rotterdam.*

Added to this is the fact that the designer is quickly, usually too quickly, attracted to all kinds of novelties. Hence, building sometimes degenerates into building of nothing but prototypes, which are not followed up by any further systematic development. In many cases it is not systematically ascertained what is suitable for a given object and what is not.

Often the choice must be restricted for economic reasons to what is available in the way of raw materials and finished products in a given region. Transport over long distances is only possible for light materials and for special equipment that only occurs once in a while. Specific regions can only be made habitable with the aid of what is potentially available in these regions and with such products as can be derived therefrom. In this connection the choice of the standard of quality is a very important matter, which concerns not so much a technical solution to a one-time problem, but rather the achievement of optimum quality for the society as a whole, *i.e.* the maximum difference between usefulness and costs.

The absence of objective data is not conducive to making the right choice and consequently an effort must be made to obtain more and better data in respect of numerous matters.

In this connection, attention should be drawn to a study carried out under the auspices of the International Council for Building Research, Studies and Documentation (C.I.B.) and relating to: technical information and performance of building products. The following is quoted from a report [1] by Dr. T. W. Parker, Deputy Director of the British Building Research Station:

"New building materials and modifications of existing materials are being produced in all countries. To gain maximum benefit from them, designers and builders need basic design data and technical advice about them, much of which can be obtained by laboratory tests or by systematic field observations. If it is desired to compare the properties of new materials with those of known materials, then precise test methods are required. When comparisons have to be made of data obtained by different laboratories, special attention has to be paid to standardisation of the test methods, to the extent possibly of internationally agreed standard methods.

There is, however, one other measure which would, it is thought, assist when an opinion on the technical merits of a product is required. It is the establishment of a schedule of generally agreed headings for the information to be sought. This would help to secure uniformity and completeness in the presentation of test data and the evaluation of technical qualities and would be of particular value in connection with products being introduced into one country from another.

[1] *C.I.B. Bulletin 1958/4 Bouwcentrum, Rotterdam.*

Although most of the data required for any particular material or product will be obtainable by laboratory tests, it will be necessary on some points to make direct observations on the behaviour of the material as used in existing buildings, if suitable examples are available.

It is convenient when considering what information is required to assess the probable performance of a building material, unit or component, to deal with it on the basis of its use, *i.e.* whether it is intended for walling, roofing, flooring, services, etc. In each of such groups it may be possible to provide a list of the points on which information is required in order to judge whether and how a material can be used in a particular type of building, what precautions have to be taken during and after erection, and the probable subsequent behaviour of the material.

In addition, in view of the great variation in the materials and products falling under one heading, it would propably be useful to have an introductory statement which would enable the prospective user to know immediately whether the subject was of any interest to him. This statement should include brief information on the following points:

(*a*) Purpose
(*b*) General description; chief components
(*c*) Indication of size; method of handling
(*d*) Origin of technical data
(*e*) Reference to existing standards or specifications.

Taking as examples products used for walling, the detailed information required can be separated into two main groups, one concerned with the characteristics of the material itself and the other with the characteristics of the walls built with the particular material. A third group deals with the factors that have to be taken into account in evaluating durability.

1. Characteristics of the material or product
    (*a*) Type and manufacture
        (i) Composition (including chemical analysis, if relevant)
        (ii) Properties of component materials
        (iii) Methods of manufacture
        (iv) Sizes and weights; uniformity.

    (*b*) Physical properties
        (i) Density
        (ii) Strength – compressive or transverse strength, etc., according to type
            – variation with age
            – variation with moisture content
            – variation with temperature

     (iii) Elasticity, creep

     (iv) Moisture expansion and drying shrinkage

      (v) Water absorption, porosity and saturation coefficient

     (vi) Permeability to air and water

    (vii) Soluble salt content

   (viii) Resistance to crystallisation of salts

     (ix) Frost resistance

      (x) Thermal conductivity

     (xi) Combustibility, spread of flame

    (xii) Colour, texture, general appearance

   (xiii) Reflection (radiation coefficient)

   (xiv) Light transmission

    (xv) Hardness; resistance to scratching

(c) Working characteristics

      (i) Ease of transport; ability to withstand rough handling

    (ii) Precautions required for storage on site

   (iii) Ease of cutting

   (iv) Availability

(d) Economics

      (i) Cost

2. Characteristics of walls constructed with the material or unit

(a) Construction

      (i) Ease of handling (size, weight, shape) – necessary plant or tools

    (ii) Need for temporary supports

   (iii) Method of construction

   (iv) Method of jointing

     (v) Need for special units

   (vi) Speed of erection

   (vii) Method of external finishing

  (viii) Method of internal finishing

    (ix) Cost per unit area of wall – materials, labour, transport

     (x) Maintenance, maintenance methods and costs.

(b) Data required for the design of the construction

      (i) Strength and stability – basis for structural design

    (ii) Durability including freedom from cracking

   (iii) Expansion and shrinkage

    (iv) Rain resistance

    (v) Fire resistance

    (vi) Thermal insulation

    (vii) Sound insulation and sound absorption

    (viii) Liability to vermin infestation

    (ix) Adaptability for varying layout.

3. Durability

The durability of a building material is a complex property depending on several characteristics of the material and on the way in which it is used in a building. In many cases no single or group of laboratory tests gives sufficient information on which to base a reliable estimate of durability.

    Much of the information concerning the durability of building products is based not so much upon laboratory tests as upon general experience in normal conditions of exposure. Particularly important also is the question of the severity of exposure of the material not only as affected by the climate of the country, but also by the particular position in the building. Thus parapet and free-standing walls provide more severe exposure conditions than the walls of a building.

    Aspects relating to durability that should be taken into account and on which information should be provided are:

(a) Effect of water

(b) Effect of soluble salts

(c) Effect of juxtaposition with other materials, *e.g.* clinker aggregates and steel

(d) Effect of frost in relation to the position in the building and the liability to become very wet

(e) Effect of atmospheric pollution

(f) Effect of destructive agents introduced in a building by the particular occupancy, *e.g.* fats and oils

(g) Resistance to insects and fungi

In view of the complexity of the assessment, the information given concerning the durability of a building material should include brief details of the basis of the assessment.

4. General assessment

Where possible, there should be a general assessment of the material as seen by the technical reporter in the country of origin.''

2.5 *A better equilibrium between the technical and the functional life of buildings*

According as society acquires an increasingly more complicated character as a result of specialisation, buildings will have to fulfil more and more stringent functional requirements. Moreover, since the rate at which things are changing is increasing rather than decreasing, there is a definite tendency for the gap between the technical life and the functional life to widen even further.

On the basis of the conception that by its very nature a building is first and foremost an article of use, the nature of the problem involved can best be illustrated by comparing it with another article of use, which – like buildings – is nowadays also produced in very large numbers, *viz.* the automobile.

On an average the automobile fulfils far more exacting functional requirements than a building erected to normal standards. Yet, the automobile is rejected after as little as four or five years, while most buildings are made to last fifty if not a hundred years. The result is that the average motorist has a much more up-to-date article of use at his disposal than the user of a building. The real cause of the problem is, therefore, that our buildings are made to last far too long, *i.e.* that unfortunately we pay far too much attention to durability. The functional requirements which a building is expected to fulfil evolve much more quickly than the rate at which we can replace our buildings and the comparison with the automobile demonstrates that, as supplier of up-to-date and efficient products, the building industry in effect lags terribly behind other industries, such as the automobile industry.

The problem becomes even more complicated owing to the fact that a building is often regarded too much as an investment project and too little as an article of use. This is especially so with dwellings and as a result the building industry is constantly urged to supply durable investment projects and thus to increase the technical life of a building as much as possible. Owing to the constant housing shortage and the rising rents there is no difficulty in letting these functionally out-of-date dwellings, but the family and the individual are very seriously inconvenienced by the fact that in many respects the dwellings do not come up to the requirements of the present-day way of life.

The effort gradually to reduce the difference between the technical life and the functional life of a building can be consciously directed to three objects:

(a) application of constructions at low cost, thus reducing the technical life of the building;

(b) extension of the functional life of the building by making greater allowance for future functional requirements;

157

(c) a clear division, both technically and functionally, of the life of the main structure and that of the building units accommodated in this structure by ensuring such flexibility that, if necessary, the building units can be adopted to future requirements without most of the building having to be pulled down.

Building at low cost with a restricted programme of requirements and for a short life span is especially attractive for those regions where large numbers of people have to be provided with accommodation quickly and where little capital is available.

From the political point of view this might well be the best investment, even if it is known beforehand that with the expected rapid rise in prosperity allowance will have to be made for a planned system of replacement within a span of from 25 to 50 years.

In the technically more advanced countries also there is a tendency towards lightweight construction, but with the definite object of building at lower cost and for a shorter life span.

There is, of course, the danger of emergency dwellings of inferior quality being built and being made to last as long as normal dwellings, and considering previous experiences this is not surprising.

In many respects the great weight of our buildings is an objection and a reduction of this weight would in itself provide some substantial advantages:

(a) a saving in building costs insofar as they are due to the actual weight of the building, particularly the costs of main girders, columns and foundations;

(b) a saving in transport of materials to and on the building site;

(c) lower costs of and easier demolition.

On the whole, surprisingly little attention is paid to the costs and the difficulties of demolition, neither to the direct costs of the demolition work itself nor to the extra costs involved on account of the time required for this work, which costs make themselves felt in the form of loss of interest on the land and interruption of the operations of the concern to be accommodated in the new building. According as the building to be demolished is heavier and its construction more of a monolithic nature (reinforced concrete!), the demolition costs will be higher and often involve fabulous sums. It would certainly be of great interest if a little more attention were paid to the economic aspects of demolition.

An attempt is made to reduce the weight of buildings by making the main structure or specific parts of the building of lighter weight than can be done by the more conventional building methods. Lower weight can be achieved in two ways:

158

(a) application of building systems involving assembly of prefabricated lightweight elements on site, *e.g.* various types of wall constructions and curtain walls in particular;

(b) application of lightweight building materials, the use of which – depending on circumstances – more or less fits in with the conventional building methods, *e.g.* various types of lightweight concrete (aerated concrete) and also lightweight structural steel.

It is indeed striking that a human being weighing 70 kg can be adequately protected against the cold in winter by 10 kg of clothing and footwear and yet lives in a dwelling weighing 25,000 kg per person. On the other hand the price per kg of a dwelling is very low compared with that of other industrial products, as will be seen from table 19.

TABLE 19

	Price in $	Weight in kg	Volume in m³	Price in $/kg	Price per m³	kg/m³
Brick dwelling	4000.00	80.000	300	0.05	13.30	267
Caravan	1000.00	500	14	2.00	71.40	36
Tent	30.00	5	5	6.00	6.00	1
Motor-car	1600.00	800	3	2.00	533.30	267

Lightweight building is a difficult technical problem. It is only possible to build lighter and cheaper if large sums of money are spent on research, whereby new building materials are obtained. In the different parts of the world this research should be concentrated on the raw materials available there.

In the next twenty years or so the countries where abundant and cheap man power is available will have to make effective use of building methods involving manual labour, due allowance being made for the shortage of skilled workers. In countries where wages are high and steadily rising, low-cost building can only be achieved by reduction of man hours and by a high degree of mechanisation. In the development of building it is principally a matter of whether one is prepared to steer a definite course and spend a lot of money on research now with a view to achieving specific ends in the future or whether one is satisfied with a development that takes its own course, so that all that can be done is to make the best of it.

It is an urgent necessity, however, to place the control of building in capable hands, since it is a matter of imparting the highest possible living value to our constructed environment, placing the urgently required standardisation on a proper basis of objective knowledge and aiming at the greatest possible flexibility in time and space in view of the dynamic nature of our life.

This applies especially if it is desired to lengthen the functional life of buildings, irrespective of whether this is accompanied by a shortening of the technical life or not. This can only be achieved by acquiring a more detailed knowledge of future functional requirements by making fundamental functional studies and aiming at standard qualities, while the ends to be achieved in the future should be clearly defined and every effort made to come to an efficiently planned realisation thereof.

Moreover, we must be able and prepared to build not so much with an eye to investments of today, but rather with an eye to the functional use of tomorrow. This can be promoted by designing and equipping the adapted space in such a way that it can be used for a number of purposes. This overall effort can only be completely successful if the uncertainties of the future can be reduced to a minimum.

The effort to establish equilibrium between the technical and the functional life of a building can also be assisted by increasing the flexibility of the building. In this connection the main structure is considered as a more permanent part of the building, thus providing a greater opportunity to modify the layout of the ground plan in accordance with new requirements which present themselves in the course of time. Experiments in this direction have hitherto chiefly been made in connection with office buildings, and the experience gained would appear to be favourable. The development of flexible ground plans for dwellings, which are more difficult to realise than the variable office layout, is still in its infancy, but it certainly warrants close attention. The principal problems involved are:

(a) A floor construction which throughout the dwelling is entirely smooth underneath, so that the shifting of partition walls is not obstructed by protruding beams. Columns should as far as possible be avoided within any one dwelling. Hence, the floor will generally have to be of slab type construction and will consequently be fairly expensive on account of the large span between party walls in one direction and between exterior walls in the other.

(b) The laying on of pipeline systems. If, in keeping with the ground plan layout, the pipeline systems are also to provide flexibility, it will be necessary to make a special hollow space in the floor for this purpose, which again raises the cost of the floor. If on the other hand the location of the pipelines is considered permanent, the desired effect is lost to a large extent, because the ground plan is then much less variable and in any case it will be impossible to change the location of the "wet element" in the dwelling.

160

2.6 Minimisation of the "all-in" costs

Building is a play in many acts and involves many decisions, which implies that there is a great chance of errors. The conception that we should build as cheaply as possible is just as wrong as the effort to make everything as expensive as possible. What we are concerned with here is the minimisation of the "all-in" costs, an aim which in effect is identical with the aim to achieve optimum quality, except that the accent has been shifted. If building involves many decisions, there is every chance of making wrong decisions, which will be reflected in more than just the essential future costs.

Hence, it is worth while at this juncture to ascertain once more on what points important decisions must be made when realising a building. To simplify matters the spheres of general planning (development planning, physical planning, etc.) have been omitted here. This does not imply in any way that we are not concerned here with important decisions involving substantial costs.

In the realisation of a building the following phases and decisions can be distinguished:

(a) The phase of initial decisions on the question whether or not the building will be constructed, on its location, capacity, etc. (*basic decisions*);

(b) The planning phase, in which in the light of the primary decisions a detailed programme of requirements is drawn up which the building should meet in order to perform its functions to an optimum degree (*functional decisions*);

(c) The design phase, in which the decisions made by the designer are laid down in drawings and specifications to suit the programme of requirements (*design decisions*);

(d) The construction phase, in which the building is constructed according to the design and specifications (*production decisions*).

As more decisions are made, the degree of freedom is restricted so that, on the one hand, the extent of possible errors decreases (most errors have been made already or good decisions have been taken) and, on the other hand, the possibilities of favourably affecting the final result are reduced.

The running of a hotel whose number of beds is twice as high as the optimum number cannot be retrieved by means of appropriate detailed architectural design.

A contractor works on a lost case, however efficient his organisation on the building site may be, if serious errors have been made in selecting the location. The diagram below gives an estimate of percentages of errors that might be made within each group of decisions, classified according to the above scheme.

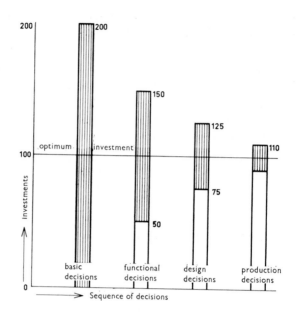

In the group of basic decisions, the decision not to build at all leads to an investment zero, whereas, for instance, the selection of the wrong capacity may easily result in twice the optimum investment (200).

In the group of functional decisions the percentage ranges approximately between 50 and 150, subject to the programme quality.

In designing, a variation between 75 and 125 per cent may be assumed, depending on the design quality, whilst in the production group this figure ranges between 90 and 110 (the optimum investment being set at 100 for each group). When the decision to undertake the construction has been made, a superimposition of errors may result in an investment 3 to 4 times as high as, or only half the amount that would actually be necessary for the project in question.

The various decisions made and the subsequent planning should be preceded and accompanied by estimating.

(a) The estimating of a building amounts to making beforehand a rough calculation of the building costs on the strength of the information then available regarding the building. In the different stages preparatory to building the interested parties will constantly be faced with the question of what costs the progressively more detailed building plan will involve.

162

This starts in the earliest stage. Even before a definite decision to build has been made and before the first sketch of the building has been drawn, the principal will want to know approximately what the building is going to cost him. At that moment he probably has very little idea what the building is going to be like and the only idea he has – and even that may be vague – is what its purpose and its capacity should be, *e.g.* a house with three bedrooms and two reception rooms, an office building for 100 staff, a church with a seating capacity for 500 people, a hospital for 100 patients, etc. It is nevertheless understandable that he wants to have an idea about the amount of money the building will involve and that he will have reason to complain if, after the plan has been made, it appears that on concluding the contract the original estimate has been greatly exceeded.

(*b*) Disappointments of this type can be avoided if:
  – at the time the basic and functional decisions are made the principal is able to make a rough estimate of the building costs and other costs;
  – throughout the design stage the architect remains aware of the consequences which the numerous detail decisions entail with respect to the building costs and, as the design assumes a more concrete shape, estimates the building costs with increasing accuracy.

It is quite usual for the architect to draw up an estimate of costs both for the provisional and for the definitive design.

(*c*) The contractors submitting tenders and sometimes also the civil authorities will likewise base their estimates on the definitive design. The former require this design to fix the amount of their tenders and the latter to decide whether they will give their approval in those cases in which the contract sum may not exceed the appropriate price standard laid down by them.

Finally, properly organised firms of contractors will, after the contract had been granted, draw up a building estimate as an element of work planning, which serves as a basis for final costing calculations.

Hence, seven different types of estimates are required, *viz.*:
(*a*) the estimate of the principal on the strength of the basic programme;
(*b*) the estimate of the principal based on the programme of requirements;
(*c*) the estimate of the architect based on the provisional design;
(*d*) if necessary, the estimate of the civil authorities on the strength of the definitive design;
(*e*) the estimate of the architect based on the definitive design;
(*f*) the estimate of the various contractors based on the definitive design;
(*g*) the building estimate as an element of work planning of the contractor to whom the contract is ultimately granted.

What all these estimates have in common is that they are preliminary estimates of the expected costs. They differ because a steadily increasing degree of accuracy is required. This increasing degree of accuracy is possible, because more and more accurate information becomes available for each subsequent estimate.

When the estimates of the principal referred to under (a) and (b) are drawn up, nothing is known regarding layout, construction, materials to be used, etc. Only the programme of requirements is known to some degree of accuracy for the estimate under (b). For the architect's estimate referred to under (c) (which is based on the sketched design) layout, construction and materials to be used, etc. are known in rough outline. For the estimates of the civil authorities, the architect and the contractor referred to under (d) to (g) (which are based on the definitive design) this information – apart from certain details – is fully known. By that time the architect can have formed some idea of the methods to be applied for production. In principle, the contractor will by then have considered and decided the manner in which he will carry out the work in rough outline, what equipment he has available and whether the contract is attractive for him in view of the size, the organisation, the work programme and the business policy of his firm.

When drawing up the building estimate referred to under (g) the contractor will have considered and decided in detail how the work will be organised.

In the design stage the architect can make a valuable contribution towards minimising costs. To this end he should abandon the traditional estimating procedure, because to ensure correct decisions he cannot possibly compare the various possibilities from the technico-economic point of view if he does not constantly keep an eye on the financial consequences.

Often the scope of his estimating procedure is still too traditional and based on the fact that, for example, all painting will be done by a single sub-contractor, which is reflected in his specifications.

To obtain a sound insight into cost prices it is necessary to know the overall building costs per element in different variations of construction and composition. In choosing the components it may occur that one wishes to know in a specific instance the price of a tiled roof or a flat roof, a wooden floor or a stone floor, etc.

In other words it is possible to compare prices and thus to assess the efficiency. The traditional estimating procedure based on trades provides a check on the efficiency of the production process, while the procedure based on elements provides a check on the efficiency of the design. In the latter case the cost of the elements can be expressed as a percentage of the total building costs or as a price per cubic metre or square metre of building,

164

whereby it becomes possible to keep an eye on the relative importance. The costs of the project can be analysed according to functional elements. Modifications and savings can be realised in a sound and justifiable manner. The effectiveness of the element procedure is determined in the first instance by the choice of the elements into which a building can be split up. This choice depends on the purpose for which the estimate is drawn up and amounts to a sound classification of the "smallest imaginable" elements.

Furthermore, it is important to make a correct choice of the variants for the elements selected. According as the elements are larger – thus composed of more components – the number of possible variants will be considerably greater. In estimating variants it may occur that one is faced with an almost unlimited selection and in practice it will be necessary, therefore to effect a sound restriction of the number of possible variants. In the case of a dwelling for example the following classification of functional elements might be used:

- soil-shifting
- foundation
- cellar closet
- floor of ground floor
- floor of storey
- vertical brickwork
- windows and doors
- stairs
- roof
- flues and ventilation ducts
- sanitary installation
- gas piping
- electrical installation
- sewer system
- finish and equipment
- outdoor installations
- miscellaneous.

The element-estimating procedure can be very useful for assessing the plan. In plan assessment, which should provide a reliable basis for sound realisation of the plan within the financial possibilities and in the desired quality, a good insight into price formation is indispensable.

An adequate evaluation for practical purposes can also be achieved without prices on the strength of experience and by making comparisons, but it is felt that this evaluation can be more precise and certainly more convincing if it is based on figures.

165

At different times it is highly desirable to know the prices of complete elements of buildings for costing purposes with a view to obtaining:

(a) insight into cost prices in the design stage on behalf of:
 – choice of materials and constructions;
 – preliminary calculation of operating costs;
 – financing;
(b) comparison of prices.
(c) assessment of plan with respect to efficiency.
(d) check on estimates of tenders.

It should be pointed out that the elements-estimating procedure will prove a practical aid to arriving at justifiable and yet sharply calculated instalment payments.

It is evident from the introduction to this section that the effort to achieve optimum solutions covers much more than just those aspects that can be influenced in the actual design phase, however important this phase may be in itself.

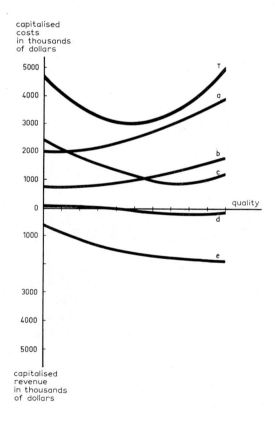

The "all-in" costs T comprise:

$a =$ building costs
$b =$ other costs involved in realisation of the building
$c =$ capitalised cleaning and maintenance costs
$d =$ cash value of the demolition costs
$e =$ capitalised other effects which the building has on the costs of what takes place in the building once it has been taken into use (apart from interest and depreciation in respect of a, b, c and d).

The object of the systematic preparation and production is to reduce $T = f (a, b, c, d, e)$ to a minimum. The curve T usually has a fairly large area within which the costs are practically identical and a minimum.

It will then depend on certain conditions what point within this area is to be preferred. If the object is to achieve low investment costs, the lowest building costs are preferred. If the wage level is expected to rise steeply, low c and e will be especially important.

Owing to lack of capital it will not always be possible to realise the aim of minimising the "all-in" costs. In that case there is no getting away from the fact that too cheap a building will ultimately prove to be expensive and this would be a regrettable state of affairs. However, minimalisation of the "all-in" costs constitutes a profitable field of work, considering the many cases in which building becomes too "expensive" as a result of wrong decisions.

3. THE ROLE OF THE DESIGNER. OBJECTIVE AND SUBJECTIVE QUALITIES
   OF THE DESIGN OF A BUILDING

When we discussed the possibilities of making our planet basically habitable by building in the shortest possible time, it was established that, in view of the considerable arrears and the rapid growth of the world population, every effort would have to be made to achieve the greatest possible volume and quality of building with the available means, *i.e.* to aim at optimum quality in building. Since the object in view is not to serve the interests of specific individuals or groups, but rather to serve the interests of the population as a whole, a socially justified quality is essential.

This conscious quality will not only lead to a better overall result, *i.e.* a larger share for all, but by better distribution it will also serve equally the interests of all the parties concerned, such as the consumer, the employer and the worker.

In building and in equipping buildings the task of the designer is a very important one, not merely because he must give an acceptable form to everything that is useful, but especially because over and above the direct

167

usefulness he must give the building or the group of buildings a subjective quality. The designer can do important work in three respects, *viz*. as industrial designer, as architect and as artist.

In industrial design it is his task, as an essential element in the control of quality, to give the industrial product an acceptable form and to create harmonious unity in a technical multiplicity.

Industrial design of building materials, building elements and standardised buildings (houses, schools, etc.) will become increasingly more important. It is clear that in these cases it is not a matter of architecture, of an original one-time conception, but one of series and mass.

In the struggle between usefulness, quantity and objective quality on the one hand and beauty and subjective quality on the other the latter will have to be the looser, unless aesthetic expression is used in the service of mass production and does not form an insurmountable obstacle in this respect.

The designer follows closely or should follow closely the trend of art. Whether they realise it or not, designers are influenced by this trend.

The task of the industrial designer consists in giving the object to be manufactured a good form on the basis of his knowledge of applied art and his good taste and of his knowledge of the function of the object in question and the requirements of mass production. A great arsenal of forms and aspects of form is at his disposal.

The guiding principle for the industrial designer is that there can be no mass production without mass consumption.

Gordon Lippincott says: "A product that is styled so many years ahead of consumers' taste that it does not receive full mass acceptance, is as badly designed as one which lags behind . . . The industrial designer is primarily a man who has his finger tips on the pulse of the consumers' acceptance."

Design must move on, however, and bring about the compromise between art and mass by keeping so far ahead of mass taste that it is just still acceptable. Raymond Loewy calls this the MAYA limit (Most Advanced Yet Acceptable).

According to Lippincott, the essential factors for industrial design are the following:

— man in relation to his surroundings
— time-knowledge of requirements
— appearance—in relation to time
-- economy—saleability
— function
— material   } directly influence design
— machine-production

168

1. FORMS
   - organic
     (biological, biochemical,
     geological, free forms)
   - abstract
     (mathematical, free forms)
   - integration forms
     (combination of the organic
     and the abstract

2. ASPECTS OF FORM
   - general aspects
     (position, sequence, move-
     ment, proportion, accentu-
     ation, etc.)
   - material aspects
     (structure, texture, model,
     colour, visual illusion,
     reflection, etc.)
   - sensory aspects
     (hardness, elasticity, etc.)

The pronounced commercial aspect of industry and retail trade often endangers the socially justified quality and the associated industrial design. Sometimes industry continues the production of inadequately designed articles, because they have a ready sale and it is feared that any change will result in the loss of a market.

In other cases, industry tries to force sales in the retail trade by constantly introducing new models, thereby influencing the consumers to buy new articles, while the existing articles are still usable. In a sense fashion is the enemy of sound design. Fashion is based on the element of surprise and has nothing to do with art, because it has a one-time effect. Fashion often degrades art to highly dated empty decoration. Hence, fashion can only play a useful part with things that are short-lived. The industrial designer should almost imperceptibly and thus in an aesthetically justified manner create a harmonious unity without emotional quality. He has an H(armonious) U(nity) function.

H U

The modern architect may not shrink from the requirements presented by the industrialisation of building, which is an urgent necessity and he may not allow himself to be tempted to indulge in a would-be fashionable originality. A building has a very long technical life (too long perhaps!) and this should be in equilibrium with the life of the design. He performs an important task in the effort to achieve optimum quality, because in the struggle to raise the difference between "usefulness" and "costs" he introduces the weapon of subjective quality. Without bringing about a substantial increase in costs, he should – in addition to harmonious unity – impart to the building emotional quality and in doing so express the essential nature of the building. The architect has an H U + function.

In the effort to create a habitable world the great significance of the architect and the town-planner will have to be demonstrated in this practical

170

work. The essential point of the architecture of the future is that, besides accepting the industrial form presented to him, the architect puts into form the essential objective function of the building and, moreover, adds something to the totality of given conditions and requirements, whereby a certain functional unity of objective qualities is created and this creation also possesses subjective quality of design. This quality of design should improve the internal significance of the building both aesthetically and psychologically and at the same time emphasise the external significance of

HU +

the building to the society in time and space in such a way that the significance of the form as such is established. This form should not only be the form of a function, but should also itself have a function.

In the sphere of design there will always be a deeply hidden remnant of mystery, which will probably for ever resist explanation, but yet it is a fact that designing, at the same time, requires a high degree of technique and skill, as well as a highly trained power of conception, which introduces unity in the sphere of multiplicity.

The significance of fine art in architecture increases according as industrial design in building and architecture based on industrialisation of the building process develop. Architecture acquires a macro-structure and develops

171

+

into grouping of masses comprising entire villages, neighbourhoods, streets, squares, and large buildings, adapted to the volume and speed of traffic. It is not always possible for the spectator and the passer-by to realise the beauty of skylines and masses, but they can appreciate the internal spatial qualities of a building. With increasing uniformity, fine arts can play an important part in the fulfilment of human need with respect to symbolism, colour, aesthetic expression and the like. The artist has a + function here. This makes it possible to enhance the personal aspect in buildings without

172

retarding the industrialisation of building. It should be realised, however, that first and foremost we are concerned here with the emotional quality of the specific form of the building.

On the strength of the conditions laid down in the programme of requirements, the general conditions which will have to be fulfilled to an increasing extent on account of the industrialisation of building and, moreover, the conditions to be fulfilled by the architect, it can now be established what objective and subjective qualities the design of a building project must possess.

A. Objective qualities of the design

1. Functional qualities
   (a) The extent to which the specified functional conditions laid down in the programme of requirements with respect to units of space, spatial relationships, flexibility, etc. have been fulfilled.
   (b) The manner in which, from the functional point of view, compromises have been found between conflicting requirements within the scope of the available possibilities (*e.g.* location of site).

2. Constructional qualities
   The manner in which the functional requirements have been realised from the technical point of view.
   (a) Main structure
   Specifications with respect to strength, rigidity, safety and insulation.
   (b) Finish
   Specifications with respect to wear-resistance, impact-resistance, sound-deadening.
   (c) Installations
   Specifications with respect to air-conditioning, lighting, sanitary equipment and transport.

3. Economic qualities
   The extent to which the design renders efficient erection possible.
   (a) Timely availability, form and completeness of specifications and drawings.
   (b) The extent to which allowance has been made for conditions on the labour market (*e.g.* the extent to which the use of scarce categories of workers has been avoided).
   (c) The extent to which use has been made of standardisation by restricting the number of types of elements and the manner in which allowance has been made for unavoidable variation in the dimensions of building materials and elements and precautions

taken to avoid unnecessary dimensional deviations during erection operations on site.

(d) The extent to which scarce and unnecessarily expensive building materials have been avoided.

(e) The extent to which a short building time can be ensured and the loss of interest during building reduced to a minimum.

(f) Building costs in relation to size, quality and purpose of the building.

4. Management qualities

(a) The extent to which allowance has been made for the need of rational maintenance and cleaning once the building has been taken into use.

(b) The extent to which the requirements with respect to flexibility and scope for expansion have been fulfilled.

(c) The extent to which allowance has been made for the ultimate elimination of the building and an effort made to strike a balance between its technical and its economic life.

B. Subjective qualities of the building

1. General

In a general way the subjective quality of a building is demonstrated by the manner in which the architect assists in creating human space within the total available space, thus enabling each human being to be protected against and brought into a harmonious relationship with his fellow beings and his environment.

2. Industrial design

The manner in which the H(armonious) U(nity) function is realised in the design of the mass-produced materials, elements and components (or complete buildings).

3. Architecture

The manner in which the architect has given to the design of the building a higher value than the sum of the objective qualities; H(armonious) U(nity) + function.

4. Fine arts

The quality of the fine arts applied in the building;
+ function.

11 Building is rational production

the limited influence of the contractor | the necessity for coordination of programme, design and production | the influence of the public authorities | the organisation of production within the limitations | human aspects | specialisation and coordination | work study | planning | quality control | personnel relations | safety inspection | maintenance of machines and equipment | administration | the barriers broken by feedback | influencing the townplan and the design | the task of the central and local authorities | teamwork

1. THE LIMITS

The contractor has the important task of erecting the building. Frequently erection takes place under the direction of and in close co-operation with the architect and such experts as may be required for the building concerned.

The contractor can influence the ultimate result only to a limited extent. By giving close attention to the erection operations he can ensure a high measure of agreement between what is laid down in the specifications and the drawings and the completed building, while by sound organisation he can reduce building time and building costs to a minimum and yet ensure a satisfactory finish. Hence, he can considerably influence the quality of production on the building site by striking a balance between tempo and finish.

In the majority of cases, however, the contractor cannot influence the programme of requirements and the design, which to such a large extent determine the efficiency and the beauty of the building, but which also form the basis of rational building.

Hence, it is here that we encounter one of the well-known weak points in the production of buildings.

It is clear that, as building becomes more and more a matter of industrialised production of large series of standardised dwellings, schools and the like, it will be necessary to co-ordinate fully the work of programme, design and production.

There are quite a number of other things over which the contractor, rightly or wrongly, cannot exercise any influence and which are yet very important from the point of view of production efficiency. We have seen that public bodies, as principal and as organisations watching over the public interests, constitute influential parties in all building. This applies not only to the central government authorities, but also in the case of provincial and municipal authorities. Moreover, the increasing influence

177

of social laws on everything concerned with labour and the great (sometimes excessive) power of the bodies active in industry itself, especially the trade unions, seriously curtail the freedom of the contractor in the execution of his task.

As a result, the contractor has become greatly dependent on the efficiency of the public authorities, particularly with respect to their policy, regulations, interpretation of such regulations and the manner in which the civil servants perform their duties. The following are the most important spheres involved:

(a) *wage and price policies*, whereby the availability and the quality of workers and materials are affected;

(b) *investment and allocation policies*, which can in rough outline determine the continuity of work and also cause excessive tension;

(c) *approval procedure* and the method of *supervision*, which can have a marked influence on the smooth running of affairs;

(d) *quality* and the timely availability of the prepared building land, complete with access roads, which can greatly influence costs and the rate of production.

An additional difficulty in the case of the last-mentioned factor is that as a rule the contractor is not free to choose the place where he is going to build, which with the house-builder is sometimes still the case. Moreover, in various towns and regions the regulations and the procedures of the local government services are widely different.

The contractor is also greatly dependent on the industry for deliveries of building materials and building elements and on the associated services rendered by jobbers and sub-contractors. It is true that the contractor can still exercise a certain amount of control over this, because he is usually in a position to choose his suppliers. Nevertheless, he is very much dependent on the quality consciousness of the industry and the attitude taken in certain circles towards delivery obligations, the manner in which the trade performs its important functions of selection, stocking, distribution and financing and the quality standards and organisational talent of the sub-contractors. The contractor himself can do a great deal in this respect by placing clearly worded orders in good time.

2. ORGANISATION WITHIN THE LIMITATIONS

2.1 *The human aspect*

Although production is constantly influenced by factors over which the contractor has little or no control, it is he who determines the quality of production, naturally within the given conditions and possibilities. This quality depends on the technical knowledge and skill of the contractor, the general foremen and the building operatives, but in view of the developments and the manner of building practised in recent decennia, it is also dependent to an increasing extent on their knowledge and experience of organisation.

In the interests of sound organisation of production, attention should in the first place be given to the human aspects on the building site. The systematic promotion of good human relations, safety, hygiene and good work-clothing is a matter of great importance.

(a) *Good human relations*   In recent decennia it has been realised more and more that the level of labour productivity is not solely a matter of perfection of machines, well designed and tested working methods, good physical working conditions and economic incentives. Experience has proved that on industrial-economic grounds alone it is undesirable to divorce the productivity problem from the place of man in industry and his opportunities to come to self-expression and self-realisation.

It would not do to concentrate all ingenuity and energy on the technical, material sphere and to take for granted human adaptation to new production methods.

Investigations have shown that, under certain circumstances, recognition, appreciation, security and contact have a greater positive influence on morale and productivity than physical and sometimes even economic working conditions.

It has been clearly evident that the attitude and the efficiency of the worker are determined by social needs, which may lie both in and outside the sphere of the concern. It has been found that groups are formed within the concern, resulting in an informal hierarchy quite separate from the official hierarchy, which can both promote and retard production.

It is not surprising, therefore, that all large concerns are paying more and more attention to human relations, especially with regard to personnel selection, staff courses, group discussions, suggestion boxes, etc., while it is gradually being realised that the capacity and the will to work are factors which can definitely be influenced.

Fortunately, these matters are now also receiving attention in the building industry, but in this particular branch of industry considerable arrears must be made up in this respect, these arrears having been caused partly by such factors as the small size of the concerns, the lack of continuity in the work, frequent changing of personnel and the constant shifting from one building site to another.

Yet, much can be done in the interests of human dignity and productivity, both by the individual firms of contractors and by the organisations of employers and workers.

179

(b) *Safety*   The furthering of good human relations is, of course, closely bound up with the effort to ensure greater safety on the building site. The managers of the concerns should realise that they are in the first instance responsible for whatever may happen to the people entrusted to their care and they should do everything in their power to ensure the full co-operation of everyone on the building site to safeguard himself and his colleagues against the risk of accidents and all the grief this entails. This is especially necessary in the building industry, which in many countries is one of the most dangerous occupations, the accidents it involves causing much human sorrow and substantial damage. This is clearly demonstrated by the following figures for the building industry and other industries taken from the *Cahiers des Comités de Prévention du Bâtiment et des Travaux Publics* of 1957.

Country	Index figures for accidents per 1,000 workers in the building industry * and other industries (other industries = 100)
The Netherlands	153
Germany	171
Belgium	215
Great Britain	138
Italy	337
Switzerland	220
France	341
Canada	291
U.S.A.	178

* *the comparison between the countries can never be quite accurate owing to differences in the insurance schemes, definition of building industry, etc.*

Moreover, the accidents in the building industry are on an average of a more serious nature. The high number and the seriousness of the accidents are evident from the fact that in the Netherlands insurance payments in the building industry amount to nearly 2% of total wages paid as against barely 1% in industry as a whole.

Both material and psychological means are available to combat accidents: provisions to make dangerous machines and dangerous places safe; the use of personal safety equipment; drawing up and application of sound, and therefore safe, working methods; correct personnel selection; putting the right man in the right place; systematic education in safe working, for the younger and the older workers and for the junior and (especially) the senior staff.

They can be applied by the building industry itself and the appointment of a special safety engineer can greatly promote safety. The managements of building concerns can also influence conditions of safety, both positively and negatively.

(c) Hygiene on the building site   Good hygienic provisions on the building site are important for human relations and human dignity. It is no exaggeration to say that in this respect the care of the workers in the building industry leaves much to be desired. It is true that conditions are not very favourable compared with other industries on account of constantly changing personnel, a certain roughness of the trade and the necessity to move from one building site to another.

Fortunately, it is beginning to be realised that this situation must be improved in the interests of human relations and – what is more – because it is evident that for the modern young workers the building trade has serious disadvantages owing to the absence of essential amenities. No serious objections would be raised to having to work in all kinds of weather, because for healthy people this has a certain charm, but the absence of reasonably good working conditions will not be accepted in the long run.

There should be washrooms to enable the men to go to and from their work clean and properly dressed, thus appreciably reducing the chance of sickness.

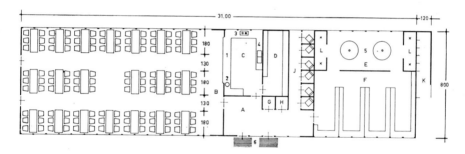

Fig. 1. Example of shed for 120 building workers

A entrance-hall	G tool closet	1 counter
B canteen	H meter cabinet	2 device for making coffee
C kitchen-buffet	J W.C.	3 gas-ring
D stores-room	K urinal	4 sink with rinsing bowl
E wash-room	L shower	5 wash-column
F dressing-room		6 foot grid

(d) Proper working clothes   More social appreciation than has hitherto been the case is due to general foremen, foremen and workers responsible for building in all kinds of weather. They have an attractive occupation, because – irrespective of the degree of industrialisation introduced in building in the future – their work will invariably be of a more constructive and individual character than mass production in industry.

A worker in the building industry will never experience the mental stress imposed by mass production, but he will from time to time have to stand up to excessively great physical exertion. Good vocational training, sound planning, efficient mechanisation and proper canteens can make the trade more attractive in this respect. If this can be achieved, the building trade will once more be able to attract more workers of the best kind, men who like to "build". These workers can then be given a good wage and proper secondary working conditions, which are attractive to them both mentally and physically.

The social appreciation – which, it must be admitted, is also associated with appearance – will grow quickly, if the workers in the building industry can claim all kinds of reasonable primary and secondary working conditions, and – once they have been obtained – make good use of them. This also means that by having proper working clothes they can be "well-dressed" on the job and by having good changing rooms they can go home attired in such a way that wives and daughters need no longer cast an envious eye on the "white collar" neighbours. The son who is suitable for the building trade will then be more inclined to follow proudly in has father's footsteps.

2.2 Specialisation – new functions

The promotion of good human relations on the building site and in the concern as a whole is a first requirement if working conditions worthy of the human effort are to be ensured. They also constitute an important element in the effort to achieve an optimum output with the means available to the contractor.

In industry, increased outputs have been attained especially by division of work and specialisation. This specialisation has developed in three directions:

(a) the concern specialises in a limited number of products;

(b) new functions have been created in the executive sphere, for which specialisation proved necessary;

(c) as a result of the division of tasks in the production sphere, mechanisation has become possible and new problems and new functions have been created.

This development is in full swing in the mass-production industry, even though it is sometimes difficult to achieve the volume of production necessary to be able to work on a rational basis (limited market).

In many countries the same trend is beginning to be noticeable in the contractors business and here again developments have lagged behind considerably. In rough outline, there is a certain amount of specialisation. There are road-builders, firms specialising in excavation work, contractors specialising in civil and industrial building, house-builders, steel construction companies, etc. Yet, the general contractor in the building sector is generally not specialised. He submits a tender for the building as drawn by the architect and erects it with such personnel and equipment as are available. The object of his tendering policy is to ensure that either he alone is invited to submit a tender or that he belongs to the limited group invited to do so. In some cases his business in confined to home-building, but even then he rarely comes to complete industrial specialisation.

It seldom occurs that a firm of contractors, after having conducted serious market research, starts to specialise in a specific type of building of a given construction. In this respect, too, the limited area of operations is often a considerable drawback.

In the supplying industries specialisation is steadily going ahead, although in many cases little or no rational standardisation has been achieved.

Apart from the one-man business, there are three types of concern with varying degrees of specialisation of functions. Besides the nature of the product manufactured, it is particularly the volume of work performed which determines the degree of specialisation required.

Even in the small business it is necessary to make a division between management and production.

In practice, this division is seldom clear-cut. The management ("the boss") sometimes does part of the work and some trusted men contribute towards management, *e.g.* by taking on orders, fixing prices, devising working methods, etc.

In the medium-size concern, both management and production must be specialised. In production, the various duties, each of which requires special training, are classified as "trades". In the management sector, the performance of the supervisory function requires the keeping of records, for which some form of administration must be set up.

Further, it is necessary to co-ordinate the various teams of workers, operating alongside each other or in turn, with a view to bringing about production of the common product. This makes it necessary to plan the work beforehand. Whereas the two split-off executive functions can be regarded as auxiliary to management, their position vis-à-vis the production department, *i.e.* the building project(s), is entirely different. The administration department is "passive", since it receives information from the site. The planning department is "active", because the plans worked out there in respect of the procedure and sequence of the work are intended to be carried out by production.

As the concern increases in size, a further division of the organisation will be necessary.

In the first place, production may involve a number of projects simultaneously. Each of these "parallel" projects must be managed on site by a general foreman.

Furthermore, the number of decisions to be taken by management increases to such an extent that a division of duties will be necessary at this level. To this end it is advisable to use as a criterion the kind of qualifications one must have to perform the function properly. In this way different kinds of functions are formed, *e.g.* commercial and technical functions, but also functions involving the collecting and processing of data (staff functions) and functions involving the taking of decisions on the strength of the possibilities presented (line functions). In addition, a distinction must be made according to the scope of the task (giving general directions or taking action in specific cases) or else in some other way, such as rendering services or work on behalf of direct production.

All these distinctions may be found in the structural diagram for a large concern given in Fig. 2.

Three of the new functions created as a result of specialisation will be discussed here, because they are of fundamental importance in the effort to achieve rational production, *viz.* work study, planning and dimension and quality control.

(*a*) *Work study*   To achieve an efficient building method, the building process should be analysed in the sequence of operations with a view to arriving at a production plan. In this production plan, called the timetable, the production factors, labour, materials and capital should be incorporated in such a way that optimum results can be attained. In rough outline, the timetable provides the answers to the questions: What, how, where, when and how much?

Optimum results can only be attained if the battle against shortages is waged in the correct manner. In highly developed countries this means mechanisation and thus building with high capital investments, and in the less developed countries, where usually ample labour and little capital is available, this means building with the accent on labour. In both cases we are faced with the important problem of the place of man in enterprise and the commercial aspect of the production factor labour.

Correct treatment of each individual worker in the concern will result in the man being suitable for his job and willing to work. An essential complement of this, however, is the systematic determination of the scope and the size of his task. The scope of the task is also understood to include the manner in which it is performed. This requires both an analysis of functions (whereby it can be prevented that a single person is made to do irreconcilable tasks) and an analysis of the work.

The work study produces a description of the work to be carried out and measures the time required to perform this work. It forms the basis for the efficient planning of the work, for correct price fixing and for a system of payments by results, if this should be required.

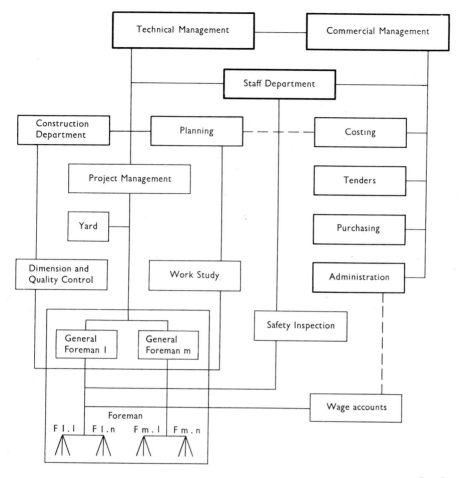

Fig. 2

   The time that can be considered as "normal" for carrying out certain clearly outlined operations must be derived – if it is to be scientifically acceptable – from observations in respect of the operation concerned or comparable operations. It has not yet proved possible to make up work times by purely theoretical means. The element of experience, *i.e.* ad hoc observations or observations previously made, is indispensable (time studies). The magnitude observed has a different value each time owing to differences between workers and differences between successive operations performed by one and the same worker.

   The object of time studies is not to gain insight into the specific output of the worker during the period of observation, but rather to establish what he and other workers are capable of achieving on future occasions. Hence, via generalisation the time study leads to prognosis. For its practical use it is necessary that the reliability of the time study should be known. The standard time is regarded solely as an average or an expected value, while, moreover, the deviations to be expected in practice must be known.

It follows, therefore, that the making of time studies is a form of statistical work, irrespective of whether the time-study man is aware of this or not. The time study is an industrial experiment, in which, on the strength of observations in respect of a complex of factors on the one hand and the associated value of the variable magnitude "work time" on the other, the laws governing the effect of circumstances (in the widest sense) on the work time are established.

Time studies can be made at very different levels of human activity. In an overall project, such as the building of a block of dwellings, involving many workers, a large number of operations can be distinguished (*e.g.* bricklaying, plastering, etc.), which often run parallel with the trades of the men.

Each operation can be subdivided into a very large number of standard work elements. A standard work element in bricklaying for example can be defined as "laying a single-brick interior wall, unpointed, in sand-lime brick". Each standard work element comprises a series of actions and each action can finally be broken down into a series of motions.

In principle, time studies can be carried out at any of the levels mentioned. The classical time study is concerned with the actions, determines their standard times and adds them up to obtain the appropriate standard time for a standard work element.

A modern method is the snap-reading method. This method does not involve the measuring of the duration of an operation or a standard work element with the stopwatch, but noting down at irregular intervals what action the worker is performing at that moment. The idea is that, if action A takes three times as long as action B, it will be observed in the course of a large number of snap readings that the worker performs action A three times as often as action B. This method was evolved by Tippett, a British statistician, and its reliability is computed with the normal mathematical-statistical means.

In recent years another method has been introduced, known as Methods Time Measurement (M.T.M.), which goes down to a lower level, *viz.* to the motions. The advantage of this method is that the same motions occur with all kinds of different operations, so that the study can be confined to a smaller number of observations than would be expected at first sight. However, difficulties are still experienced with adding up the results.

Yet another time-study method recently introduced is concerned with observations at a higher level, *viz.* in respect of operations. With this method the work times are noted of one and the same operation in a large

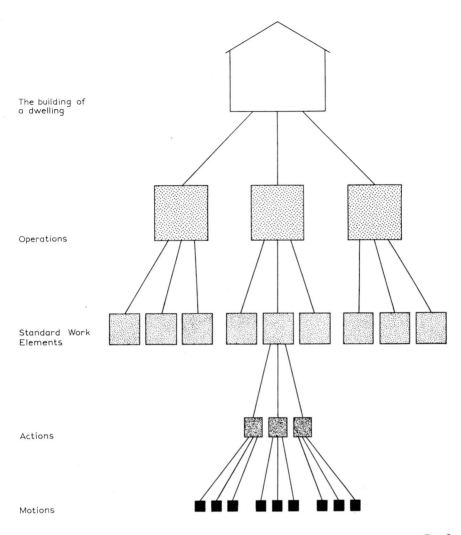

The building of
a dwelling

Operations

Standard Work
Elements

Actions

Motions

Fig. 3

number of different tasks. Whereas in the case of the conventional time-study methods the conditions must as far as possible be kept constant, in the statistical time-study referred to above it is necessary to vary the conditions or influencing factors as much as possible.

By means of special statistical techniques, chiefly the multiple correlation method, a formula is derived from the results of the observations, in which the nature and the magnitude of the effect of the various conditions are laid down.

Substitution of the numerical value of the "conditions" in the formula produces the normal work time of a given standard work element.

All time-study methods are useful and have their specific purpose. The conventional time study is indicated when in an industry a certain type of work is often repeated under standard conditions. In the building industry, where – as in the case of foundries – the work varies a great deal, the statistical time-study is an important aid.

The work study and the associated time study enable a number of essential questions in regard to the systematic approach to production to be answered. These questions concern the following points:

Planning: volume of work, number of workers, rate of building, working methods, number of workers required at a given time.
Production: division of tasks, definition of tasks, payment for tasks.
Supervision: progress, costs, price adjustment.

This systematic approach is reflected in all the various activities which can generally be classed under the heading "planning".

(*b*) *Planning*   Most buildings are very complicated things. The various operations required in their production must be performed in quick succession and the work must generally be completed at a given time, while nevertheless the most economical use must be made of men, materials and machines. Hence, it will be appreciated that improvisation, *i.e.* taking a decision at the moment that action is required, is impossible without considerable waste of time and money. Efficient production of buildings requires "thinking ahead" and "building on paper first", thus "planning".

Such planning provides the answers to a number of points, such as:
— the operations to be performed to realise the building
— the sequence in which the operations must be performed
— the manner in which each of the operations must be performed
— the time at which each operation can be commenced and in how much time it can be completed
— the number of workers, classified according to their trades, required to perform these operations
— the equipment required to perform the operations
— the materials to be used for the operations
— where the operations will be performed: on the job, on the building site or elsewhere.

In planning, the omission of any of these points constitutes a serious error. It is as in chess: it is difficult to win if you do not keep an eye on all your pieces.

Each of the points enumerated above requires a decision, after the pros and cons have been weighed. It should be borne in mind that a decision on any of these points may mean that the number of possibilities to choose from in respect of other points becomes smaller. Thus, when taking a decision on any point, it must be carefully considered what the consequences will be with regard to the other points.

To this end it is necessary as a first step to draw up a sound timetable, which means it must be determined what tasks (*i.e.* operations and part operations) must be performed and how much time each task should take at most.

The basis of modern planning methods is to look for repetitive elements in the buildings to be produced, so that also in the building industry advantage can be taken of series-production whenever possible. It is necessary, therefore, to make a project analysis and a construction analysis. The similar units thus found can differ in size. In housing projects they can take the form of whole blocks with an identical number of dwellings of the same type. In road-building they can be road-sections to be constructed one after the other. In the case of industrial buildings, the units can be a number of identical columns and/or floor sections, etc.

A list of operations is then drawn up in respect of these units of construction and it is ascertained whether one or more operations are subject to a time limit, since allowance must be made for this when determining the time "available" for each of the operations. Acceleration or delay in any one of the operations will only give rise to waiting times and will thus upset the continuity of work for men and/or machines.

Inversion of the uniformly fixed time per unit of product found for all the operations produces the "rate of building", *i.e.* the quantity of product that can be handled per unit of time. Moreover, the indivisibility of the production factors makes it necessary to weigh the disadvantages of equipment standing idle against those of workers being partly employed. With a continuous flow of human labour the intermittent use of a concrete mixer is less inconvenient than having costly installations such as tower cranes and concrete pumps standing idle.

However, once it has been established on the strength of a comparison of costs what the optimum building rate is, the timetable can be drawn up in rough outline. An example of such a timetable, in a simplified form, is shown in Fig. 4.

This drawing clearly illustrates the repetitive operations of the series of identical constructional components of the building. It also shows at what moment certain auxiliary equipment becomes available at the end of a cycle of operations for further use.

Subsequently, the quantities of material and labour required for each phase of operations are laid down in a production specification, which forms the basis for the secondary planning, of which the building site organisation plan

189

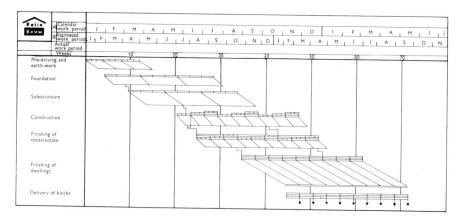

Fig. 4

is certainly the most important. The principal object of this plan is to reduce transport costs to a minimum. However, the consequences of a (good or inferior) building-site layout, orderliness, neatness and safety are equally important.

It is quite impossible to work smoothly and safely in the chaos shown in Fig. 5.

It will not be difficult to see that Fig. 6 presents a much higher degree of efficiency.

The efficiency of production can be promoted by the use of offtake schemes for materials and equipment in the sphere of work planning, which indicate the cycle of the tasks of workers and teams of workers, as well as the use of time distance diagrams, which enable the number and the capacity of the vehicles to be determined.

Route tables tell the truck drivers what to collect or deliver and where. Similar routing instructions enable the skippers of barges to be given accurate instructions, for example, with large-scale soil shifting. All these forms of primary, secondary and detail planning constitute as many means to assist in achieving efficient production of buildings.

When extending the efficient organisation of a single project to a number of projects, it appears straight away that series-production of similar units is invariably possible, irrespective of whether the successive units are located close together or some distance away from each other. It will be clear that once an organisation has been set going for the production of a given project, it will retain its advantages if it can be immediately transferred on completion of the work to a subsequent project of a similar organisational structure.

(c) *Quality control*   The significance of quality control in the building

190

Fig. 5

Fig. 6

191

industry depends on the extent to which modern industrial methods and prefabrication based on standardisation and mechanisation are introduced. Quality control can be applied to individual products, batches of products and processes.

The essential basis for any activity concerned with quality is a clear definition of what is understood by quality and of the requirements that must be fulfilled.

For some quality properties the method of determination has been standardised, *e.g.* measuring with caliper gauges and sometimes the standard construction has been laid down in standardisation sheets. A clear method of determination is necessary in all cases.

It will often be necessary to confine quality control to sampling, because for batches or a process one hundred per cent inspection is usually impossible or very uneconomical. The samples should be representative of the whole batch or process. They should be of adequate size and, in view of the many factors that can exert their influence, the samples should be correctly distributed over the batch or process. For the purposes of quality assessment the inspection results must be compared with standards, due allowance being made for the chance variations in the samples in a statistically acceptable manner. Quality control should as a rule not be confined to acceptance or rejection of products actually made, but must also be directed towards the improvement of the articles manufactured or designed in the future.

The influencing of quality and maintenance of quality standards are, therefore, very important aspects of quality control. The undesirable quality fluctuations must be corrected by feedback[1]. If the feedback principle is to be used effectively, the process must fulfil the following three conditions:

(*a*) There must be a regulating mechanism enabling the process changes to be controlled.

(*b*) The result must be capable of being measured, *i.e.* a standard must be available, against which the results can be checked, so that the deviation can be established.

(*c*) Both measurement and control must take place quickly, so that the correction initiated by the deviation occurs during the process and thus – from the point of view of time – is relevant.

Quality can be influenced on the whole in a number of different ways, such as quality recording (making the quality visible), co-ordination of actions, training of special functionaries responsible for quality control, improving the quality consciousness of management, etc.

---

[1] *Feedback is a notion originating from cybernetics, i.e. the science concerned with the study of self-regulating processes. The feedback principle is encountered in a variety of spheres.*

In the contractors business the need will be felt for a new functionary, the quality analyst, who is made responsible for quality control in the concern. He will have to devote special attention to the quality of dimensions, because an adequately high standard of dimensioning in production constitutes one of the fundamental conditions for the development of industrialised building. This applies to the materials and elements brought to the building site and to the work on the building site.

Relevant investigations[1,2] have shown that it is an urgent necessity to devote greater attention to dimensional accuracy in industrialised building, whereby considerable economies can be achieved.

The inaccuracy which occurs in respect of the materials supplied is caused by mutual differences or random error and difference between the standard and the average of the actual dimensions, *i.e.* the systematic error.

It is usually easier to reduce the systematic error than the random error, which requires a deeper study of the production process.

The quality of dimensions in building is not solely dependent on the variations which occur in the dimensions of buildings, but also on the permissible tolerances on these dimensions. The quality is bad if the variations are great and the tolerances small. The dimensional quality is good if the variations are about equal to the permissible tolerances.

If the variations are considerably smaller than the permissible tolerances, the dimensional quality is then not so good, because the relatively slight variations are unnecessarily small, which in practice usually means that a cheaper working method with larger variations could be adopted.

The diagram (Fig. 7) indicates what measures can be taken to improve dimensional quality with a view to reducing the amount of adjusting work to a minimum and thereby making further industrialisation of the building process possible.

In practice, the measures to improve dimensional quality amount to reducing the variations in the dimensions and increasing the tolerances. The former can be achieved both by reducing the variations of the building materials and by reducing the variations occurring as a result of operations on the building site.

In the manufacture of building materials the variations can be reduced in three ways. The method which according to practical experience is the most obvious one and the least drastic is the application of a system of statistical quality control in the factory. This makes it possible to reduce the variations by exercising greater care in the manufacturing process. If

1 *Dimensional deviations in house-building. Consultants for Applied Statistics, in collaboration with Bouwcentrum and the Quality Control Service for Industry. Rotterdam 1956.*
2 *Investigation into dimensional accuracy of some building materials. Bouwcentrum 1959.*

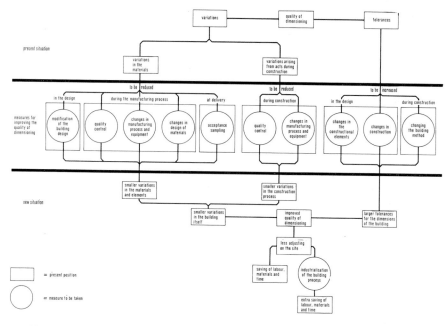

Fig. 7. *Improving the quality of dimensioning in the construction of dwellings*

it appears that the results are then still inadequate, more drastic measures can be adopted, *e.g.* the purchase of machines operating with a higher degree of accuracy. In the diagram this method is defined as "modification of process and equipment". It is also possible to modify the design of the materials in such a way that more accurate manufacture becomes possible.

A very simple and yet drastic method of reducing the dimensional variations of building materials is the application of an acceptance sampling procedure, whereby all articles deviating excessively from the standard are rejected and, if necessary, returned. This method is undoubtedly very effective, but must be handled with the necessary care.

With regard to the operations performed on the building site the application of statistical quality control is likewise the most advisable procedure as a first step to achieving a reduction in the dimensional variations.

Especially in the initial stages of building, *viz.* the setting out of dimensions and the location of the fundamental building elements, the application of statistical quality control is highly desirable.

In the course of building a reduction of variations can also be achieved by using different equipment and different working methods. The changes in the process also include changes in the method of setting out the dimensions of the building.

Finally, the variations in the dimensions can also be greatly influenced

194

by the architect. In consultation with suppliers of building materials and with the contractor the architect can arrive at a choice of materials and construction which ensures greater accuracy of dimensions. It is quite possible, for example, that two small spans together produce a more accurate result than a single large span.

All these measures can result in smaller variations in the dimensions of a building and can thus lead to better agreement with the standard.

As stated earlier, a better accuracy of dimensions can also be achieved by increasing the tolerances instead of decreasing the variations. It is generally possible to change the design in such a way that larger tolerances can be applied. These changes can be brought about both by a different construction of the building materials and by a different construction of the building. For example, one method of supporting a beam can permit of a greater tolerance on the distance between walls than another.

In a few cases it will be possible to apply larger tolerances by altering the organisation, but this will not lead to large-scale results.

In the foregoing it has been explained how it is possible to reduce the variations on the one hand and to increase the tolerances on the other. These measures together will result in a better dimensional quality. Consequently, less adjusting work will be necessary on the building site, thus culminating in a considerable saving in labour, materials and building time.

Once this has been achieved, the time has come to consider adapting the entire building process to the new conditions. The greater uniformity, both as regards dimensions and the essential operations to be performed, will constitute a sound basis for further mechanisation of the building process. However, since it will no longer be necessary to correct dimensions on the job, it will also be possible to revise the methods employed in work which will have still largely to be done by hand.

(d) *Other important aspects*   As the building concern grows in size and consequently the distance between management, executive staff and especially workers becomes greater, it appears that contact between "high" and "low" is inclined to lose its personal character and is more and more reduced to the level of "paper-work".

The self-identification with the concern, *i.e.* the personal effort on behalf of the concern, is born from the confidence which the worker has that "the concern" is also interested in the wishes and the opportunities of the individual. Even for the most "human" management it is unfortunately impossible to give this attention to each individual, unless he has delegated this aspect of his executive function (personnel relations). This means that in this sphere, too, an "expert" takes over the care of these wishes and opportunities and, insofar as this is then still necessary.

195

For, here again it is the line functionary who must ultimately (also) do it himself.

This also applies to the executive personnel at the lowest level, the general foremen and the foremen. Despite the frequent changing of executive personnel on the sites, it appears that the majority of the workers are not solely interested in their pay packet at the end of the week, but their confidence in the justness of the measures taken or to be taken constitutes a much stronger tie and has a greater stimulating effect.

This aspect must be given every attention in the selection and training of executive functionaries at this level by or on behalf of the personnel department.

One of the ways in which human relations can be handled by the line functionaries is by ensuring safe working conditions. The services of an expert are required to work out the necessary safety measures and in particular to persuade the general foremen and the workers to apply these measures. He is the safety engineer, who on behalf of the personnel department assists on the building site in this particular aspect.

As the industrialisation of building proceeds and more and more manual labour is replaced by machines, it becomes necessary to pay special attention to the regular maintenance of machines and equipment. There is still far too much neglect in this respect.

A timetable, a team of well-trained mechanics, carefully compiled instruction manuals for the use and inspection of machines, as well as a sound system of recording the use and the costs of machines and equipment, constitute the essential basis for the proper functioning of the department responsible for this work.

As the small concern grows into a medium-size concern it is necessary to pay special attention to administrative specialisation. This applies to an even greater extent in the case of the large concern, where the supervision of the daily business, purchasing, checking of costs, estimating and subsequent adjustment of prices in respect of building projects have become very important and where the keeping of wage accounts also requires special care.

The technical aspect of estimating could be put back into its proper perspective if greater use were made of the quantity surveyor as an independent authority, thus appreciably reducing the contractor's responsibility for the quantities of materials used or to be used.

With increasing specialisation it is not sufficient to ensure an efficient division of functions and tasks, but it is equally important to arrange proper co-ordination of the specialised activities.

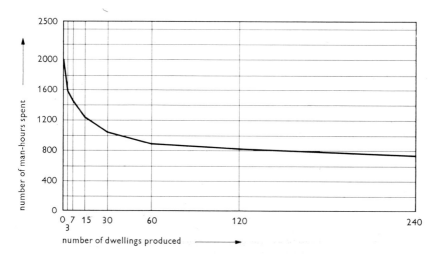

Fig. 8 Single type of dwelling

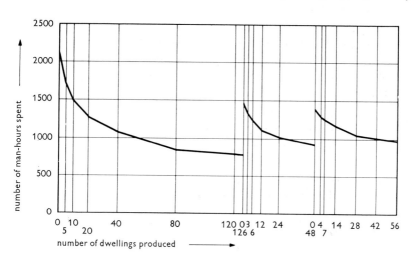

Fig. 9 Different types of dwellings

3. HOW TO BREAK THROUGH THE LIMITATIONS

Even the best attention to organisation cannot lead to rational building in every respect, as long as the contractor's freedom of action remains as limited as it usually still is.

He cannot organise his work properly if in most cases he receives the drawings bit by bit as the building operations proceed. The advantages of standardisation and repetition in production cannot be fully developed if, owing to unwarranted variety and lack of continuity, the building industry

197

is not given the opportunity of discovering the advantages of continuity of work, division of work and efficient mechanisation.

Hence, the contractor must not only study the possibilities presented by modern industrial organisation, but he should also ensure that the barriers are broken down in such a way that by means of feedback all stages of planning are affected.

The actual building operations can be made to proceed with a high degree of productivity by ensuring efficient division of work and using teams of specialised workers of such size that the different teams can be kept working continuously and consecutively. This applies especially if the project is of a sufficiently large size to produce a gain by routine work. This routine gain will be greatest if continuous production can be maintained on, for example, a single type of dwelling, as is evident from Fig. 8. The change from one type to another results in a temporary loss of man-hours, but even then a considerable gain is achieved because the organisation is kept intact (see Fig. 9).

It is not sufficient, however, that the contractor secures the specialised knowledge to be able to impart an efficient rhythmic character to the building operations. The design should allow for this possibility, as otherwise this knowledge will only be of theoretical value. That is why feedback is necessary.

This does not only apply in the design stage, when the choice of materials, construction and design is very important to create conditions conducive to rational building, but it also applies in the town-planning stage, in which very important decisions are taken, which ultimately affect production. In this stage also it is possible to promote rational production without detracting in any way from other values, as may be seen from the Figs. 10 and 11, in which a project (plan 1) involving a combination of high and low buildings was ultimately replaced by another project (plan 2), fulfilling exactly the same requirements, but which – unlike the original project – could be realised on a rational basis.

In the second project, allowance was made for the fact that with the given construction a building cycle of 24 dwellings in the case of the blocks of flats and one of 28 dwellings in the case of the single-family houses made it possible to use the teams of workers on continuous rhythmic production, which resulted in a considerable gain as compared with the first project[1].

It is the task of the central government authorities to create, in collaboration with the local authorities, the right climate for rational building with a view to achieving the essential reduction of building costs and increased building capacity whilst attaining a more conscious quality.

[1] *Example: Work of Foundation Ratiobouw, Rotterdam executed in collaboration with the municipality of Hengelo, The Netherlands.*

Promoting continuity

— Regulation of the building industry to avoid a lack of work or excess work.
— Promotion of capital formation and canalisation of the flow of capital to building, partly with a view to achieving a decrease in the rate of interest.
— Greater continuity in the government policy with respect to financial assistance in house-building, school-building, etc., in order to promote better planning of local activities and to avoid waste in the form of loss of interest, loss of capacity and revision of building plans.

Simplification

— Clear government regulations, available to all, with respect to building plans and an effort to reduce subjective assessment of plans by government authorities to a minimum.
— Ensuring uniformity of estimates and of calculation methods for government authorities, management and contractors.

Promoting standardisation

— Further unification of building regulations.
— Government assistance in promoting standardisation and repetitive building.

Promoting the reduction of building costs and improving quality

— Reducing transfer fees in respect of buildings and building land.
— Supervision of any action aiming at a restriction of competition, whereby the prices of building materials would be maintained at an excessively high level.
— Promotion of building research and documentation.
— Promotion of teamwork.

Teamwork will have to break down the barriers between planning, design and production, and an effort should be made to create greater unity in the overall task.

This applies in countries where supply is controlled from one central point and in cases where design and production are placed in the hands of a single private or government enterprise, as well as in countries where the stages of town-planning, programming, design and production have hitherto been almost completely isolated from each other.

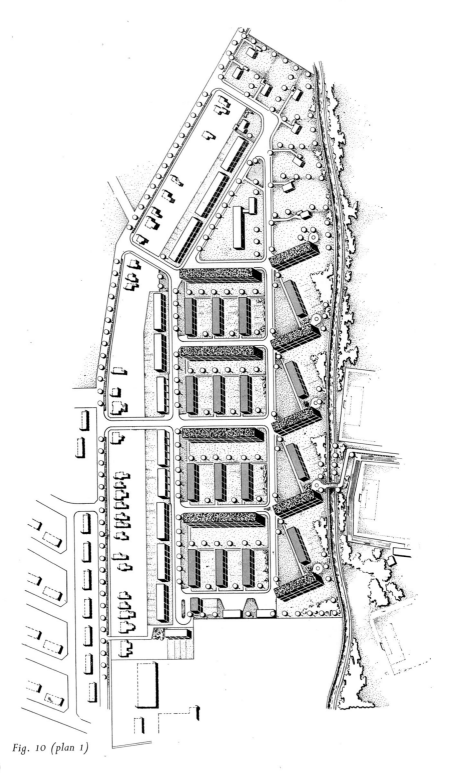

Fig. 10 (plan 1)

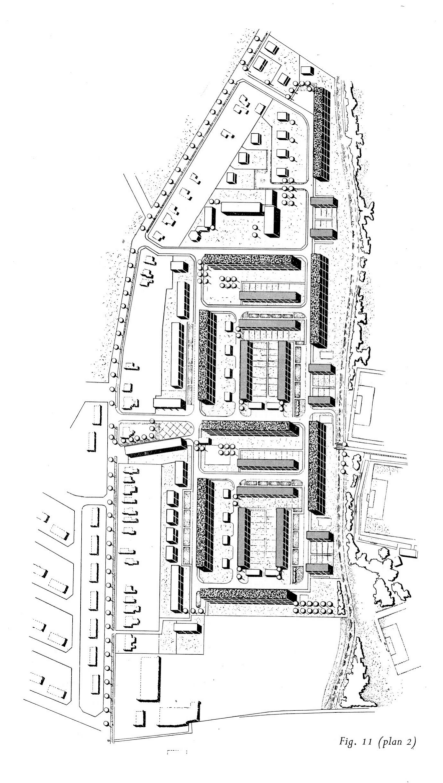

Fig. 11 (plan 2)

In the first two cases it is an internal matter of a public body or a private enterprise. In the third case it is a matter of co-ordinating the work performed entirely independently by different bodies, firms or persons and where the tie is the principal at one end and the completed building at the other end.

In all cases a characteristic feature of teamwork is the willingness to co-operate on the part of all the members of the team. This means that each member unconditionally accepts an exchange of views during which all kinds of data, standpoints and considerations are openly discussed. Each member must be prepared as it were to account for his own work and views, while the other members whose work is not involved must take part in the discussions whenever they feel that the expression of their views can contribute towards the overall results. The members have equal rights to express their opinions, thus in the discussions they are equals. All this is an essential condition for success.

The work in respect of which consultation and co-ordination are required varies considerably. In the first place there are the provisions and activities which to a large extent come in the sphere of the public authorities and are of a programming nature. Examples are the local house-building programme and the associated town plans. Other matters closely connected with this are the division into building tasks and the availability of building land. In addition, there are activities directly concerned with the realisation of a specific project. This chiefly concern the design of the architect, fitting this into the town plan (and the possibility of modification), the constructions and the production of the building.

It is not practical on the whole to set up a team to cover all these activities. Especially in large cities, where a large number of projects are involved, such a team would become much too large and various experts forming part of the team would only sporadically be brought into the discussions. For these cities, therefore, it is advisable to make a clear distinction between the programming team (engaged in the first group of activities, directly concerned with the building programme) and the various building teams (whose work is confined to the problems concerned with the realisation of a specific project). The object is in all cases to express in a building the knowledge and experience of many in order to achieve optimum fulfilment of the need for buildings, which must be realised by rational organisation whilst respecting human dignity.

In the effort to achieve this object numerous difficulties will be encountered and special measures will, therefore, have to be taken to obtain the necessary building output. The problems involved are concerned on the one hand with the in many respects still underdeveloped building research, documentation and rational transmission of knowledge and on the other hand with the manner in which these matters are approached on national and international levels. These points will be discussed in the last part of this book, which deals with "acceleration".

Part three: ACCELERATION

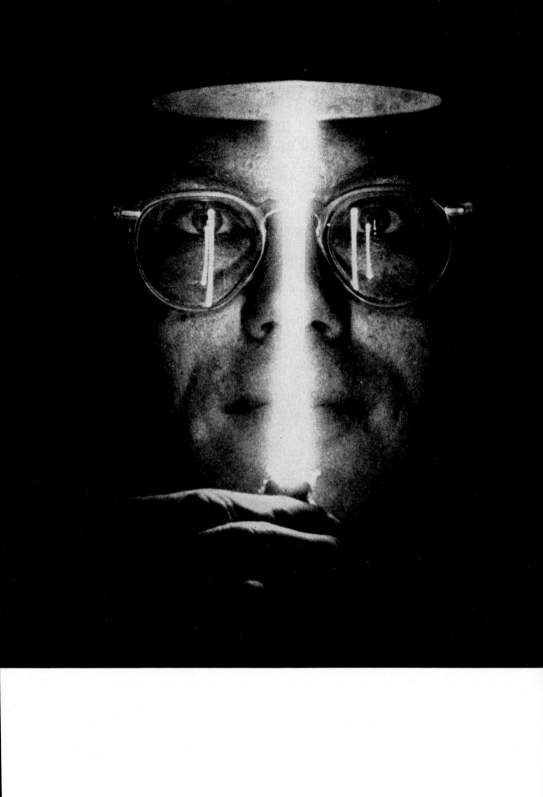

12 Building research and development

the aim: better living conditions | accidental discovery, linear invention, multi-dimensional planning | arrears in building research | basic problems: the skeleton of building activity | functional research: usefulness | technical research: realisation of functional requirements, technological basis of production | organisation research: large scale framework and efficient production | development work: from prototype to mass production

1. OBJECT, SCOPE AND BASIC PRINCIPLES

On the strength of past experience man is constantly engaged to-day in taking decisions with an eye to the future. He wants to reduce the uncertainties of the future to a minimum with a view to achieving a higher degree of control over society and over his personal life. Man is beginning to realise more and more that he cannot be satisfied with a future over which he has little or no control.

When taking these decisions he is constantly faced with the problem of making a choice and his efforts should be directed towards making the optimum choice from the available alternatives. His intuition – however indispendable this may be – is inadequate and he cannot rely exclusively on the opinions of others. He needs facts and he must know the relationships between the essential factors which wholly or largely rule the game.

It is impossible to achieve optimum functioning of our society without a good deal of thought and preparation, without optimum intellectual investment, without research and systematic development work. We all know, however, that in our personal lives and in society as a whole we are concerned first and foremost with certain essential criteria, which do not constitute subjects for research in the ordinary sense, such as truth, justice, integrity and honesty, courage and love, beauty, faith and hope, freedom to develop as an individual and as a group. But we are also beginning to realise how important the ordinary things of everyday life are: the manner in which man exists or should exist and especially also how our fellow men exist.

The ultimate aim of research and development should be to improve directly and indirectly the means of livelihood of man and to promote an accelerated balanced development of society.

For thousands of years accidental discoveries have been the basis of acceleration of progress, which was moreover supported by experience

207

obtained with the aid of intuition and trial-and-error methods. In this phase, progress was extremely slow and its scope small, one of the reasons being that the capacity to foresee the future was limited. It is remarkable to note how very much the world of to-day is still in this stage of thought and action.

The phase of invention proved to be a considerable step ahead. Man must now have the imagination to visualise a certain aim and to direct his activities to and divide them over a certain period with this aim in view. The radius of prognosis and action was increased, but in the main was still of a linear nature. It will be clear that this phase constituted an important gain, but at the same time strongly promoted an unbalanced development.

Under the influence of technical progress interdependence is rapidly increasing and consequently it is not only necessary to correct existing unbalance wherever it is found, but also to ensure a balanced development in the future by means of a different and more systematic approach. To achieve this, however, it is necessary that the entire development of the world should enter into a systematic planning phase. In this phase the accidental discoveries and linear invention will remain very important, but they must be incorporated as valuable additional elements in a planned multi-dimensional development backed by research. In this planned development, adequate room must be reserved for "idle curiosity", which should be made to serve the really important things in our lives.

Fortunately, fundamental changes are evident everywhere. Even in his time, Hubert Spencer envisaged a social development in which gradually more attention would be given to the interests of others. In industry it has been noticeable in recent decennia that personal interests and technical progress are no longer the only yardsticks used to determine industrial policy. Actions are now also prompted by the feeling of being responsible for a large number of people. Especially since World War II there has been a tendency to pay attention to the human being, not to the "*homo economicus*", who is expected to be capable of adapting himself to any new production method, but to the human being of flesh and blood, who does not allow himself to be driven by economic motives alone.

Following the line of thought introduced by Julian Huxley, we can therefore characterise two eras in our present century by referring to the period that lies behind us as "the era of economic man" and to the period lying ahead of us as "the era of social man".

As we have already noted, there has been a decided shift of our attention to other interests. Before the first world war the western world occupied itself almost exclusively with the technical control of the forces of nature. In an age devoted to economic exploitation and the creation of wealth, the human being with his problems was almost entirely forgotten. It is evident, however, that gradually a certain amount of priority is being given to the human problems rather than to the strictly economic problems. This does not mean, of course, that in the era of social man economics is regarded as a matter of secondary importance, but rather that an attempt is being made to make economics function on behalf of mankind.

We are beginning to understand that the period in which engineering and economics almost fully control the conditions of life has reached its last phase and that in order to be able to build up consciously a healthy, balanced society priority must be given to social and psychological factors.

This creates the conditions necessary for a society worthy of mankind, made possible by free men and women who are prepared to accept the consequences of the fundamental principles of democracy and of the growing interdependence, while engineering and economics are further developed in the service of mankind in order to break through the vicious circle of hunger, sickness and poverty and lay the foundation of personal happiness and prosperity for the individual and of the economic strength of the society. It is in this way that human beings can be freed from their daily cares to the extent that they will gain a clearer insight into the things that really matter, the essence of life.

Research and development should ultimately be directed towards achieving a better social functioning of our society, when important psycho-sociological and socio-psychological problems will present themselves.

Improvements in the social sphere usually necessitate a strengthening of the economic basis and improvement of spatial functioning, which should be developed simultaneously. The means available to man consist for the greater part of technical knowledge, capacity for organisation and natural resources.

Improvement of spatial functioning on behalf of man and society implies adaptation of the available space by building and civil engineering. Through adaptation of space to human requirements, strengthening of the economic potential and influence on social functioning, building is directly and indirectly associated with the essential problem with which we are faced, viz. the creation of favourable conditions for the development of man and society. This is all the more true because when creating a building we are concerned not only with material aspects, but, in addition, the architect in his capacity as artist imparts quality to the building, which is closely related with the essence of life.

In the foregoing, we have ascertained the enormous tasks with which man is faced in building and the large amounts of money that will have to be invested to make the world habitable for all within the span of this century.

It is clear that much will depend on whether optimum use is made of these enormous annual material investments. This means a lot of building

209

research, a rational transmission of knowledge on the basis of objective, practical and active building documentation.

In this respect also, considerable arrears must be made up in the sphere of building; it is remarkable to note how little of the overall volume of production is devoted to building research. Whereas in the aircraft industry for instance up to 10 per cent and in the pharmaceutic industry up to 5 per cent of production is devoted to research and development, in the sphere of planning, building, housing and civil engineering this figure lies between 0.1 and 0.2 per cent in some countries, and in many other countries it is even lower or non-existent. In this statement no allowance is made, of course, for what is being done in industry in the way of research with respect to specific materials that benefit building and other branches of industry.

If we consider it normal that in building and civil engineering 1 per cent of the production is spent on research and development, the capacity of research, documentation and development will, expressed in terms of money, have to grow from 100 million dollars, which is roughly the amount now spent on this work, to 1,500 [1] million dollars, in 1999.

Thus, the volume of building research and building information will have to be increased fifteen times in a few generations. Especially in the first ten years, this increase will have to be very fast to enable the rapidly increasing building capacity to be used to maximum effect.

To be able to use the available building capacity to the best possible advantage this capacity should be studied in close connection with the social, economic and spatial development in order to ensure that building and overall development influence each other as favourably as possible. In this connection building research is faced with a number of basic problems, which must be solved in order to be able to make a concrete general development programme and give the right direction and the appropriate speed to the growing building capacity.

In order to achieve a practical method it is recommended that the approach be made in a number of successive stages, *i.e.* using two- and more-stage planning (Tinbergen). This method is to be preferred to a method that aims at answering all the questions simultaneously. To this end, the economic development possibilities can be used as a starting point, provided they are consciously used for improvement of the social infra-structure, but the object of this should not be exclusively to improve the economic possibilities.

One of the first decisions will then concern the desired rate of growth

---

[1] *1% building capacity in 1999 equals 3,000 million dollars (see Table 11, page 35). Assuming that 50 per cent of this amount would be spent in industry, 1,500 million dollars would correspond to the 100 million dollars mentioned above.*

of the economy as a whole, expressed as an increase in the national income over a number of years. On the basis of this increase it can be calculated with the aid of the capital coefficient for the country as a whole and the average delay between investment and the increase in production, how the income should be divided between total consumption and total investments.

The second stage of economic planning concerns the distribution of the volume of investments over the various branches of industry in such a way that a maximum national product is obtained, while at the same time a number of equilibrium conditions are fulfilled. These conditions imply that the available production capacity must just be fully used, that the production for each of the branches of industry must be just sufficient to meet the demand (for consumer goods, capital goods and semi-manufactured products), that the balance of payments is sound, etc.

In view of the large number of relations between the magnitudes, a correct choice can only be made with the aid of a mathematical model that expresses these simultaneous relations.

2. BASIC PROBLEMS

The improvement of the development of man and society from the social point of view and the accompanying essential economic growth involve a number of basic problems in the spheres of physical planning, building and civil engineering:

(a) the desired volume of building and the distribution thereof over the various sectors (dwellings, schools, factories, etc.);

(b) the optimum use of skilled and unskilled labour, national natural resources and capital;

(c) the research resulting therefrom for the desired development of building technique in connection with the available raw materials; the desired labour intensity and the capital intensity associated therewith; possibilities of self-help, aided self-help, mutual aid and other forms of co-operation on a non-profit basis;

(d) the choice of the quality level, among other things in respect of housing, in connection with the number of units to be produced and the building costs per unit, the hygiene functions, the function of protection against nature and the more sociological functions of housing;

(e) the financing methods for the building of low-cost housing and other social and economic basic projects (water supply and control, power, transport, basic industry, schools, hospitals, etc.);

(f) the effort to achieve the best possible distribution of the population and capital in space, for which research is necessary into the optimum size of the population agglomerates. This requires a quantitative insight into the cost functions for the urban infra-structural provisions (power, transport, communications, schools, etc.) dependent on the size of the agglomerates of population, the optimum size of public services and the level of transport costs per unit of product;

(g) the transport motives for people and goods in connection with the effort to achieve an optimum solution for physical planning of neighbourhood, town and region, whereby–partly as a result of a conscious development of public transport–it becomes possible to satisfy demand fully by a relative decrease in transport;

(h) the development of optimum standardisation on behalf of society as a whole and the individual, in which connection an appropriate cost price calculation per functional element should be made.

Apart from the basic problems, the research for planning, building and civil engineering can be subdivided into three categories of problems.

The first category, which at the same time determines the manner in which the other problems are tackled, relates to functional research. This should be taken as the starting point if it is desired to direct building research to the ultimate aim: improvement of the functioning of our society on behalf of the individual, the family and the community. Here we are not interested primarily in the buildings as such, but rather in the way in which they function. In this connection the notions "function" and "functioning" should be interpreted in their widest sense. The second category that can be distinguished relates to technical research on behalf of the best possible technical realisation of the functional requirements to be fulfilled by buildings.

The technical realisation presents a number of small- and large-scale organisation problems, *i.e.* management problems, which constitute the third category.

Hence, research for planning, building and civil engineering can be split up into three sections, which cannot be treated independently, namely function, engineering and management.

3. FUNCTIONAL RESEARCH

Firstly: Functional research, resulting in a thorough knowledge of how an individual building, a neighbourhood and a town should be designed to ensure that it will have the highest possible living value for the future. This means research which is directed to determining the requirements to be fulfilled by the constructed environment in order that, for the individual and for the society as a whole, the necessary functions can be performed under optimum conditions.

This functional research is not, of course, a new branch of pure science, such as physics. It is, however, an as yet little used method of approach, in which use is made of the results and sometimes also of the methodics of other sciences. To quote the late Karl Mannheim, the great sociologist, one might well speak of an example of specialisation in problem units and of an associated essential multi-dimensional approach. Functional research borders upon numerous branches of science, such as physiology, psychology, sociology, etc., but also upon engineering and economics. It enters the sphere of economics, because we have to keep a constant eye on the economic consequences of alternative possibilities.

Functional research must furnish information regarding programmes in the widest sense for adaptation of space by building and civil engineering, down from the single space unit to the individual building, group of buildings, street, neighbourhood, district, town, region, country, group of countries and ultimately to the whole world.

Functional research is concerned with a number of problems associated with the various phases involved in the programming of individual buildings and combinations thereof. In view of the basic programmes to be drawn up, it is of great importance that a number of efficient methods should be worked out for solving problems related to capacity and location and for drawing up management schemes for the various communities belonging to the frequently occurring types of buildings (hospitals, schools, townhalls, old people's homes, etc.). To this end it is necessary to work out standard ratios for the expected use (number of cases per thousand inhabitants, per thousand pupils, etc.) and for the expected costs per functional element (cost per bed in tourist hotel, cost of cleaning per square metre of floor area, etc.). On the strength of the methods developed and the available standard ratios a basic programme can be efficiently worked out for any individual building of a commonly occuring type without involving high costs and serious loss of time.

Another type of work that is encountered as a result of systematic development of functional research is the definition of frequently occurring functions and the corresponding spatial consequences. With the aid of work analysis it is possible to devise in each individual case the most efficient working method and to determine the space element on the strength thereof.

This information can then be used for efficient space-unit research, *i.e.* the drawing up of programmes for individual space units, where certain functions can be performed. The following aspects are involved:
(*a*) dimensions (length, height and width);
(*b*) climate (air, sound, temperature, humidity, colour, wind, hygienic atmosphere, psychological climate);
(*c*) properties of floor, ceiling and walls, which partly determine the

functional value of the space unit (resistance to impact, dustfree, foot warmth, sound absorption, etc.).

A fourth important group of activities can be put under the heading layout research, which involves investigation of the most efficient grouping of space units into departments, departments into buildings, buildings into neighbourhoods, neighbourhoods into towns and towns into regions.

This involves studies concerning contacts, traffic and transport and the drawing up of organisation schemes, etc.

Together with research of functions and space-unit research, this layout research can result in a number of practical programmes for commonly occurring space units, departments and types of buildings, while to an increasing extent attention should also be given to larger units, such as neighbourhood, district and town. In these programmes, costing constitutes an indispensable element.

4. TECHNICAL RESEARCH

The second category of research problems is concerned with technical research in the sphere of building and civil engineering. This technical research on the one hand involves matters relating to the technical realisation of the functional requirements of buildings and on the other hand should provide the technological basis of rational production.

Since the object is technical realisation of functional requirements, to be achieved by means of rational production, it would seem desirable to put technical building research on a functional basis. In this category there are also a number of basic problems relating to climate, the load-bearing structure and the general development of the materials of construction to be used, viz.:

(a) technical research to determine how water of desired quality and in the desired quantity can be made available in the right place, how use can be made of and daylight the energy of the sun on behalf of space units with controlled illumination level and temperature, and how efficient use can be made of wind and other natural conditions;

(b) design and calculation of contructions based on superimposed loads and safety factors, which are determined from an adequate volume of statistical data with the aid of the theory of probabilities, the object being to achieve optimum quality of construction, whilst keeping the probability of failure below a permissible limit.

(c) research in respect of raw materials, manufactured materials and elements suitable for lighter and cheaper building.

Apart from these basic problems, technical building research can be subdivided into a number of main groups. The first group concerns research resulting from the functional requirements to be fulfilled by the space units. This research relates to the desired dimensions, the desired climate and the requirements which the boundaries of the space unit must fulfil to suit the users. The climate and the requirements of the boundaries are typical subjects for technical space research.

To meet the requirements in respect of climate, the space will have to be protected against the effects of the weather, while if necessary the air inside the space unit must be heated or cooled, moisture must be added or removed, and furthermore, undesirable constituents must be removed and desirable constituents added.

Hence, the research will on the one hand have to be directed towards obtaining a better insight into the problem of insulation and moisture transport in exterior walls, the relationship between insulation and moisture content, and the development of high-grade insulation materials with favourable mechanical, chemical and practical properties, while on the other hand it should be directed towards the development of installations for heating and cooling, ventilation and air-conditioning, both for large-scale application and for use in cases where the highest degree of perfection is desired.

With respect to lighting, there is a tendency to regard daylighting as a matter of secondary importance, while more and more attention is given to means to exclude daylight and sunlight. Considering the demand for higher illumination levels, it will certainly not be easy to meet the requirements inside a building by applying exclusively or largely daylight. The psychological effect of daylight and sunlight is so great that further research in this sphere, such as determining the daylight factor and the degree of sun-access beforehand, is essential. An important aspect in this connection is the development of special types of glass (and other transparent materials). In the case of artificial lighting, efforts are made to obtain a higher light efficiency and a better colour, a longer life and a greater light output per light source, while naturally the aim is to reduce the production, installation and maintenance costs.

In the acoustics sector, the experiments and applications of electronic equipment are both interesting and important. It has already proved possible to lengthen or shorten the reverberation time of a hall by electronic means. In the sphere of building acoustics the research will be directed, *inter alia*, to the development of sound-absorbing materials with special properties and to the construction of lightweight walls with a high degree of sound-insulation. With regard to noise abatement, special attention will have to be given to the industrial sector. Far too many machines, apparatus, means of transport, etc. are built without due attention being paid to efficient noise abatement.

In this category the technical problems with respect to floors, walls and ceilings relate to the surfaces of the materials used. Research should provide better insight into the resistance to mechanical, chemical and physical influences, and the properties associated with comfort, reflection of sound and light, etc. and should be directed towards improving the quality of the spatial boundaries in these respects (*e.g.* maintenance and durability).

The second group of technical building research problems comprises the technical problems resulting from the functional requirements for transport of human beings, goods, gases, liquids and power between spatial units, and communications between such units in order to establish auditive or visual contact. We are concerned here with the technical problems associated with the building of roads, the construction of ports, canals, locks and bridges, etc., the problems associated with the laying-on systems for water, gas, electric power, fuel, waste materials, compressed air, telephone, pneumatic conveyor tube systems, telecommunication, television by wire, calling systems, etc., and further the installation of lifts, escalators and the like.

On account of the rapid development of facilities and requirements, research in this sector has usually been erratic and without any clear line of approach. So long as it is not known with any degree of certainty in what direction the supply and distribution of power will develop, it is a risky affair to draw up a long-term research programme.

It will in any case require a system of close co-ordination to match internal and external transport and communications. The internal provisions will not only be affected by the services of the public utility companies who supply gas, water, electricity and possibly heat and by the services of those responsible for the removal of refuse and waste materials, but they will be equally affected by the provisions made on behalf of external transport.

The third group of technical problems is encountered in the technical realisation of the functional horizontal and vertical layout of the individual space units and departments in buildings, the individual buildings in neighbourhoods, the neighbourhoods in towns and the towns in regions. For that reason the land should be prepared for building, and load-bearing structures must be developed, including the associated technico-functional main elements, such as foundations, floors, walls and roofs. The object is to find sound technical solutions to meet the requirements of free spans, flexibility and facilities of expansion and other practical requirements.

Important factors here are strength, rigidity and safety and thus the attempt to achieve optimum quality (durability and maintenance). The development of research in this sphere is not always assisted by the existing regulations, which as a rule do not make allowance for the latest insight, for which highly specialised knowledge is necessary. Moreover, since these

216

regulations differ from town to town, it will be appreciated that the resistance to change is particularly strong.

In addition to the research in respect of design and calculation of constructions, which we have regarded as a basic problem and on which the future economy of the load-bearing structure will to a large extent depend, there are a number of important associated research subjects. The development of new methods for the joining of elements, especially the glued joint, deserves full attention. Practicable solutions are required for roof and floor structures with a lower weight and a greater span than have hitherto been customary. Considerable interest is being displayed in cheap interior wall elements of appropriate durability. These problems belong partly in the last of the main categories into which building research can be divided. They relate to the choice of building materials and elements required in addition to the main load-bearing structure for filling up, finish and further functional completion of the building.

The principal points here are quality to meet modern practical requirements, suitability for new construction methods, durability, price and appearance. Building research in this sphere covers technical problems in respect of raw materials, the manufacture of building materials, and transport in the factory, from the factory to the building site and on the building site itself. Building materials cannot be regarded separately from the transport facilities and the mechanical equipment. They should be developed jointly and simultaneously. Special importance must be attached to the technical problems concerned with consistency of dimensions and interchangeability. These can be solved only by the application of modern methods of quality control.

5. ORGANISATION RESEARCH

Thirdly, we need research with respect to methods of organisation that will enable management of building production to be improved. On the one hand large-scale problems are involved, relating to a country, a town and a branch of industry, while on the other hand there are small-scale problems chiefly relating to the building site and to the internal organisation of the individual concern.

For organisation research also it is possible to indicate a number of basic problems that are associated with the typical difficulties of building. From one aspect, building is of great significance for the overall development of a country. It is an activity in which the national and local authorities and the community are concerned in many ways, viz. as principal (roads, bridges, schools, townhalls, etc.), as subsidiser (low-cost housing, schools, hospitals), as planner (regional and town plans), and as supervisor (beauty,

217

objective quality and safety). From another aspect, building can develop soundly only if adequate use is made of individual talent, such as that of the architect, the engineer, the contractor and the worker. It is an essential organisational problem to establish an overall apparatus that will make efficient building possible with due observance of the great interests which the community must watch over. Another typical organisational problem that presents itself in building is the introduction of more unity in the work connected with building. Planning, programming, designing and production are still far too often performed one after the other, while insufficient allowance is made for difficulties and possibilities encountered in a subsequent phase. Unity and optimum building activity can be achieved only by teamwork and feedback.

It will be clear that the essential objective is to attain optimum quality, whilst ensuring that the difference between usefulness and costs is a maximum. To achieve this, the development of a perfect calculation technique is a first requirement. Optimum achievements can be obtained only in a work atmosphere in which the results of research in respect of human relations are fully reflected. Hence, three subjects can be indicated as basic organisational problems of building:

(a) the evolution of a system of building administration in country, region and town together with appropriate legislation, bye-laws and regulations to control total activity (continuity), and division of activity to develop a sound system of financing and to maintain quality and safety. Special attention must be given to the danger of considerable loss of time and money owing to complicated regulations, and of excessive rigidity owing to inadequate adaptation of regulations to the rapidly developing building technique and wrongly placed responsibilities;

(b) organising teamwork in such a way that by an efficient system of feedback rational products and a high living value of buildings are combined. This teamwork should take place against a background of cost data, which can be obtained by working out a calculation system providing a comparison of costs when making a choice, so that by improvement of working methods, comparison of constructional possibilities in respect of technical functional elements, standardisation and repetition it is possible to achieve optimum quality;

(c) the study of human relations in the building industry with its typical temporary ties to place, object and workers, whereby – partly promoted by hygiene on the building site and by safety – pleasure in work and high outputs are obtained.

For the rest, organisation research covers numerous subjects, which can be divided into two main groups and are to some extent associated with the basic problems referred to earlier.

In the case of the large-scale problems it is generally a matter of how to integrate overall development and building in such a way that by making optimum use of the national resources they have the greatest beneficial effect on each other. This involves problems of differentiation, specialisation and integration of the building industry, as well as problems relating to capital requirements, distribution of building capacity in space and time and according to the purpose of the individual buildings. An important problem is the continuity of building and consequently also the organisation of everything concerned with the timely availability of land prepared for building.

The large-scale problems often relate to such matters as centralisation or decentralisation, delegation of authority by the central government to other public bodies, division of tasks between government authorities and private enterprise.

Small-scale organisational problems on the building site and in the workshops chiefly relate to improvement of human relations, hygiene and safety, improvement of working methods, planning of production, fixing tariffs, layout of building site and workshops, improvement of transport and mechanisation, etc.

Special attention will have to be given to dimension and quality control and to promotion of standard conditions in general.

Apart from the problems more directly associated with the work, there are still a number of other problems regarding the internal organisation of the individual concern, such as administration, calculation, financing, etc., which also deserve attention. In this connection one of the difficulties is the small concern, which frequently occurs in the building industry and appears incapable of achieving a sound system of accounting. This problem can be solved by encouraging these small firms to set up a joint accounting office to take care of their accounts.

6. DEVELOPMENT

There is little sense in research work as such if it is not followed by a direct or indirect improvement of the product to which the research relates. This is particularly a difficulty in the building industry, where so much unco-ordinated activity takes place and unity can only be sought prior to production (with the principal) and after production (in the finished product). Many buildings are prototypes, which as a rule are not followed up with series production. There is no continuity in the development.

With complicated production problems no improvement of any kind can be obtained quickly without systematic development work. Systematic development work at the same time prevents the research work being split up into a number of small subjects, which on the face of it would not appear to be interrelated. Systematic development work also leads to unity in research activities.

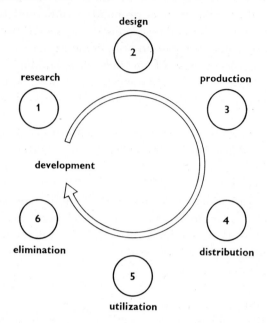

The development of any new form or activity pattern can be analysed as a process, comprising six characteristic and interacting phases[1]:
— research (analysis)
— design (synthesis)
— production (formation)
— distribution (dispersion)
— utilisation (performance)
— elimination (termination)

To achieve a rhythmic and balanced continuity in development, there must be a progressive elimination of the old along with the emergence of the new. Such continuity requires a close correlation between the research and elimination phases of the development cycle.

This definition of development does not imply any deliberate destruction of the old merely because it is old, nor does it demand the creation of something new solely for the sake of novelty or as a change in "fashion". So long as the old serves a need, it clearly should continue in use.

The objective in developing new forms and patterns is to satisfy those

[1] from Development Index, K. Löwberg-Holm and C. Theodore Larson, 1953, University of Michigan, Ann Arbor, Michigan.

emerging needs of man that cannot be met adequately by existing forms and patterns.

In order to apply directed development in building, a system of feedback will have to be devised as indicated below:

> research
> design of prototype
> production of prototype
> analysis of prototype
> feedback (design and research)
> design of series product
> production of series product
> analysis of series product
> feedback (design and research)

There is no sense in extensive development work unless standardisation, mass production and repetition are accepted. It is only in this way that a well thought out development cycle can be achieved, which can lead to rational production and a high living value of our buildings.

There is an important matter, however, which must not be overlooked, *viz.* transmission of knowledge. Without transmission of knowledge rapid development is impossible, because in that case the right knowledge and experience cannot find its way to the right place at the right time.

In our present-day world with its increasing differentiation and specialisation, transmission of knowledge is becoming more and more a factor of importance. Without exaggeration, the development of an efficient system of transmission of knowledge is one of the most important basic problems of our time, inseparably bound up with research and development. It is for this reason that it has been made the subject of the next chapter.

13   Transmission of knowledge

a problem of integration of knowledge and practice | the sources and the users | documentation and storage of knowledge | transmission of knowledge by unilateral and multi-lateral methods | aids: sound, written word, image | the barriers: resistance to change, linguistic barriers.

1. THE PROBLEM

If we define the problem of the transmission of knowledge as bringing (1) the right knowledge by (2) the right route at the right time to (3) the right place, and if we realise that (1) involves problems of content, volume and form of knowledge, that (2) involves problems of resistances to be overcome (*e.g.* the resistance to change) and barriers to be cleared (*e.g.* the linguistic barriers) and that (3) involves problems of easily accessible storage and efficient application of knowledge, we begin to discern the first vague contours of this subject.

integration

knowledge	‐ ‐	buildings

In its simplest form it is a problem of integration, which did not involve any particular difficulties when the world was still little differentiated and specialised and when knowledge, experience and production were practically in one and the same hand or practiced by people working in very close collaboration.

Communities were small and readily surveyable, while communications within these communities, being a very essential condition of transmission of knowledge, could develop in a natural manner.

This natural communication was disturbed by the development of our society, which considerably shortened distances, joined highly divergent communities and brought totally different civilisations in contact with each other and even made them interdependent.

In this situation, man was not entirely powerless. Ever since the first day of their existence human beings have used all kinds of natural forms of communication, they have had contact with each other by sounds, signs or language and thereby influenced each other's behaviour. Human intellect, however, has put human communication – unlike that of animals – on an abstract level (use of symbols) and has developed all kinds of technical means on behalf of communication. By putting communication on an abstract level and especially by development of modern means of communication it was possible to establish contact technically between very remote areas.

This did not remove a number of obstructions to complete integration of the now generally available knowledge and the generally applied visible building practice. Differentiation and specialisation have separated theory

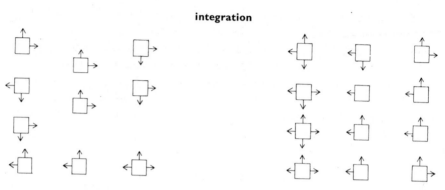

integration

sources of knowledge   **building practice**

and practice. Man, used to unchanging or gradually changing conditions, offers resistance to the drastic changes made possible by the enormous volume of new knowledge becoming available. Where peoples meet, they still remain separate owing to differences in language and customs. The highly developed technique of communication releases a flood of knowledge and information over a world which in many respects is not ready to receive and use it.

This leads us to the function of transmission of knowledge, which can be outlined as follows:
– bridging the gap between science and practice
– overcoming differences in language and behaviour between nations and differences in behaviour and mode of expression between groups
– overcoming resistances
– leading the constantly increasing flood of knowledge into proper channels.

In our present-day society this means that transmission of knowledge is developing into a specialised task, of which we shall now study a number of elements more closely.

224

2. THE TASK

In order to bridge the gap between science and practice observation and analysis are necessary in two directions. Science must know the requirements of practice, while practice must know the possibilities presented by science. This necessitates market research on the one hand and an inventory of the sources of knowledge on the other.

To sort out the many kinds of knowledge a suitable documentation technique must be developed that would facilitate the registration and the opening up of sources of knowledge.

Another task of documentation is to tag and store the knowledge in such a way that it is easily accessible at the time it is required. This makes it necessary also to transform the knowledge by means of active documentation in order that quality, quantity and form are adapted to the requirements of the user.

A special chapter (14) will be devoted to the most important elements of documentation. In making knowledge independent of time and space storing problems are encountered and intermediate stores are necessary. The two most important stores are the practitioner's office and the information centre. The practitioner's office will be dealt with in Chapter 14, while the information centre will be discussed in Chapter 15.

Documentation lays the foundation for making knowledge transmittable, independently of time and space. At this stage the transmission of knowledge has not yet been established. This is done by disseminating information and by education, not with the sole object of enabling the practitioner to familiarize himself with the knowledge and to apply it in practice, but also to enable him to learn to live with it.

To this end numerous methods and means have been developed, of which the most important will be given in the following section. In this last round we return to the starting point, the sources of knowledge, as new requirements are created and the transmission of knowledge becomes an activity promoting research.

In the comprehensive sphere of transmission of knowledge a number of typical obstacles must be overcome. The two most important obstacles are the resistance to change and the linguistic barriers, which will be discussed in the last section of this chapter.

3. METHODS AND MEANS

We can transmit knowledge, experience, a message to others:
- by word of mouth and by technical means of communication to convey speech;

- in writing or printing and by technical means of communication to convey the written word;
- by displaying or demonstrating, either in the natural form or in two- or three-dimensional representation, thus with the aid of the image as a means of communication;
- by enabling the user to acquire the knowledge himself (assisted and directed by others), by allowing him to discover and experience it, the accent being placed on his self-activity.

It will be clear from the above brief survey of methods for transmission of knowledge that these methods can be split up into two categories. Transmission of knowledge by means of sound, writing and image, thus by telling, writing or showing, invariably tends to be unilateral, *i.e.* the person transmitting the knowledge is engaged in a unilateral action, while the person acquiring the knowledge is engaged in listening, reading or looking, without these actions being mutually adapted. These are called unilateral methods.

The transmission of knowledge in which the learner is stimulated to self-activity presupposes a constant contact between teacher and learner, which provides an opportunity to observe each other's reactions and enables the teacher to adapt himself to any gaps in the knowledge of the learner that become apparent in the course of the process and any difficulties he may have in assimilating the knowledge. We then speak of multi-lateral methods.

(a) Unilateral methods

The following are examples of transmission of knowledge utilising unilateral methods:

(1) Sound:

the lecture (a discussion after or during the lecture makes it possible to sound the reactions of the listeners; this, however, is generally not sufficient to achieve proper adaptation between the lecturer and the listener);

radio;

(2) Writing:

written advice (a certain amount of adaptation to individual require- ments is possible);

report;

direct mail (adaptation to requirements of groups is possible);

journals;

documentation sheets;

newspapers;

(3) Image:

exhibitions;
films;
television.

A characteristic feature of the unilateral method is that it is on the whole directed to groups of users. This means that the cost per user can be relatively low, a feature, however, that is accompanied by a relatively low efficiency of the transmission of knowledge.

The lack of adaptation to the user (absence of feedback) is offset by a check on the results of the transmission of knowledge. The simplest check lies in the economic plane. If the user is asked to pay for the services rendered (entrance fee, licence fee, subscription, etc.), the number of visitors, listeners, or subscribers can in the long run be used as a yardstick to ascertain whether the transmission of knowledge fulfils a need. Other means to achieve some sort of adaptation are the enquiry, questions and answers in journals, newspapers, radio programmes, etc.

Institutes that have a specific task in the sphere of transmission of knowledge (information centres) are particularly interested in establishing a systematic contact with organisations of users, likewise with a view to overcoming the lack of adaptation.

(b) *Multi-lateral methods*
   Examples:

   the instructional course (instruction in its completest form comprises demonstration, explanation, practicing, checking, repeating, and finally supervision of the application of the acquired knowledge in practice);

   the experiment, or – particularly in building – the experimental building (the transmitted or self-acquired knowledge is applied in a practical situation of limited size, in order to acquire certainty and confidence for full-scale practical use);

   competitions, scholarships (the activity on the part of the person transmitting the knowledge is confined to defining the problem and providing facilities for solving it; the solution, *i.e.* the acquisition of knowledge, is then left entirely or almost entirely to the learner);

   classroom tuition (the transmission of knowledge is confined to demonstration, explanation, practicing and checking; as a rule self-activity, repetition and practicing, which must result in skill in application, are lacking).

227

These are only a few examples. Moreover, there are many intermediate forms, such as correspondence courses with set papers and supervision of the work, courses with partly written and partly oral lessons, etc.

The characteristic feature of the multi-lateral methods is that they can be very effective on account of the constant adaptation that occurs between teacher and learner. The disadvantages are that the cost per learner is high, that the teacher and the learner must speak the same language and that the teacher must fulfil very exacting requirements in regard to his capacity for adaptation and reaction and must have adequate training in educational techniques.

A very specific characteristic of multi-lateral methods is that they present an opportunity to make the learner accept important knowledge even if at first he does not recognise its importance. In other words, multi-lateral methods can have a strong demand-creating effect.

(c) Aids for transmission of knowledge

Aids for the transmission of knowledge are those means that are applied with a specific method to make the transmission of information possible or to enhance the effectiveness thereof.

A brief survey, which is by no means exhaustive, is given below.

(1) Sound:

electronic amplifier, tape recorder, radio, telephone, telegraph, musical illustration;

the form of the spoken word (language, choice of words, rhythm, rhyme);

(2) The written word:

reproduction techniques (typing, hectographing, stencilling, rota-print, printing, photography, micro-photography, die-line printing);

the form of the written word (typography, layout);

(3) The image:

demonstration in natural form (living image), exhibition in natural form and in the form of scaled-down models, graphs, drawing-board, flannel-board, photograph, film strip, film, diapositive, projection, epidiascope (direct and overhead), printed illustration;

the form of the image (exhibition design, film shots, etc.).

The use of the aids is of course not restricted to the methods with which they are mentioned. On the contrary, almost invariably an attempt will be made to overcome the shortcomings of a selected method by making use of aids according to other methods. The lecturer, for example, likes to make use of films and diapositives, while the writer likes to use illustrations, etc. The essential point is that the assortment of aids is composed in such a way that they neutralise each other's shortcomings as much as possible. Transmission of knowledge, for example, with the aid of a large number of diapositives will have to be supplemented by means of sound. Transmission by the spoken word needs to be supplemented above all by pictures, etc. It is necessary to use all these various methods in transmission of knowledge to ensure that the right aid is available at the right time.

4. THE BARRIERS

(a) The resistance to change

There is always an affective resistance to anything new, anything unknown and thus not experienced. This applies especially in the case of old trades such as building, in which much is still determined by tradition and fundamental changes can be introduced only with difficulty. The remarkable fact is that in building much is done differently in an irresponsible way solely with a view to creating an appearance of originality, whereby all kinds of fashionlike features are obtained. What we are concerned with here is the making of changes on the strength of acquired scientific knowledge and generalised experience and it is of the utmost importance that they are introduced in the correct way, making allowance for emotional and sensorial resistance.

In the emotional sphere, allowance must be made for the fact that human beings have a tendency to forget those things that consciously or unconsciously displease them. One forgets things if one selects. Furthermore, they have a tendency strongly to defend old customs and methods, which perhaps have never been given any serious thought, on the basis of unsound principles as soon as they are confronted with the possibility of change.

In developing activities in the sphere of transmission of knowledge allowance must be made for this resistance mechanism in man.

Hence, when introducing new systems and methods, attention must be given both to the conscious attitude of the person or group to whom the knowledge is to be transmitted and to the unconscious motives. The latter can be effected in the same way as in motivation research, which is developing in propaganda and advertising. When introducing new ideas it may well be a good thing to play what might be called a "signature tune", whereby the new is joined with something familiar.

Transmission of knowledge also meets with sensorial resistance. Each group (people or race) has a certain preference for the use of specific aids for transmission of knowledge. This can find expression, for example, in the phenomenon that one people may be sensorially better adjusted to visual perception, while another people may be better adjusted to auditory perception. In transmission of knowledge it must be considered and, if necessary, empirically ascertained beforehand which aids suit a given group (people) best.

Methods which are based on a culturally unusual sensorial manner of perception do not produce optimum results. Moreover, this sensorial distinction must also be taken into account within a people and thus the aids for transmission of knowledge must be adapted to suit requirements. Groups with a limited education, for example, offer more resistance to transmission of knowledge via literature study than more educated groups.

On the whole it is true to say of persons in the building trade that they read little, but like looking at drawings, photographs and completed buildings. It is not surprising, therefore, that most building periodicals reserve a lot of space for illustrations and often contain little text (too little!). This is likely to lead to a certain amount of superficiality, unless special care is taken to give what is essential in as few as possible words.

(b) The linguistic barriers

As stated in Chapter 1, the world has at once become smaller and greater. We have almost reached the point where we have all become neighbours living in one big neighbourhood, in which little is left of the isolated way of life of groups or peoples that has prevailed for thousands of years.

Natural communication is being replaced by technical communication and in this connection it is no longer appropriate that we should exclusively have a system of "natural" languages. Children learn foreign languages, dictionaries in two and more languages are compiled, new foreign words are taken over untranslated (*e.g.* sputnik), but this does not remove the linguistic barriers for transmission of knowledge. This constitutes one of the most important obstacles to rapid elimination of the unbalanced situation in which the world finds itself. In addition, new knowledge is emerging at an enormous rate, while specialisation is developing further and no country is large enough now to be self-supporting in the sphere of science. All countries need each other. Each country is underdeveloped in certain respects and can learn from another country, one country more than another.

This can be solved only if we learn to understand each other better, both in the literal and in the figurative sense.

If the linguistic barriers could be removed, there would be a much better chance of achieving the international division of work that is so essential in order to avoid duplication and thus to derive maximum benefit from the best intellect that the world possesses. This is especially important in the sphere of building, because the problem of building is so very complicated and can be divided into thousands of scientific compartments. Here, the solution can only be found in international co-opera-tion. The linguistic problems cannot be solved at short notice in a direct sense by creating an artificial world language, that would enable everyone to understand everyone else, and this is not exactly necessary. However, it can be done at short notice, at least in the sphere of science, by creating a number of transformation stations, linguistic centres, where certain trans-lation work can be taken care of systematically. The aim should be to evolve a system in which the quantity of translation work is reduced to a minimum. This can be achieved on the one hand by making a very careful selection and by reducing the volume of the material to a minimum and on the other hand by making a choice from the languages used (overall effort to be minimised). This choice of languages cannot be made by rational thinking alone (key language), but allowance must also be made for the relationship existing in certain parts of the world between certain languages.

The most rational solution is shown below. The system has one key lan-guage and all the national linguistic centres know two languages, the key language and their own language.

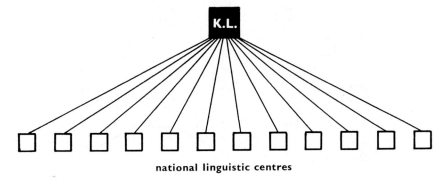

national linguistic centres

diagram with one key language

The key language chosen should be that language for which $N.i. =$ maxi-mum, where N is the number of people who speak this language and i the number of scientific contributions which this language region produces annually per one million inhabitants. Though no accurate figures are avail-able for i, it may nevertheless be assumed that English is the only language that can be considered for use as the key language.

This conclusion is supported by the data published by Unesco in 1957 [1]. Estimates, in this case not of numbers of inhabitants (the readers of the future) but of present-day readers, *viz.* of numbers of scientists and tech-nologists capable of reading publications in certain languages, proved that

[1] *Scientific and Technical Translating and Other Aspects of the Language Problem, Unesco, Paris 1957.*

English was both the language most read and the language mostly chosen for scientific and technical publications.

However, languages not only serve to permit knowledge to be transmitted in written form; they also make possible oral exchange of thought, which is often indispensable. The latter takes place at all kinds of scientific congresses, while tourism in all its forms often furnishes a contribution in this respect. This form of communication is frequently most intensive between adjoining countries whose languages are to some extent related. This raises the question whether a system comprising a number of regional linguistic centres with associated regional key languages would not be preferable to a system with a single key language. The languages that could be considered for this purpose are those with a high value for $N.i$ or those for which a high value can be expected in the near future. The languages that enter into consideration as regional key languages would then be, for example, English (1), Russian (2), French (3), Spanish (4), German (5) and Chinese (6).

This would result in the following diagram:

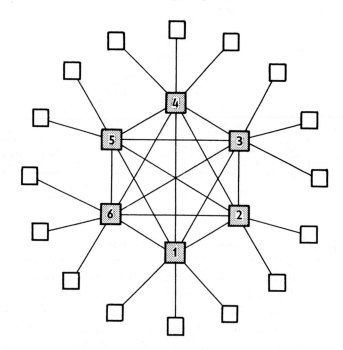

diagram with six regional linguistic centres

In this case there are two disadvantages:
(*a*) to transmit knowledge, for example, from Italian in the French region

232

to Rumanian in the Russian region it is necessary to translate three times as against only twice if one key language were accepted;

(b) the traffic between the regional centres makes it necessary for each of these six centres to operate in six languages.

The first disadvantage would be acceptable only if the traffic within the regions were much more intensive than between regions and if in this way less resistance were created.

The traffic between the regional centres could be simplified if these regional centres would together accept English as the key language. This would certainly result in considerable simplification in the traffic between the regional centres, but in most cases the number of times that translations would have to be made would increase. To translate from Italian via French to Rumanian, via Russian, it would be necessary to make an intermediate translation into English and hence the material would have to be translated four times.

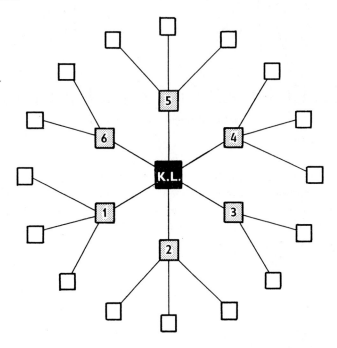

diagram of six regional linguistic centres with one interregional key language

It will be clear that this solution can be acceptable only if it is indeed possible to indicate a number of regions, six for example, each comprising a number of language areas, whithin which the traffic is much more intensive than is the case between the regions.

However, the trend is in the opposite direction insofar as certain

233

areas are less isolated. Yet, it is worth while to give some attention to an intermediate form, a system with two regions, namely English (1) and Russian (2), not so much because this could be considered as an improvement of the weak point of the solution with one key language, namely a lack of language relationship, but rather because the world happens to be divided into two regions, in which the social organisation is run along very different lines.

The extent to which the traffic within the two large regions is more intensive than between these regions depends especially on the development of scientific traffic between the Soviet Union and China.

The diagram then looks as follows:

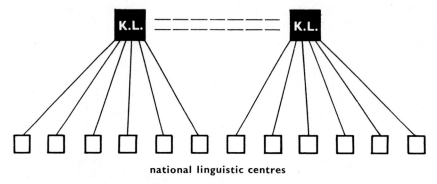

national linguistic centres

diagram with two key languages

The solution of the linguistic problem is heavily laden with all kinds of irrational elements. Taking a rational view it is a matter of decisionics with a view to arriving at an optimum solution. Probably one key language is the most rational, while the system with two key languages has the greatest chance of success.

14 Documentation

independence of time and space / unity in multiplicity by classification and standardisation / from unplanned reading towards planned reading by signposting / from undirected knowledge towards directed knowledge by active documentation / storage in the practitioner's office and information centre / basic and special subject-training of building documentalists

1. THE BASIC PRINCIPLE: UNITY IN MULTIPLICITY

In the previous chapter we have seen that one of the most important phases in transmission of knowledge is the recording of knowledge with a view to rendering the knowledge transmittable, independently of the individual or the group possessing this knowledge.

This is effected almost invariably in writing, while especially in building the drawing and the photograph play a very important part.

Knowledge recorded in a documentary way constitutes the practical starting point of transmission of knowledge. Knowledge recorded in writing can assume all kinds of forms, of which books, correspondence courses, periodicals, pamphlets and documentation sheets are the most common forms.

By documentation, knowledge can be made independent of time and space, so that it can become available anywhere precisely at the moment that it is required. Moreover, by means of documentation it must be ensured that the person requiring the knowledge can find it quickly in the form that suits his particular purpose. To achieve this both in the national and in the international spheres the knowledge should be classified, while a common line of thought must be developed.

This will make it possible to introduce unity and balance in the rapidly growing multiplicity of specialised subjects. A few figures will emphasise the need to introduce unity in the multiplicity. According to recent investigations the annual number of publications at present amounts to 200,000 books and 80,000 periodicals, of which approximately 30,000 furnish original contributions in roughly three million articles.

In the sphere of science and engineering alone the annual production is 50,000 books, 40,000 periodicals and 200,000 patents. In this connection it should be realised that no figures at all are available for the production in the eastern part of the world. The classification of knowledge and the development of a common line of thought based on this classification can

237

be effected by drawing up and accepting as universally as possible a specific classification system. Dependent on requirements, two possibilities can be distinguished in this respect:
– an attempt is made to give an objective and systematic survey of overall human knowledge;
– the effort is confined to classification of a specific part of human knowledge or activity based on a specific point of view.

An example of the first classification system is the Universal Decimal Classification. It does not pretend to give a system of the sciences, but it aims at grouping associated subjects together. In this respect it is sufficient if the detailed classification fulfils certain scientific requirements.

Examples of the more restricted classification of a limited sphere of human knowledge and activity are the selection from the UDC specially compiled for the building industry, which has been published in many languages under the title "Abridged Building Classification", (ABC) [1], and the SfB system of classification [2] developed in Scandinavia. This system can render good service in the sphere of practical building. This is due to

[1] *Published on behalf of CIB by Bouwcentrum, Rotterdam.*
[2] *For further systems see: International Building Classification Committee: Recent Developments in Building Classification, Copenhagen 1959.*

238

the fact that the nucleus of the system is related solely to functional elements, components, building operations and materials, and that it is not intended as an exact definition of certain phenomena, but as a practical classification, which at the time when the system was compiled was especially sought for classification of building specifications and bills of quantities.

Attempts are being made to achieve the essential unity by means of the widest possible application of sound classification systems, but the development of filing systems that fulfil the divergent requirements of general libraries, specialised libraries, research institutes, information centres and last but not least practitioner's offices is also of essential importance. The requirements of the centres of documentation referred to above are indeed highly divergent.

We shall now deal with three possibilities:

(a) for the general library and the specialised library which classify the available documentation, for example with the aid of the UDC, filing amounts to finding the best solution both from the economic and the practical points of view, a solution that will often be independent of the classification system used. At most, the filing system in this case is a less refined version of the classification system applied.

(b) For the practitioner's office matters are quite different. The fact that the number of articles in periodicals, pamphlets and commercial catalogues exceed by far the number of books in the documentation available here and the requirement that personnel not trained as documentalists must be able to find the requited material quickly, make it desirable in this case that the classification system applied is at the same time the key to filing.

The SfB system briefly referred to above is intended to be at once a classification system and a filing system for the practitioner's office.

(c) In the case of the information centre, which aims at bridging the gap between theory and practice, a combination occurs of the requirements and possibilities of the general or the specialised library and the practitioner's office. On the one hand it is possible here to limit the volume of the available documentation material, because a system of collaboration exists with the institutes mentioned under (a), where the material can be obtained on loan. On the other hand the regular contact with the practitioner, who will come to the information centre when his own documentation proves inadequate, makes it necessary that a certain amount of documentation material should be readily available at any time. If in the information centre the filing of suitable documents is done as simply as possible and accroding to a pattern that appeals to the practitioner, the information centre can effect a saving in labour, because the visitor will then search for the required documentation himself.

Classification and filing cannot fully perform their task of introducing the greatest possible unity in the multiplicity if at the same time a series of supplementary conditions are not fulfilled.

The first problem that should be mentioned is that of terminology,

Recommendations on the form of documents*

Classified information must be capable of being filed. The following points are recommended:

1. *Format of papers for filing should be A4 (210 × 297 mm) with prepunching for filing, two holes c - to - c 80 mm, symmetrical in height and with centres 10 mm from the left edge of the paper.*

2. *Publications for filing should have the filing reference printed in a 45 × 20 mm box on the top right-hand corner of the front page. The box should be divided into two by a horizontal line. The upper part is reserved for SfB-notations, the lower part for UDC numbers.*

Recommendations on the classification of documents*

UDC numbers should be chosen according to the UDC selection "Abridged Building Classification", (ABC).

SfB-notations should be chosen according to SfB tables.

* From "A Building Filing Manual", IBCC report No. 5, 1959 included in "Recent Developments in Building Classification", Copenhagen 1959.

which presents itself as soon as there is any question of national and international exchange of knowledge. It is true that even in one particular language it is not always quite clear what is meant by a specific technical term, but the real difficulty begins when an attempt is made to understand the meaning of a technical term in another language and to find a technical term in the first language which entirely covers the same notion. As a rule this will be impossible unless an international standardisation of technical notions has been set up beforehand, supplemented by technical terms in each language, having exactly the same meaning.

It will be clear that the compilation of a classification system suitable for use both nationally and internationally amounts to a terminological codification which must have been preceded by a standardisation of technical notions.

Furthermore, attention must be drawn to the great importance of standardisation of format of documentation material and of layout both for pages and for complete documents.

The ideal of any practitioner who wants to work efficiently will undoubtedly be that he should receive all periodicals, documentation sheets, pamphlets and commercial catalogues in one and the same format with a standardised layout, so that he knows immediately where he can find the classification provided by the publisher. If, moreover, he can file the loose-leaf documentation, which is already punched with standardised holes, immediately in standardised files, boxes and the like, the unity in multiplicity will have become reality for him, especially if the documentation received presents as much as possible in the fewest possible words and, for example, facilitates comparison of the material because the subject has been treated in an identical, previously standardised manner.

In like manner, the accessibility of the material in libraries and information centres demands standardisation of format and layout and in general of the material means of documentation.

2. THE PRINCIPLE: MORE KNOWLEDGE FROM LESS PAPER

(a) The problem

Although a universal classification system and logically associated arrangements for the unification of the material means of documentation form the indispensable basis for systematic promotion of transmission and transport of knowledge, they do not in themselves amount to more than a common line of thought, which is the starting point for joint action.

This line of thought points in a specific direction, but it does not indicate the routes along which and the means of transport whereby the written knowledge is conducted towards practical application.

It must be realised that in practice there is an increasing number of uncontrolled routes and means of transport, which all lead to the limited reception station of the user. For the user the quantity is too great to handle and the information offered is not sufficiently classified to enable him to make an efficient choice to suit his actual requirements.

This overloading compels the conscientious user who wishes to keep up-to-date in his particular sphere to make a haphazard choice from the material, which is seldom ready for use. He is simply obliged to follow the method of unplanned reading of undirected knowledge and even if he manages to do a lot of reading, this will make him suspicious of any attempt to make him read more. Quite rightly, he has a fear of being faced with even more paper. He will experience the efforts of the experts in the sphere of transmission of knowledge as a real assistance only if they enable him to make a quicker and more directed choice from the multitude of material and make it possible for him to acquire more knowledge by reading fewer words.

His real problem is his personal reading efficiency. Hence, joint action to be taken must be directed towards reducing the quantity of paper and words and at the same time towards increasing the information offered, by concentrating and directing it to a higher degree to the ultimate user of the knowledge. The essential point is to build up an action in such a way that first the various categories of users now compelled to indulge in unplanned reading of undirected knowledge are guided towards planned reading of the available undirected knowledge and later towards planned reading of directed knowledge.

(b) Planned reading

The first problem is therefore to enable the user of the knowledge to make an efficient choice from the available literature to suit his requirements. This problem exists for all categories of users, the building practitioner, the highly specialised research worker, the professional building information centre, etc., because practically none of these categories are able to read what they should like to read and ought to read.

Hence, there is on the whole a strong need for an efficient system of signposting the available material, which constitutes the basis for a directed choice. This signposting means in effect sorting, classifying and signalling the material. The documentation activity to achieve this end does not include the processing of the available material, *i.e.* its activation, and is therefore known as passive documentation.

The signal or the system of signals which the documentalist sets up for the practical user must as far as possible meet the requirements of speed and exhaustiveness.

Speed is essential, because otherwise there will be little value in the signal furnished, since the object of this signal is to enable the practitioner to remain up-to-date.

Exhaustiveness, however, is equally necessary, because otherwise the object of planned reading is not achieved. The requirements of speed and exhaustiveness, however, contain contradictory elements.

It is possible, for example, by means of brief bibliographical references regarding a given subject quickly to signpost the existing flow of information, because the assistance of the expert on this subject is not required for making such simple signals.

However, as soon as an attempt is made both to make the signal itself more exhaustive and to make it contain clearer indications regarding the content of the signalled information, the production of the signal requires more expert knowledge and also more time. To put it briefly, the making of a good building science abstract requires expert knowledge and time.

In signposting we are, practically speaking, concerned with two large groups of data, viz.:
– the sources of knowledge;
– the flow of published information.

The signposting of the sources can be effected by compiling "Directories", which systematically signal such sources, preferably with a clear indication of the scope of their activities and their programme.[1]

Such sources are research institutes, documentation services, technical information services, and also journals. Here the compilation of efficient catalogues is a primary means to assist the practitioner passively in his attempt to keep up-to-date.

The signposting of published information can be effected by a system of signals. The nature of the signal is to a large extent determined by the chosen compromise between speed and exhaustiveness.

The simple bibliographical reference can be furnished quickest. The annotated bibliographical reference, which – for example in at most thirty words – provides some indication as to the value of the signalled publication, is somewhat more complete.

The indicative abstract is considerably more complete, but it is more difficult to produce. An initial element of active processing of the signalled material is introduced in the case of the informative abstract.

The choice of the type of signal is now also dependent on the prospective user.

An information centre will benefit from a regular abstract service, since an institute of this kind wishes to receive a lot of information on a large

[1] An example is the "Directory of Building Research and Development Organisations", published on behalf of CIB by Bouwcentrum, Rotterdam, 1959.

number of subjects and consequently it needs a system of exhaustive signals, which facilitates selection for own use.

The highly specialised expert feels the same need in his limited field of work. We are concerned here with the passive secondary product derived from the original publication, but which is directed to complete orientation.

This product, however, is not so suitable for the building practitioner, because his naturally large sphere of interest would make it necessary for him to read a very large number of abstracts, which he would undoubtedly not experience as reading efficiency but just as a new flood of paper. Hence, he would derive greater benefit from the quick and simple signal, which the brief reference – either annotated or not – can give him. Provided the speed of delivery does not adversely affect these signals, the brief annotation can be of great use to him. On the whole, however, passive documentation is not suitable for the building practitioner who reads little. As far as he is concerned the bibliographical reference and the abstract must therefore be regarded as semi-manufactured products of the library or of the information centre.

A careful enquiry into the real needs of the various categories of users must form the essential basis for building up any system of passive signals.

(c) Directed knowledge

The signposting by means of passive documentation is an aid to bring the user from unplanned reading to planned reading.

However, it does not offset the disadvantage that, with a few exceptions, the signalled flow of information denotes knowledge which in the light of the immediate and specific requirements of the individual user must be called undirected.

It is precisely in this sphere that we find a possibility to promote strongly reading efficiency by preparing available information for ready use by categories of users whose requirements have been carefully determined, and by processing, converting and putting together in a comparable manner similar information, thus active documentation.

If a practitioner is offered condensed data regarding a subject in his sphere of interest, in which experts have worked up a lot of available but dispersed information on that subject, it will be possible for this practitioner to obtain a relatively large amount of information by considerably less reading. This object is achieved by building up a system of processed data.

The simplest form of collected processed data is the digest, which aims at drawing attention to existing knowledge in a brief, businesslike, but especially in a palatable form. This object is approached even more closely in the so-called trend report, which is intended to give an exhaustive snapshot of the state of affairs in regard to a certain subject.

The same results can be also effectively attained by other forms of active documentation, directed either to products and materials or to specific subjects. In the sphere of products and materials the property accounts, which vary between the standardised picture of objective data based on research and the standardised presentation of data furnished by the producer, are of some importance.

The essential aim in the processing of selected subjects is to furnish, against a background of a concise general picture of the typical problems encountered in regard to these subjects, a series of comparable data regarding the various possible solutions to the problems.

Other important documents are those giving systematic analyses of completed buildings, compiled in such a way that they permit of mutual comparison.

Furthermore, the results of studies can be processed in such a way that allowance is made for transmission of the knowledge to a certain category of users.

The production of this active documentation requires a high degree of expert knowledge of the subject matter concerned. If the active documentation is fairly complex, as is the case for example with active documentation on a series of theatres, its production will actually require a team of experts.

3. THE AIM: USEFUL KNOWLEDGE READY FOR USE

It has been clearly illustrated in the preceding chapters how complicated building is and how much theoretical and practical knowledge must come together for a building of optimum quality to be created. On one occasion is has made us ask: "How can we realise the knowledge of so many in one building?" [1]

On the one hand we are concerned with the quality, the quantity and the form of knowledge and on the other hand with the storage of knowledge. The practitioner should have the easiest possible access to the knowledge. In this connection his own office plays a limited yet very important part, because it must be possible for the knowledge he needs regularly to be efficiently filed there.

The documentation needs of the practitioner [2] are:
– well arranged files for papers, related to his day-to-day work;
– an office library, consisting of:

[1] J. van Ettinger and L. M. Giertz: "How can we realise the knowledge of so many in one building?", Building and Housing Research, Bulletin 8, United Nations.
[2] The following has been taken (in brief) from: "Some fundamental and practical aspects of transmission of knowledge" by L. M. Giertz, J. van Ettinger and K. L. de Vries, CIB Congress 1959, Rotterdam.

(*a*) a set of books, including handbooks on subjects of his professional interest;

(*b*) a set of binders or folders for the storage of the stream of useful sheets and pamphlets, such as:

reports, standards, codes of practice, regulations, trade catalogues, etc. that enter into his office in an ever-increasing amount;

– an easy access to knowledge he does not possess in his own office.

Usually the practitioner will not have so many books in his office library that the arranging of them would present him with great difficulties. The classification of books is not his main problem; it is more a problem of official libraries and abstract services. Practitioners mostly seem to prefer books, but even if books were used to a greater extent than is the case today, it remains evident that they must be complemented by other types of documents, containing an additional quantity of new information, such as reports, regulations, standards, codes of practice, trade catalogues and all other kinds of current information, including the notes and working papers of the practitioner himself.

The practitioner dislikes all these pamphlets and sheets in different formats, although they are offered to him as an aid for his work. The publishers of such documents apparently are not aware of the fact that nowadays the amount of such documents has grown to such extent that great difficulties are caused when they must be stored in the practitioner's office, and that the practitioner simply cannot keep pace any longer with the ever-increasing stream of these documents.

The practitioner will ask for a method to arrange all his documents (papers, pamphlets, leaflets, etc.) and preferably also his type drawings, according to one "easy" system of classification, and by the word "easy" he would mean two things:

– main grouping in accordance with his way of thinking (the pattern);
– simple notations for these main groups.

This method of arranging documents in a practitioner's office is what is usually called filing.

Documents (excluding books) to be filed must comply with precise demands in three respects, *viz.*: format, classification and perforation.[1] This determines as it were what those who publish something (excluding books) should make allowance for in the future.

If we want to ensure that the useful knowledge is ready for use and easily accessible, we are concerned not only with selection and transformation problems, but equally with storage and activation problems.

However well organised a practitioner's office may be in documentation

[1] *See Agreements International Council for Building Research, Studies and Documentation (CIB) General Secretariat, Bouwcentrum, Rotterdam.*

matters, the practitioner will again and again run into problems, for which he has no answer at hand. This raises the question of his need for access to the enormous amount of knowledge, spread all around him, or even hidden from him. After a trial over many years to introduce abstract cards into the practitioner's office so as to cover at least part of those documents the practitioner does not possess himself, CIB-documentalists, who are active in the field of the abstracts exchange, have now arrived at the conclusion that the best access to hidden knowledge is for the practitioner not to keep his own files of abstract cards but to keep in direct contact with a professional information centre.

In addition to a well-organised practitioner's office we need Building Information Centres not only to solve the storage problem of knowledge, but also to transform knowledge and to facilitate transmission of knowledge with all available means.

4. TRAINING OF BUILDING DOCUMENTALISTS [1]

More and more organisations and firms wish to establish documentation departments. Therefore it is not for the sake of information centres only that assistance is given to the training of documentalists. It is apparent that there are few people with the necessary experience to build up and run such departments and to manage them on the basis of personal experience, and equally there is a dearth of qualified assistance. Consequently, the training of documentalists must be a matter of serious concern to all those who realise the importance of documentation as a foundation for research and as a step towards rationalisation. Documentation can serve many fields of knowledge and practice.

Training therefore must embrace two stages: a basic training in documentation and a specialist training directed towards the particular subject field.

Training facilities for the basic training are directed towards the particular subject field in several countries mostly on a private (non-governmental) level. As far as is known today, in no case is it regarded as full professional training. The syllabuses today contain so many features in common that one can say that the lines of the basic training are generally recognised. Essential differences are shown, however, in the weight given to certain aspects.

Nevertheless, in various countries the basic training of documentalists covers the needs.

It is otherwise with courses for documentation training in a particular

[1] *Miss C. Müller: "Some fundamental and practical aspects of transmission of knowledge", CIB Congress 1959, Rotterdam.*

subject field; whoever is in practice as a subject documentalist today, has grown up in the job without outside help.

Firstly three points must be stressed:

(1) Special-subject training cannot stand alone: it is essential to have a basic training first and to extend this for the particular subject.

(2) Only documentalists who have worked for some time in a documentation centre in their particular specialist field after their basic training should be admitted to subject training, so as to ensure that they have a thorough knowledge of the subject and its documentation needs.

(3) Subject training in documentation can be conducted only by people who have built up their own organisation and are thoroughly conversant with the subject field and documentation technique.

Turning now to the main theme "Training of building documentalists" it will be seen that these three principles form a programme of work.

The training of building documentalists, it seems, is essentially an international job. There are two reasons for this:

(a) there are not sufficient people with the required experience in the country concerned;

(b) a substantial part of the work lies in the sphere of international exchange of knowledge.

The main points for the training programme are as follows:

(1) Organisation of building documentation.
(2) Special functions of building documentation.
(3) Building up a building documentation centre.
(4) Work flow in a building documentation centre.
(5) Classification systems in the building field.
(6) Establishment and running of technical building information services.
(7) Literature handling.
(8) Costing for installation and operation of a building documentation centre, for literature handling and information service.
(9) Time and work control in a documentation centre.
(10) Reader relations; telephone and written inquiries; visitors' reading room.

15 Building information centres

*different types of information centres | the stages on the
road from theory to practice | Bouwcentrum, an all-round
building information centre | the supply of knowledge | the
production of knowledge | the transformation of knowledge |
the transmission of knowledge*

In the previous chapters it has been explained how the flow of knowledge
should be canalised and promoted in various ways to ensure that the transmission of knowledge takes place in such a way that it is applied in practice.

It has become evident that this canalised flow of knowledge cannot in
its full volume and in its original form be directed to the practitioner's
office.

We are concerned here on the one hand with the problem of storing
knowledge and on the other hand with the problem of transforming knowledge. It might be possible for certain large categories of users to have the
transformation done at the source, whereby studies, books, periodicals and
pamphlets would acquire a more active form directed to transmission of
knowledge. This, however, will not do away with the problems of selection,
making the information from various sources comparable and laying on
"stocks" greater than the practitioner can keep in his own office. Special
provisions are necessary. Such provisions can be made in Building Information Centres, which can be set up in different forms:

1. Building research and information centre.

   A building research institute can be combined with an information
   department, which ensures that the knowledge created in the institute
   is put into a suitable form for transmission to the user. For the institute
   itself a documentation department is set up, which serves as information
   centre for the research workers of the institute.

   Activated by enquiries received, information is furnished which covers
   a wider field than the institute's own research work.

   An advantage is that an institute of this kind has a thorough knowledge
   of subjects coming within the sphere of its own research work, but a disadvantage is that as a rule no special attention is given to the manner
   in which the knowledge is transmitted and that usually the field of
   work covered is limited.

2. The building documentation and information centre.

   In a technical library for example – either associated with a university or not – a department specialising in building is set up. Books and periodicals available in the department are systematically gone through and sometimes the department also has printed matter issued by industry, working drawings of important buildings, patents, unprinted studies, photostats, etc. Enquiries can be submitted to the information department, which are answered by referring to the appropriate literature. Sometimes a centre of this type also runs an abstract service, for which a subscription can be taken out.

An advantage of such a centre is the objective atmosphere in which the work is done, but it has the disadvantage that very often the documentation remains passive. This involves the real danger that the accent will lie on documentation rather than on information and that the information to a certain extent fails to find its way to building practice.

3. Building exhibition and information centre.

The practical sphere is approached more closely by the permanent exhibition of building materials, elements and components, usually also including furniture, fabrics, lighting fixtures, etc., complete with an information department.

The primary object of this information department is to give factual data on what is to be seen at the exhibition, based on information furnished by industry. The information capacity is usually extended by arranging reading room facilities, with national and foreign periodicals, and by collecting information on materials not exhibited.

It is an advantage that samples and models are available when giving the information, but the disadvantages of this type of centre is the risk of insufficient objectivity and the danger of the exhibition dominating over the information aspect.

4. A specialised building information centre.

A particular branch of industry establishes a common centre, which may be associated with the material used (*e.g.* wood), the building element (*e.g.* steel windows), a building aspect (*e.g.* insulation) or a building type (*e.g.* houses).

This centre, sometimes the secretariat of a society, starts by making propaganda and setting up an information service. Usually the latter is at first very one-sided. Gradually a more or less joint development activity is started up as a result of the numerous queries posed or difficulties encountered by the members in practice. This and the knowledge that too much propaganda will ultimately damage the interests at stake may lead to an efficient development and information activity, which on account of the propaganda element usually has a high penetration capacity. The latter is promoted as a rule by practical experiments, demonstrations, etc. There remains, of course, the disadvantage of insufficient objectivity, which, however, will not constitute a very serious objection for the critical user.

It is illustrated by the examples of the forms that building information centres can take that it is dangerous to speak of such establishments in a general sense without giving some indication of the aspects characterising the individual centre. The name "building centre" is at present used by a large number of institutes all over the world, but the nature and volume of their activities, however, are widely divergent. Conversely, many institutes are engaged in the sphere of transmission of building knowledge without this being evident from their names. We shall now endeavour to gain some insight into this situation.

In transmission of knowledge we can distinguish (provided we accept a number of simplifications) the following stages on the long road from theory to practice. We can see these stages as a series of intermediate stations along this road, provided we realise that – fortunately – some of these intermediate stations are repeatedly passed over.

Knowledge is:
- developed by, among other things, *research* and *experience*
- laid down in *sources* such as books, reports, periodicals, etc.
- indexed by passive documentation in libraries, bibliographies, abstract services, etc.
- adapted to the needs of the practitioner by *active documentation*
- transmitted to the practitioner by *information* in word and writing
- transmitted also by visual presentation in *exhibitions*, fairs, etc.
- instructed in courses by *training*
- applied and extended in *development work* and *experimental building*

and thus goes into practice.

On the strength of the distinction made in respect of the various stages referred to above it is possible to characterise institutes engaged in transmission of knowledge according to their nature. An attempt in this direction has been made in Table 20, giving a survey which, of course, is by no means exhaustive.

With the aid of this survey we can now distinguish various information centres, but it is expressly pointed out that each building information centre can be:
- a general centre, if it does not operate from a specific point of view or interest, but intends to serve building in a general sense, or
- a special centre, if it has chosen a specific subject (material, element, trade). In this case the word "special" in the name will, of course, be replaced by an indication of the aspect concerned, *e.g.*, timber centre, contractors' centre, etc.

253

TABLE 20

	Research experience	Sources	Passive documentation	Active documentation	Information	Exhibitions	Training	Development work and experimental building	Type of centre
Universities, etc.	x	x	x	(x)			x		
Publishing bodies		x		x					
Research institutes	x	x	x		x				
Libraries		x	x		x			(x)	(1)
Documentation centres			x		x				(2)
"Building centres" (limited sense of the word)			x	x	x				(2)
Training centres				x	(x)	x	x		(3)
Professional (industrial) organisations			x	x	x	x			(4)
Productivity centres		(x)	x	x	x		x	(x)	(6)
Development institutes			x	x	x	x	(x)	x	(6)
Bouwcentrum	x	x	x	x	x	x	x	(x)	(7)

(x) aspect of varying importance

Hence, the following can be classified as building information centres:

- Building research and information centres (1)
- Building documentation and information centres (2)
- Building exhibition and information centres (3)
- Building training and information centres (4)
- Building development and information centres (5)
- Multilateral building information centres (6)
- All-round building information centres (7)

The figures shown between brackets have been used in the last column of Table 20 to denote some of the institutes mentioned there as building information centres. The reader will no doubt forgive the author if he devotes a few words to an example of the last-mentioned type, Bouwcentrum in Rotterdam, with which he is so closely associated.

Bouwcentrum came into being in a natural way. It comprises all the essential elements referred to in the foregoing and is characterised by a high degree of independence, which it has secured by accepting, right from the start, the form of a self-supporting and non-profit-making institute.

Very soon after its official opening in 1949, Bouwcentrum was able to depart from its one-sided status of exhibition and information centre, by establishing very close co-operation with a number of other institutes founded during the war.

At that time (1943), when the official authorities were forbidden to make preparations for post-war plans, the author was asked to collect statistical data on behalf of the Netherlands Government reconstruction policy after the war. This work was done in collaboration with members of the staff of the Bureau Documentatie Bouwwezen (Building Documentation Bureau) (B.D.B.), specially set up for this purpose. Together with a number of management experts, the author started the first building management course in 1943; this formed the basis for the department in charge of courses now operating in Bouwcentrum, where annually 600 students (young contractors, administrators, general foremen, work analysts, tariff calculators) follow various specialised courses given according to modern didactic methods. Likewise in 1943, the Foundation Ratiobouw was set up, whose task was to promote rationalisation of building.

This institute at first directed its efforts mainly to technical research in respect of both traditional and non-traditional building methods, in collaboration with T.N.O. Later, attention was also given to problems of organisation on the building site, for which a special department was formed. In 1945 the weekly "Bouw" was founded, covering social-economic, technical, architectural and management problems.

Gradually the co-operation with Bouwcentrum became very close, because in due course all these institutes were placed under a single Management and Board. Since 1955 they have all been accommodated in the same building, *viz.* Bouwcentrum.

In this way, Bouwcentrum grew from a single foundation and an idea into a collaborating group of institutes with great versatility and housed in a single building. This versatility was further enhanced because, in addition to exhibitions, information and the courses referred to above, Bouwcentrum also became active itself in the sphere of research. To this end the choice fell on the almost virgin field of functional research.

This activity resulted in studies and information on the programming of houses, schools, hospitals, homes for old people, factories, etc., for which special departments and in some cases even special foundations were set up in Bouwcentrum. In co-operation with "Bouw" and "B.D.B.", Bouwcentrum developed a great documentation activity. In collaboration with others, special departments and new foundations (steel, wood, brick, concrete, etc.) were also established in the technical sphere, while the co-operation with T.N.O. was greatly intensified.

The advice service is very active in all kinds of spheres, so that members of the staff are constantly involved in the planning or execution of about 100 buildings, while about 250 visitors per day ask numerous questions on practical points. (In 1958 about 35,000 personal, written and telephone enquiries were answered.)

The overall versatility became even greater because in the building were accommodated a number of institutes whose task was to study the application of mathematico-statistical methods in mass production (quality control) and in "decisionics", and who were also engaged in work analysis, with which the author was also concerned. These institutes are not active solely in the building industry, but also in other branches of industry. In this way, the underdeveloped sector – the building industry – is experiencing a highly beneficial influence from more industrialised mass production methods employed elsewhere. Owing to the large variety of aspects of the study, advice and development work, as well as documentation, exhibition and information activity, the overall organisation is quickly acquiring a fully unified task, which can be divided into the following parts:

(*a*) the supply of knowledge
(*b*) the production of knowledge
(*c*) the transformation of knowledge
(*d*) the transmission of knowledge.

The overall organisation closely resembles an industrial concern and is being increasingly operated as such. It has business ends and for this reason it is operated on the "non-loss" principle in order to preserve its independence and to be able to meet the social obligations with regard to the staff, but it also has an ideal and this explains why it is operated on the non-profit-making principle.

To an increasing extent the overall activity is being directed to investigation into the need for knowledge of the practitioner and to the conscious effort to conduct the flow of knowledge in such a way that it is ultimately applied in practice.

It appears that it is only possible to work efficiently if the greatest possible co-operation with others is maintained in order to avoid duplication and to ensure that national co-ordination is achieved in due course. In this way optimum achievements can be attained.

A. SUPPLY OF KNOWLEDGE.

(1) *incoming books, periodicals, non-printed studies,*
codes of practice, specifications,
documentation systems,
pamphlets, brochures,
advertisements, etc.
films,
recorder tapes, gramophone records,
photographs,
drawings,
diapositives, etc.

(2) *building materials, elements and components of buildings, machines, tools and means of transport for building, in which knowledge and experience is given implicitly and sometimes explicitly by objective data of industry.*

(3) *teamwork with outsiders (institutes), which make their knowledge and experience available in the discussions.*

(4) *the interviews with those who submit enquiries.*

259

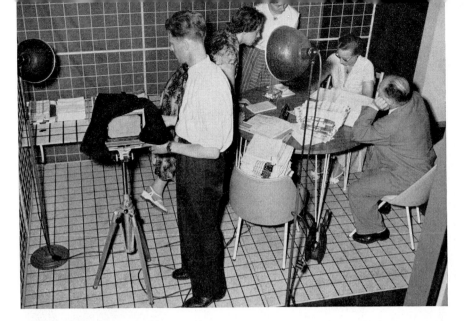

B. PRODUCTION OF KNOWLEDGE.

(1) *by controlled experiments*
    (investigations in laboratories, in the field, in experimental workshops, in respect of experimental buildings or on experimental building sites).
(2) *by controlled sampling,*
    the statistical method
    (investigations in industry, on building sites, in completed buildings before and after they are taken into use).
(3) *by collation/joining of existing elements of science and experience to form new combinations from literature, by interviews, in team discussions.*

261

C. TRANSFORMATION OF KNOWLEDGE.
bibliographies
abstracts
documentation sheets (scientific, T.C.D.)
data sheets
articles in periodicals
books
courses (syllabuses, manuals, drawings, diagrams, etc.)
exhibitions
photographs
diapositives
films
gramophone records
models (scaled-down and full-scale).

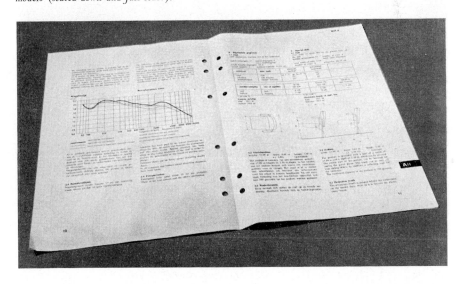

263

D. TRANSMISSION OF KNOWLEDGE

information)
advice) *individual and group*
research)
exhibitions
distribution of printed matter
radio and television
courses (correspondence and oral)
congresses
press conferences, interviews with representatives of newspapers and periodicals.

16 Acceleration

fundamental unbalance / accelerated change on well-planned basis a necessity / basic conditions: mutual trust, reduction in cost of armaments, transfer of income and knowledge, birth control / acceleration of public and private capital movement from rich to poor countries / economic and social investments / acceleration of international exchange of building knowledge / a long-range U.N. programme of concerted international action in the field of low-cost housing and related community facilities

In many parts of the world and on the dwellings of many hundred millions of people the sign "uninhabitable" would be quite appropriate. By far the greater part of mankind lives in an uninhabitable world, because the essential basis of a healthy physical and mental life is lacking. Despite all the technical progress and the enormous economic strength of certain regions and groups there are probably to-day more poor people than 50 or 100 years ago. The fundamental unbalance is becoming more and more pronounced, especially since, unlike in former times, this unbalance is now accompanied by the rising expectation of the poor of the earth that for them also better times are ahead. Moreover, interdependence is greatly increasing.

Mankind is beginning to realise more and more that changes are necessary to break through the vicious circle of hunger, sickness and poverty, and that conditions must be created which provide an equal chance for all to attain a higher standard of living. These must be fundamental changes, which themselves introduce other changes and thus start a development that takes care of its own acceleration.

We are already late in starting such a development, because rising expectations that are not fulfilled quickly lead to a deep feeling of disappointment and frustration with all the danger this entails for the poor and the rich alike. Hence, there is much that will have to be done soon in order to accelerate all constructive development in such a way that through a growing mutual trust and understanding by visible progress the destructive forces in man and society are reduced.

The dangerous situation in which the world now finds itself compels us as it were to choose as our aim the making of a habitable world for all, which must be achieved before the end of the present century. This makes it necessary to work out plans and to make prognoses despite all the uncertainties which they entail. Even if we realise that there is only a small chance of complete success, it is essential in this time of great uncertainty to set ourselves a concrete aim.

For we need a practical ideal, hope, which can act as a blood transfusion and create new energy, especially if from time to time a part of this aim reaches visible realisation. It is a good thing to remember, however, that ideals can also poison the blood if they turn out to be idle fancies and hope disappears because practical results are not forthcoming.

The creation of a habitable world for all is not a problem that is solely important for the so-called under-developed and semi-developed countries. Considering the number of slums that can often still be found in even the most prosperous countries and how many essential things for man and society are still lacking there, we can hardly call even these countries a habitable world for all and great changes will also be necessary there. Moreover, in the so-called developed countries there are still many under-developed areas and in these countries also there is still fundamental unbalance, which should be combatted as quickly as possible with greater force.

To achieve this habitable world enormous investments will be necessary, which should not only be made available in the form of capital and labour, but should find expression especially in a change in human thought and in the degree of devotion to the task.

As Mannheim put it quite appropriately[1]: "It is only by remaking man himself that the reconstruction of society is possible".

What all countries should have is the courage to look ahead, to make prognoses, to set aims for the benefit of all the people, even if it is fully realised that there are many uncertainties. It is no longer a matter of "laisser faire" or planning, but rather a matter of uncontrolled action or properly planned efficient action, a matter of bad or good planning. Good planning should be directed towards eliminating the fundamental unbalance and promoting a balanced growth of prosperity throughout the world, while an effort should be made to achieve maximum freedom and self-determination for each country and in each country for each group and each individual. Planning can have a positive value only if it is based on the creative tendencies in society, i.e. if it controls living forces without suppressing them.

It is necessary, therefore, that a new balance should be struck between the individual and collectivity, in the knowledge that both are important and that both can be a source of great forces, which together will lead to optimum prosperity.

The problem of achieving this synthesis can be approached from two directions. It can be approached through individualism, starting from the strong personal forces of the individual and pursuing jointly such sound and clear collective aims (also expressed quantitatively) that fundamental social unbalance is eliminated.

It can also be approached through collectivism, starting from collective aims, but utilising to an increasing extent the great force inherent in the individual effort. In the latter case also we can speak of a useful collectivity if social unbalance is eliminated and the individual is given a reasonable chance of personal development.

The difference in approach may appear—and can in fact be—very great, especially in the beginning, which leads to great contrasts. When cri-

[1] *Man and Society in an Age of Reconstruction*, New York 1951.

269

ticising the latter (collective) approach one calls one's own system democratic and the other totalitarian and when turning against the former (individualistic) approach the terms capitalism and socialism are used as contrasts.

This contrast could in itself prove quite useful ultimately to achieve an optimum, if it were not that terrible weapons might be used in the struggle to prove each standpoint and if the complete destruction of our society did not hang over our heads as a potential danger.

The systematic lie and brainwashing based on fear threaten the sense of freedom and the sense of truth, which are present in all human beings to a greater or lesser extent. Fear is also used for building up enormous armaments and can exert such pressure on the individual that he begins to believe that his safety can be secured only by the complete destruction of others.

In an unpublished article Tinbergen writes [1]:

"The significance of these ideological differences for the fate of the world population has grown to the present dramatic level because of the technical development in armaments. This has brought us to the point where the world consists of two main power centres, both in the possession of new weapons. The use of these weapons would bring devastation of a completely different nature from that known up to and during the Second World War. There still appears to be an insufficient realisation of the fact that the nature of this devastation is much more serious than the difference between the two socio-political systems. If we make an attempt to analyse what are the things in life that make for human happiness in its higher forms, it is my contention that, however bad the capitalist system may be to a convinced communist, the effects of a big nuclear war are worse, and however bad the communist system may be to a convinced democrat, the effects of a big nuclear war are worse.

The bi-polar system of the atomic stalemate, which represents the organisation of our present safety system, does work in quite a few circumstances; this cannot be denied. Yet the risks of its being unstable in other possible circumstances are only too clear. These risks are increased by the tendencies of some smaller powers to develop their own nuclear armaments. It remains pressingly urgent, therefore, to search for other solutions."

A solution must be found and the essential point is to develop – before it is too late – sufficient mutual understanding and trust to establish a common basis for winning the peace.

If the distrust – a very costly distrust – could be gradually made to

[1] *Some Problems of Co-existence.*

disappear, it would not be long before the world could be given a healthy basis for a balanced development and it would be possible in a few decennia to lay the foundation for a world habitable for all.

A co-existence based on fear would then perhaps gradually change and a rapprochement would be made possible, provided at least that we were prepared to accept the further consequences of this aim – a world habitable for all.

The highly developed countries, who to a large extent have solved their economic and technical problems and who have large numbers of trained people at their disposal, should in their own country take up the struggle against everything that is still under-developed with greater energy. It would be true to say that if they wish they can help themselves. In the under-developed countries, however, the situation is quite different. They are still at the mercy of nature and largely still live on the border line of existence. Consequently, they are unable to save and they remain on the border line of existence because they do not save. They cannot sufficiently invest in directly productive projects, which are often so very essential for raising the national production in a short time, let alone give adequate attention to the essential improvement of the social infrastructure, which will become a decisive factor after a somewhat longer period.

They are often unable to solve the difficult problems with which they are faced owing to a lack of cadre and skilled workers. Their economic position is often very unstable, because they are dependent on a single agricultural or mineral product and often a considerable part of their efforts is in vain as a result of a bad harvest or a change in world market conditions.

What is achieved is usually hardly sufficient to make up for the growth in population, which is assuming alarming proportions as a result of the improved medico-hygienic provisions and unrestricted fecundity (see Table 3, Chapter 3). This leads to an exhausting race between economics and fecundity, with impoverished masses coming more and more into the foreground; they will demonstrate their rising expectations in an increasingly aggressive manner but do not know themselves how they can contribute towards improvement of their lot.

From the need to increase the investment capacity in the under-developed countries and from their inability to save enough themselves it follows that they must be helped in some way or other, which amounts to a transfer of income. This constitutes all the more reason for the highly-developed countries, which still have many serious problems of their own, to increase their productivity as much as possible and to reduce their cost of armaments.

Owing to the lack of sufficient cadre and skilled workers it is necessary to pay serious attention to international transmission of knowledge and to regard education and training as one of the most important problems. The transfer of income, however, should be properly planned and in many cases should be combined with transmission of knowledge. Hitherto the transfer of income and the transmission of knowledge have had too much of an accidental character, which is also evident from table 21.

TABLE 21[1]

NET INTERNATIONAL ECONOMIC AID PER HEAD OF THE POPU-LATION RECEIVED FROM THE NON-COMMUNIST COUNTRIES DURING 1957/8 (IN $)

I. Countries with a national income of less than $ 100 per head		II. Countries with a national income of between $ 100 and $ 200 per head		III. Countries with a national income of more than $ 200 per head	
Afghanistan........	1.4	Brazil	−0.4	Argentina.........	0.7
Bolivia	9.8	Ceylon	2.7	Chile.............	7.9
Burma............	1.4	Formosa	7.9	Colombia	6.6
Cambodia........	8.7	Dominican Republic	0.1	Costa Rica.......	12.5
Ethiopia	0.5	Ecuador	1.6	Cuba.............	0.5
Haiti.............	1.1	El Salvador.......	1.5	Israel.............	25.6
India	0.6	Ghana............	0.2	Lebanon	4.6
Indonesia	0.3	Guatemala	5.0	Mexico...........	1.6
Jordan............	24.6	Honduras	2.2	Panama...........	7.8
Korea	14.7	Iran..............	5.2	Uruguay	1.4
Laos	22.5	Iraq..............	0.7	Venezuela........	0.1
Liberia	4.9	Libya.............	23.8		
Nepal	0.8	Nicaragua	6.5		
Pakistan	1.6	Paraguay.........	5.2		
Saudi Arabia	0.2	Peru	6.5		
Sudan	0.1	Philippines	2.0		
Thailand.........	1.1	U.A.R.: Egypt.....	0.4		
Vietnam	19.0	Syria	0.2		
Yemen	−				

Owing to the often accidental manner in which technical assistance has been given, it has not always been possible to achieve optimum effect. This need not be a very serious disadvantage in the initial period, because experience must be gained in many respects and numerous experiments are invariably necessary. It is now high time, however, to take up the struggle against the fundamental unbalance in the countries and between countries in a more systematic way, and to do this we need a world development plan, as well as national and regional development plans.

A clearly defined aim can be of great psychological importance, an indispensable guide for everything that has lagged behind. In development

[1] United Nations, Statistical Yearbook.

planning one should have the courage to follow a long-term economic policy, although the short-term successes should not be overlooked, if only for psychological and practical reasons.

The investment policy followed should be directed to the human being, because ultimately we are concerned with his mental and physical health, his energy and his happiness. Hence, development planning should not be solely directed to economic aims and clearly defined sociological and cultural aspects should not be overlooked.

The important points are to avoid fluctuations in economic conditions in the widest sense, to eliminate excessive tension in the distribution of income and to avoid an excessively rapid transition from old to new patterns of civilisation. It is also important to avoid disturbances of equilibrium in the trade relations between industrialised countries and countries with little or no industry. It is necessary to avoid unemployment resulting from rapid one-sided mechanisation and also to avoid an excessive rate of urbanisation. Another aim should be to reduce hate and fear and to remove the boredom which may result from this. There is a tendency sometimes not to pay sufficient attention to this boredom, but as the tension resulting from fear and hate disappears the struggle against boredom, especially when more spare time becomes available, will constitute an important problem.

A world-wide prosperity plan, incorporating plans for food, health and education, and resulting in building programmes, plans for reducing the cost of armaments, for birth control, transfer of income and transmission of knowledge, can only be realistic if it is borne by a powerful and constructive international co-operation based on clearly formulated national co-ordination. It is only after it has been established where and how on a national and regional basis the fundamental unbalance can best be tackled that an effort can be made to achieve definite international co-operation within the framework of a world-wide prosperity plan.

Conversely, world-wide aims must be drawn up in rough outline to furnish useful national and regional starting points. Setting ourselves an ideal, both at a national and an international level, and creating political starting points can only be a beginning of the realisation of an efficient system of communications to make co-operation possible in both a horizontal and a vertical direction. In the horizontal direction this co-operation must cover the political, scientific, educational and practical spheres. In the vertical direction it must be achieved both nationally and internationally, cutting right through all these horizontal spheres to achieve realisation as quickly as possible on the basis of political necessity and decisions.

Acceleration of everything that is constructive to break through the vicious circle of hunger, sickness and poverty and to make the world habitable for the greatest possible number of its present and future inhabitants is a practical ideal which in itself will probably meet with little resistance, but we should realise right away that the most important consequences of this will be:

(a) conscious development of mutual trust and understanding, as a basis for international co-operation;

(b) an appreciable reduction of the cost of armaments and acceptance in principle of the fact that a considerable part of the funds becoming available must be used on the basis of international and national development planning to facilitate a rapid and balanced development of under-developed regions and of the own country;

(c) transfer of income and transmission of knowledge with a view to realising the desired development on the basis of domestic effort;

(d) promotion of birth control within the possibilities presented by the individual conceptions of life to achieve a sufficient rise in the standard of living with the available means.

The world finds itself in the fortunate position that the feeling that much will have to change in a relatively short time is gaining ground.

Diplomatic international consultation at all levels is accelerating, increasing attention is being given to technical assistance, idealists and realists are occupying themselves to an increasing extent with growing international co-operation, and countries are forming themselves into groups under some heading or other.

The world is in motion, but the threat remains and thus also fear. There is still no peace in the hearts of men, nor in the social and international spheres. Whereas there seems to be a willingness to accept the almost insane consequences of modern warfare, there is not yet a willingness to accept fully the problems involved in winning peace and in defending the rights of man by making the world habitable for all.

Yet there is reason for moderate optimism when one considers how much aid is already being given to the poor countries by the rich countries.

As will be seen from table 22 the movement of capital between the rich and the poor countries is taking place in various ways, namely in the form of multilateral and bilateral aid and in the form of private capital movements. An intermediate form of the first two is the aid via regional organisations (Colombo Plan). The aid is given in the form of grants and loans under various conditions.

As regards volume the bilateral aid is the most important, and also includes the furnishing of capital to overseas territories (*e.g.* by France and The Netherlands). Of the bilateral aid mentioned under (*a*) in table 22 the United States furnishes the largest amounts. The most important organisations (of that country) are the International Co-operation Ad-

TABLE 22 [1]

CAPITAL (PUBLIC AND PRIVATE) FURNISHED BY RICH COUNTRIES
TO POOR ONES IN MILLIARDS OF DOLLARS PER YEAR

Outside the communist bloc	
(a) Bilateral public aid (1956/57)	2.1
(b) International aid (United Nations and International Bank for Reconstruction and Development (1956/57)	0.2
(c) From long-term exports of private capital and share in the revenue of oil production (1956/57)	1.5
	3.8
By Soviet bloc	
(d) To non-communist countries (average 1955/58)	0.7
(e) To communist countries (average 1955/58)	0.5
Total	5.0

ministration and the Development Loan Fund. An example of the regional organisation is the Colombo Plan, which in effect is not a plan, but a form of co-operation between a large number of Asiatic countries receiving aid (*e.g.* India, Pakistan, Ceylon, Burma, Indonesia and the Phillippines) and a number of countries furnishing capital (United Kingdom, United States, Canada, Australia and Japan). The most important financial aid furnished by the United Kingdom is effected via the Colombo Plan. In the bilateral aid referred to above, the grants exceed the loans.

The multilateral aid chiefly takes place via the United Nations and its specialised organisations. Apart from the normal technical aid to which all members of the United Nations contribute, there has been since 1949 the Expanded Technical Assistance Program to which a large number of countries make an extra contribution on a voluntary basis. This technical aid consists chiefly in sending out experts and in granting fellowships, and only to a limited extent of purely financial aid.

The purely financial aid is given by the World Bank (International Bank for Reconstruction and Development). Not all the United Nations countries are members of the World Bank; the Soviet Union for example is not. The World Bank furnishes loans only to Governments who are at the same time members of the Bank. After careful investigation into the economic aspects of the projects concerned the loans are furnished only if there are no facilities for obtaining private loans. Further, the Govern-

1 *Sources: (a)–(d) Netherlands Economic Institute based on U.N. Statistical Yearbook 1958 and G.A.T.T. Trends in International Trade 1958; (e) rough estimate.*

ment must guarantee the loan. The projects financed by the Bank are concerned with power, transport and agriculture.

An affiliated institution of the World Bank is the International Finance Corporation (IFC), which grants loans to private enterprise in the under-developed regions on purely commercial terms.

As sources of financing economic development the institutions mentioned are inadequate. There are, especially, insufficient financing facilities for projects which do not produce an immediate revenue and which, therefore, are not attractive for the private investor (the so-called infrastructure projects). The object of the Special United Nations Fund for Economic Development (Sunfed) was to fulfil this requirement.

Up to now this proposal has not been realised, because the most important countries – particularly the United States – do not wish to co-operate in this plan as long as the expenditure for defence is at its present high level. In 1958 the Special Fund (funds: $ 100 million per year) was set up as a predecessor to Sunfed. This fund finances projects which will promote the execution of larger projects, *e.g.* surveys, research, training and experimental projects.

At the last annual meeting of the World Bank it was decided to set up an International Development Association (IDA). The object of this Association was to grant credits on very favourable terms (low rate of interest, if required in local currency and long-term redemption). The capital would be $ 1,000 million. The proposal is still to be worked out. In addition to public aid, private investments are also indispensable, not only because they are considerable in volume, as appears from Table 22, but especially because in this way capital, know-how and usually employment are at once made available to the developing country.

Eugene R. Black, President of the International Bank for Reconstruction and Development puts it as follows [1]:

"The great industries of the United States of America, Britain and of Europe have, by and large, been built up by private enterprise in an environment of political and economic freedom. Those industries have been remarkably successful, and their contribution to the prosperity and the economic strength of the more advanced countries have been the envy of the rest of the world.

Why, then, isn't there a very simple answer to the problem of promoting industrialisation in the developing lands? Just let those countries follow the course already followed in North America and Europe; let them rely on and give full scope to private competitive enterprise; and then they, too, will know the full benefits of modern industrial development.

There is, of course, a fundamental part of the truth in this answer. But

[1] *International Industrial Development Conference; San Francisco; October 1957.*

a truth which may seem to us so very obvious is not at all obvious to the leaders and peoples of a large part of the world. They are skeptical of private entrepreneurs and investment – and particularly of foreign private entrepreneurs and investment. Sometimes, unfortunately, past experience has given them reason for such skepticism.

They are, in any case, impatient to see progress. Impressed by the great need for industrialisation, they feel impelled to take quick action to promote it. From a feeling of urgency, or for other reasons that seem to them valid and compelling, governments feel they have no alternative but to found industrial ventures of their own as state enterprises.

It is an oft-repeated truth that economic development depends primarily on domestic effort, and that foreign capital plays, at best, a marginal role. Yet the assistance provided by foreign capital, if effectively employed, can make a crucial difference.

And to-day, the underdeveloped countries have perhaps more need for that margin of assistance than at any time in the recent past. For as development has achieved momentum, it has created large new demands for capital that are as yet unmatched by any comparable increase in domestic savings. If the momentum so dearly gained by these countries is not to be lost there must continue to be, over a sustained period, a steady growth in the amount of foreign investment available to them. If that momentum is lost, then we will find ourselves at a turning point in world affairs, because the human, economic and political consequences that will follow are likely to be disastrous.

Where can we find the investment that continues to be needed for development? A good deal of it will come from public sources, both national and international. Now, I hope and believe that there will be some increase in the public funds available. But the plain political reality is that no increase in public funds is likely to come close to matching the growth in the legitimate capital needs of the developing countries. In the long run, those countries cannot obtain the additional external resources they must have unless, in addition to attracting public funds, they also succeed in attracting substantial amounts of new private investment from abroad.

Fortunately, the increase in the need for foreign private investment comes at a time when, despite the shortage of capital everywhere, the interest of industrial firms in the advanced countries – and even of the purely financial investors in those countries – in venturing abroad has also been increasing. There has been a remarkable change in this respect over the past decade. As communications have quickened, awareness of the opportunities offered by overseas investment and operations has grown. The underdeveloped countries no longer seem so far away or so unfamiliar

277

and the risks of investment in at least some of them no longer seem so fearsome. To-day, it is broadly true, I think, that the opportunity to attract foreign private capital is there for those nations which have the will and courage to grasp it.

I have spoken of the need to attract foreign private capital as urgent. But even more urgent for the developing countries is the need to build up a strong domestic private sector – to encourage their own entrepreneurs to devote their talents, their energies and their capital to the creation or expansion of productive enterprise.''

Private investments can be promoted to a considerable extent if the correct form is found to protect the private investor against losses which can occur through changes in the political situation in the countries concerned. To this end guarantees of his own government, tax facilities and other means are available. These private investments are quite indispensable, because it is necessary that all facilities should be utilised to strengthen the economic power of the under-developed countries. The greatest benefit can be derived from these investments if they are made within the framework of clearly defined aims of a conscious social and economic international policy. Tinbergen [1] feels that to this end an international economic policy must be developed, having the following aims which should in effect be brought to some quantitative expression:

(a) Real incomes per head of the various regions of the world should converge rather than diverge or as a minimum diverge no further. This means a more equitable distribution of income between regions.
(b) Development in the more prosperous countries should not stop, although it may have to be slowed down somewhat if aim (a) is to be fulfilled. This implies that for the world as a whole investment may have to be speeded up.
(c) Prices of primary products should be stabler than before.
(d) Balances of payments should be more in equilibrium than before.

For the purpose of achieving these ends we have given four basic conditions (see page 274). Another important matter is the manner in which the economico-political possibilities are utilised, the wage policy is handled to check a rise of wages out of proportion with productivity, and the international trade policy is developed to achieve greater international stability.

David Rockefeller, Vice-President of the Chase Manhattan Bank is of opinion that in this connection the measures announced by the American Government in recent years deserve special attention, viz.:
(a) expansion of markets by regional agreements;

[1] *Aims and Means of an International Economic Policy*.

278

(b) lowering of tariffs (Reciprocal Trade Act);
(c) greater investments in the under-developed countries, and also greater private investments, by establishing world and regional development banks;
(d) promotion of greater economic stability by expanding the means of the International Monetary Fund and assisting in stabilising prices and making currencies convertible.

The views of leading experts given above and the many forms of international aid which are developing clearly illustrate how extensive and how complicated the problem is with which the world is faced in its growing effort to make our planet habitable for all. To achieve this before the end of the present century much more is necessary than is now being done and can be done. Consequently, special attention will have to be given to the organisational form in which the accelerated aid will have to be cast.

It is only possible to do much more if the mutual understanding and trust between West and East grows to such an extent that the cost of armament can be considerably reduced. If this is to be promoted it will be necessary to give attention to the world population as a whole and not only to those who at present are regarded as politically mature. Estimates [1] of the world population for 1960 and 1970, divided into rich and poor countries, present the following picture of the expected growth of the world population.

TABLE 23

FORECAST OF GROWTH OF POPULATION 1960–1970

	Population increase in millions			%
	1960	1970	1960–70	
Rich countries (North America, Australia, New Zealand, Europe, and U.S.S.R.)	850	950	100	12
Poor countries (Latin America, Africa, Asia)	2060	2520	460	22

The growth of the population of the rich countries is on an average a little over 1% per year, while this figure for the poor countries is about 2%.

The development of the income per head of population is such that in the rich countries it even shows a greater relative increase than in the poor countries [2].

Hence, the development is exactly opposite to what is desired. The

[1] Source: U.N. "Future Growth of World Population", 1956.
[2] Source: Netherlands Economic Institute based on U.N. and I.M.F statistics.

question is: how much capital or income must be transferred annually to the poor countries in order to obtain the same relative increase in the income per head of population in the poor countries as in the rich countries. In 1957 the income of the poor countries which were members of the United Nations Organisation was 128 milliard dollars[1]. For the same year the income for the non-members can be estimated at approx. 40 milliard dollars.

In 1960 the income of the poor countries of the world, which together have a population of more than 2,000 millions, will be approx. 180 milliard dollars. Assuming that it will take a few more years before it is possible to bring the assistance up to standard as regards volume and organisation and before the poor countries will be able to make sufficient useful investments, an income of 200 milliard dollars can be taken as a starting point for the poor countries.

If it is desired to effect a permanent improvement in the conditions in these countries and thus to make them habitable as quickly as possible, it will be necessary to follow a long-term economic policy and thus to give serious attention to improvement of the social infrastructure. Here also considerable arrears must be made up. This means that for every 1% improvement of the national income 4% net investment will be necessary, because the building of dwellings, schools, hospitals, etc., produces very little short-term economic yield. Assuming once more that the national incomes of the world as a whole are raised annually by 3% and that we wish to attain a situation in which the poor countries acquire a relatively somewhat larger increase in income per head of population than the rich countries, it is possible to make the calculations shown in Table 24.

TABLE 24

GROWTH OF POPULATION AND DESIRED INCREASE
IN INCOME IN %

	Rich countries	Poor countries
(a) Growth of population	1	2
(b) Desired increase in income per head of population	1.75	2
(c) Increase in national income from (a) and (b)	2.75	4

To achieve this increase of 4% per year for the poor countries on the basis of a national income of 200 milliard dollars a net investment of 16% is necessary (inclusive of the improvement of the social infrastructure by the building of dwellings, schools, hospitals, etc.). This means an investment of 32 milliard dollars per year. Assuming that the under-developed and the semi-under-developed countries can themselves save

[1] Source: Netherlands Economic Institute based on U.N. and I.M.F statistics.

6%, *i.e.* 12 milliard dollars per year, a capital movement of 20 milliard dollars from the rich to the poor countries would be necessary to achieve this end. This is only possible if the cost of armaments is greatly reduced. If this is done as illustrated in Table 13 on page 37 and if the capital movement is made to increase as the funds become available, the situation would be as illustrated in Table 25.

TABLE 25

5–YEAR PLAN FOR ACCELERATION OF CAPITAL MOVEMENT FROM RICH TO POOR COUNTRIES IN MILLIARDS OF DOLLARS

	Existing capital movement * kept constant	Extra available by reduction of costs of armaments **	Economic investments	Social investments	Total investments	Further additional capital available in rich countries
1960	5		5		5	—
1961	5	9	7.5	1	8.5	5.5
1962	5	19	10	2.5	12.5	11.5
1963	5	29	10	5	15	19
1964	5	40	10	7.5	17.5	27.5
1965	5	52	10	10	20	37

* *see Table 22, page 275*
** *see Table 13, page 37*

It would be possible in 1960 to lay the foundation for the international policy which would enable the cost of armaments to be reduced during the following five years. In 1961 the economic investments in the poor countries could be increased and the correct organisational form for the international aid established.

In the same year, preparations (training, pilot plants, establishment of development centres, etc.) could be made for the improvement of the social infrastructure in the poor countries. The realisation of the social defence could be gradually taken in hand. After the five years the investment possibilities in the poor countries could have improved as a result of sound preparatory work to such an extent that the maximum amount of foreign capital could be taken up.

The above plan can only be successful if adequate domestic effort can be developed in the poor countries, if saving can be promoted and a sound organisational form can be found for the overall development activity. To manage this plan would be an excellent task for the Economic and Social Council of the United Nations, which might well instill new life in the United Nations. All the existing forms of assistance and activation could be expanded and the whole could be incorporated in a system of

Rotterdam: a symbol of Europe's reconstruction

1939

1940

1959

international, regional and national banks and organisations for development and reconstruction. Private enterprise could be given a place of its own in this setup with a view to obtaining the greatest possible amount of know-how in a practical way on behalf of the desired industrialisation, etc. All this would have to be done on the basis of clearly formulated and quantitatively specified prosperity plans in order to derive the greatest possible benefit from the extra investments. Important preparatory work is already being done by the Special Fund. Paul G. Hoffman, Managing Director of the United Nations Special Fund, said on this subject[1]: "The significance of the role of the Special Fund must be seen in the total framework of a greatly increased program of capital investment from many sources. The spending of a comparatively small amount on the projects with which the Fund will concern itself will lay a solid groundwork for the investment of many times that amount in revenue-producing development programs aimed at improving the living conditions of millions of people in the less-developed countries. The minimal goal which I have outlined as worthy of seeking during the next decade – raising the annual rate of increase of national income in these lands to two per cent. – will be possible only if the necessary preparatory work is done."

The special place which building and civil engineering occupy in this setup will be discussed in greater detail in the following chapters.

2. ACCELERATION OF INTERNATIONAL EXCHANGE OF BUILDING KNOWLEDGE

It is certainly useful to emphasise once more that a habitable world can be created only on a basis of domestic effort. The fact that this requires a lot of aid makes no difference.

When Europe emerged from the second World War impoverished and a victim of destruction, it was the domestic effort that made it possible to wage a successful war against the forces of hunger, poverty, despair and chaos. What the American people did to assist in bringing this effort to a successful end in a relatively short time by rendering assistance in kind will always remain of inestimable value. The manner in which this was done bore witness of great wisdom. In his now historic speech at Harvard on 15th June, 1947, the late General Marshall said in effect: "Let the countries of Europe get together and formulate a plan for their own recovery; then the United States can consider what it will do to help Europe to put it into effect."

This excellent combination of a great domestic effort and efficiently directed international aid did not fail to produce results. Europe conquered its difficulties in a very short time. It recognised the relationship between

[1] Source: Speech to the U.N. Economic and Social Council, Geneva, 16 July 1959.

prosperity and productivity and is now building up a society in which, whilst retaining the greatest possible individual freedom, social justice and economic strength are being further developed by international co-operation. It need hardly be pointed out that this also presents new difficulties, which must be overcome.

If one is entirely dependent on the domestic effort a difficult and long road lies ahead, with a constant risk of failure. In that case, the account for building up the economic strength can only be presented to the people concerned. The people of the country can only pay off this account by an almost superhuman effort, lower consumption and restriction of personal freedom. What this means to the individual is clearly evidenced by the 40 years of privation and struggle in the U.S.S.R., which have resulted in the economic and technical strength which that country is now gradually building up. It is satisfactory to note that especially in recent years—now that the initial and heavy struggle for the existence of the U.S.S.R. as a collectivity has been brought to a successful end—more and more attention is being given to the weal and woe of the individual in that country.

North America, Australia, New Zealand, Western Europe and the U.S.S.R. are the principal regions that can be classed as the rich countries. This does not mean, however, that there is not still a lot to be done before we can speak of a habitable world even in those countries. The great importance of know-how and cadre and skilled workers was clearly demonstrated by the rapid recovery of Western Europe after the war. The difficulty of developing anything that has lagged behind in a country where know-how and cadre and skilled workers are not available to a sufficient extent has become quite evident from the international aid of the last 10 years.

One of the great problems for the development of under-developed countries is, therefore, the acceleration of international transmission of knowledge with a view to accelerating the development process in these countries by training and education. Knowledge is necessary for drawing up a sound development plan for the country, making wise investments, setting up a modern production apparatus, and achieving functional and rational building. Furthermore, knowledge and insight are necessary to enable people to live with all these new things.

Transmission of knowledge invariably has two difficult aspects, the teacher and the learner. To be a good teacher it is necessary to have a good knowledge of the subject, but also to find the right didactic approach. In international transmission of knowledge between countries with such divergent civilisations and prosperity levels it is not a simple matter to transmit the right knowledge in the right way. It is advisable, therefore, that those engaged in this work should have received careful training, for otherwise the teachers will make serious mistakes.

Transmission of knowledge is possible, however, only if it meets with a certain amount of receptivity, if the people want to learn and acquire skill. People should realise that things can and must be done differently and they should be willing to break with the old routine, resignation and super-stition. The aim to achieve a habitable world for all requires energy and enthusiasm. It is necessary, therefore, that transmission of knowledge should be preceded and accompanied by a process of psychological conditioning to create the right atmosphere.

(a) *Growing United Nations' activity and greater concentration*
It is a fortunate circumstance for our present-day world that—besides the growing activity of the rich countries in the bilateral technical assistance programmes and the growing interest displayed by private industry and investors—we have at our disposal the United Nations Organisation with its special agencies and organisations for technical assistance and the grant-ing of credit. It is precisely the United Nations Organisation that makes such an important contribution towards creating the right atmosphere owing to its neutral position; moreover it has the especially important task of accelerating international transmission of knowledge. The United Nations is displaying an increasingly keen interest in everything concerned with planning, housing and building. This finds expression in particular in the acceptance by the Economic and Social Council of the most impor-tant proposals of the Inter-Agency Working Party on Housing and Related Community Facilities for the extension of low-cost housing and related community facilities. This proposal for concerted international action for the period 1961–1965 is given in full in section 3 of this chapter.

The working party comprised representatives of the United Nations (U.N.), the International Labour Organisation (I.L.O.), the Food and Agricultural Organisation (F.A.O.), the United Nations Educational Scientific and Cultural Organisation (U.N.E.S.C.O.) and the World Health Organisation (W.H.O.). Contributions were also made by the Economic Commission for Asia and the Far-East (E.C.A.F.E.), the Eco-nomic Commission for Africa (E.C.A.) and the Economic Commission for Latin-America (E.C.L.A.). This certainly proves the great importance attached to acceleration of the construction of low-cost housing.

This programme was the fortunate result of many years of work in the spheres of planning, housing and building of the U.N. Headquarters and the specialised organisations and commissions mentioned above.

(b) *International courses for planning, building and hydraulic engineering*
A growing activity worthy of attention concerns the international courses, which promote very intensively the transmission of knowledge in the

spheres of planning and building. The most important work in this connection is performed by Bouwcentrum, Rotterdam, The Netherlands, the Inter-American Housing Centre, Bogota, Columbia, and the School of Architecture, London, United Kingdom.

The object of the International Course on Building [1] is to acquaint planners, engineers and architects from developing countries with the methods required to achieve a systematic solution of the building problem. To this end the course, which takes six months, is divided into a theoretical and a practical part.

In the theoretical part these methods are dealt with as a group of four specialities (planning, programming, technique and organisation) complemented by the theoretical background of transmission of knowledge. The practical part, which takes four months, serves to give the participants an opportunity to specialise in a subject of their own choice within the framework of the course and to practice the application of the methods of approach discussed. It is also possible for the participants to bring along a project from their own country and to solve the problems of this project in the Netherlands with the assistance of experts. In close consultation with the participants it is ascertained beforehand for each one of them which study programme is the most suitable. During this practical part of the course each participant is coached by a member of the staff and sent to an institute, a bureau, etc., to acquire the necessary practical knowledge.

Although the envisaged specialisation of the participants in a given direction is very useful to assist in solving these specific problems in their own countries, it has proved of great importance in countries where extensive specialisation has already taken place that each building technician should acquaint himself with the subjects belonging to the spheres of others. To be able to work in a team it is necessary that the members of the team should know of each others problems and of the progress made in respect of the other man's subject.

A similar activity on behalf of developing countries is displayed by the Inter-American Housing Centre in Bogota, Columbia. This centre operates under the supervision of the Organisation of American States (Division of Housing and Planning). Its work forms part of the Programme of Technical Co-operation. Every year from March to December this centre gives a course on low-cost housing for post-graduate students, using a combined method of classroom, workshop, laboratory and field work.
The curriculum of the course is as follows:
– Orientation course (first period – approximately two weeks).

[1] *Organised by Bouwcentrum, Rotterdam, The Netherlands, in close co-operation with the International Federation for Housing and Planning and with T.N.O. (Organisation for Applied Scientific Research), The Hague, The Netherlands.*

286

- Field trips and visits.
- Basic course (second period – approximately one month).
- Special short courses.
- Training projects (third period – approximately six months)
- Short summary course.
- Individual projects (fourth period – approximately one and a half months).

A course along more or less the same lines is given by the Department of Tropical Architecture of the School of Architecture in London. This course of training for qualified architects from tropical countries (and for architects who intend to work in tropical regions) was started in 1957 and is given under the direction of Dr. O. H. Koenigsberger. It takes six months and consists of two parts: studio work and lectures on special subjects relating to tropical conditions.

In addition to the three courses referred to above, mention must be made of some other important activity in the sphere of building and civil engineering. Under the direction of Mr. G. A. Atkinson, B. S. (arch.), A.R.I.B.A. the British Building Research Station at Watford, Hertfordshire, England, gives a course for architects and civil engineers in the overseas service on a number of technical subjects, followed by excursions. This course lasts one week. The City and Guilds of London Institute gives an overseas certificate course for training young building technicians. This course lasts three years, but involves only from 6 to 8 hours of training per week. Half of the training is given in the form of lectures, the remainder being devoted to tutorial work, drawing office and laboratory work.

Apart from the international courses on planning and building, special attention should be drawn – in view of the aim put forward in this book – to the International Course on Hydraulic Engineering organised by the Technological University of Delft, The Netherlands, and by the Netherlands Universities Foundation for International Co-operation, The Hague, The Netherlands. The International Course on Hydraulic Engineering is open to those who have received a thorough preliminary training in engineering. Practical experience in civil engineering will be very desirable in order to derive the maximum benefit from the course. A degree in civil engineering (or a related branch of study) of some university or other institute for higher education is the minimum requirement for admission. The duration of the course is 11 months (from October to September).

Arrangements have been made for every participant to choose a programme that will be of most use to him. To facilitate this choice three programmes have been compiled from the subjects given in the course. These are:
- Tidal and Coastal Engineering (including harbours).

– Reclamation (including ground-water recovery).
– Rivers and Navigation Works.
If, with a view to his plans for the future, a participant should prefer a combination of subjects other than that provided by one of these three branches of study, he may submit a special programme for approval. Such approval will generally be granted if the special programme of study does not disturb the balance between basic and practical subjects.

(c) Other international activities. Professional and industrial exchange of building knowledge

Besides the work of the U.N. and its special agencies and the international courses referred to, there are also numerous other international activities which constitute a valuable contribution towards international exchange of building knowledge, but space does not permit a detailed account of these activities. Important work is being done in the sphere of planning, housing and building on behalf of, among others, planners, architects, engineers, contractors, industrialists, and labourers. Furthermore, co-operation on an international level is in progress with respect to the most important building materials, such as brick and tiles, concrete, steel, timber, etc. Subjects such as light, sound and heat insulation, as well as other important matters associated with building, are receiving increasing attention in the sphere of international exchange of knowledge. This exchange of knowledge takes place within the individual professions, trade unions and industries, as well as between these groups and the buyers of goods and services. As a rule they serve a much wider aim, namely to promote productivity and quality of building by disseminating useful knowledge, even though this knowledge sometimes contains an element of private interest.

As examples of regional international activity, mention should be made of the work of the O.E.E.C. (Organisation for European Economic Co-operation) and of the High Authority of the European Coal and Steel Community. In recent years both organisations (the former through the European Productivity Agency) have given a great deal of attention to problems associated with building, particularly house-building. An important contribution was made towards accelerating the international exchange of building knowledge, especially regionally, by financing projects for studying important building problems and by organising international seminars, study trips, prize competitions and exhibitions. It is unfortunate that the building section of the European Productivity Agency could not be brought to full development, partly owing to lack of funds, especially in recent years, and partly – largely in the beginning – because use was made of a number of national building productivity centres, which mostly proved a failure.

The High Authority of the European Coal and Steel Community is making effective use of an existing organisation, the International Council for Building Research, Studies and Documentation (C.I.B.), ensuring efficient performance of its work.

Although it must be admitted that any international activity in this sphere deserves our praise, there is invariably a risk of confusion if such activity cuts through the work of existing, properly functioning organisations. There have been years when the same experts – their number is limited – were made to meet over and over again to discuss practically the same subjects, but each time on behalf of a different international organisation, without any attempt at co-ordination being made. This caused great confusion and a waste of time, and the after-effects of this are still evident to-day. It is high time that national and international systems of co-operation should be drawn up, so that a higher degree of efficiency can be achieved.

(d) Growing activity of C.I.B.

In Europe this unsatisfactory state of affairs was recognised fairly soon after the war, the principal subject in mind being building documentation. The Economic Commission for Europe, especially the Housing Sub-Committee – later called the Housing Committee – realised that properly organised co-operation could prevent a lot of duplication and consequently could appreciably raise the effectiveness of the work of the limited number of real experts available. Largely as a result of Belgian initiative the C.I.D.B. (International Council for Building Documentation) was founded in Paris in 1950. Three years later in Geneva this organisation was transformed into the C.I.B. (International Council for Building Research, Studies and Documentation). In this way an international, non-governmental organisation was set up under the auspices of the United Nations, and it received a so-called consultative status with the Economic and Social Council of the United Nations.

The original intention was to establish an institute promoting contact between experts, in which working parties were formed with a view to studying subjects of common interest.

The work of the C.I.B. developed in two directions, *viz.*:

– The joint study of the various documentation techniques with a view to drawing up common rules and methods so as to promote unity in the large variety of available literature and documents, as well as the organised exchange of information.

In this way the C.I.B. carries on the task of the former C.I.D.B.

– The joint study of selected subjects in committees, which subjects are of interest to the committee members. This concerns co-operative research or study on the basis of a division of work. The C.I.B. has committees for studying such subjects as "Calculation of constructions and safety factors", "Rain penetration in walls", etc.

Moreover, a start was made with the dissemination of the results of the work of the C.I.B., as well as of the member institutes of the C.I.B. The normal channel for this is the three-monthly C.I.B. Bulletin, but in 1959 the transmission of the acquired knowledge was organised on a broader basis for the first time at the first international C.I.B. congress, which was also open to non-C.I.B. members. It is the intention to organise such congresses once every three years.

The general assembly of the C.I.B., in which its authority is vested, consists of its full members, *i.e.* national, governmental or non-governmental, non-profit-making institutions, which are experienced and active in a large part of the field of interest of C.I.B.

The C.I.B. has such members in practically all European countries and to an increasing extent also in non-European countries. They are the larger building research and documentation institutes of national and sometimes also of wider importance.

In addition, more specialised institutes are members of C.I.B. They specialise either in specific building materials, such as concrete, wood, steel, etc., or in specific technico-physical, technico-sociological, technico-economic or other more limited problems of building. This category of associate members also includes Directorates of Ministries, which desire to maintain close contact with the work of the C.I.B.

The C.I.B. also includes a number of leading experts as individual unattached members. The fact that, in addition to the work of institutes, the manufacturer and the builder have a large share in the development of building, even though they do not belong to the non-profit-making category, found expression in the creation of a category of supporting organisations of the C.I.B. In this way these organisations can participate in the work of the C.I.B. and make their particular contribution towards the objective research and objective information envisaged by C.I.B.

The C.I.B. promotes co-operation and integration of effort, while a large amount of freedom is allowed for independent initiative, thus avoiding undue regimentation. Originally the co-operation thus achieved was limited to European institutes, but the C.I.B. is gradually attracting more and more members outside Europe and the trend of development is towards a world organisation.

(e) An international chain of building information centres
When considering what has been done in the sphere of international transmission of knowledge during the last ten years, it is certainly evident that there has been a great and remarkable achievement, but that on the other hand overall organisation is not yet complete.

In the entire field of technical assistance some 8,000 devoted experts have worked in some 140 nations and territories and 14,000 fellows have studied abroad during these ten years. Thousands of international seminars, study trips and exhibitions have been organised and hundreds of thousands of publications issued, resulting in a greatly increased contact between people from a variety of countries who have the same or practically the same difficulties and interests.

A rapidly growing activity is also noticeable in the sphere of planning, housing and building, but there are still quite a number of unfulfilled requirements, that stand in the way of efficient progress. Both on a national and on an international level four horizontal planes of co-operation can be distinguished, with vertical co-operation cutting right through these four planes. The four important horizontal planes are the political plane, the scientific plane (fundamental and applied), the plane of transmission of knowledge (education and training) and the practical plane.

The ideal-situation is, of course, that something practical is done as soon as possible after a political decision has been made, *i.e.* that political decisions should indeed result in more, less or different building, generally requiring a special activity in a scientific sphere and action in the sphere of transmission of knowledge.

From the national point of view the organisation of building requires a building development and information centre, which co-ordinates the

291

results of research, carries out research on subjects not explored by others and which ensures that knowledge finds its way to practice in the appropriate form and promotes the practical application of this useful knowledge. From the international point of view also these building development and information centres are essential because optimum international co-operation can be achieved only if there is sufficient co-ordination on a national level.

On the other hand, the national building development and information centres cannot operate efficiently if a properly organised contact with other countries is lacking. Both in the national and international spheres it is not necessary for each centre to know everything or to do everything itself, but it should know who are the experts and what they are doing. To achieve efficient co-operation, both nationally and internationally, an international chain of building development and information centres is necessary, adapted to the national conditions in the countries concerned, but at the same time structurally so alike as to promote a smooth international exchange of knowledge.

The realisation of the international transmission of knowledge requires, besides a network of building development and information centres as a machinery for organisation, unity in presentation and special international publications.

The building development and information centres should closely cooperate with existing national general development institutes in the developing countries. This is necessary to ensure that general development and building influence each other as favourably as possible. For practical reasons acceleration of international transmission of knowledge will have to be confined to a limited number of subjects. Even then, a certain degree of completeness can be aimed at by setting up a sound international bibliographical service. It is impossible to be complete in the more active forms of international transmission of knowledge (active documentation, seminars, courses, pilot projects, etc.). Here a selection would have to be made.

It is a very fortunate circumstance that the Inter-Agency Committee of the U.N. referred to under (a) in this chapter has already laid down the main theme for international co-operation in this sphere for the coming years. As the extension of low-cost housing and related community facilities is of exceptional importance, also within the framework of this book, the complete text of the proposals of this committee, which were accepted by the Economic and Social Council of the U.N. in 1959, have been incorporated in the next section of this chapter. It would seem of great importance that all the organisations and institutes which can promote the action planned should give these proposals their full support. Within the framework of this planned action an efficient chain of building development and information centres would be of great value.

292

3. EXTENSION OF LOW-COST HOUSING AND RELATED COMMUNITY FACILITIES [1]

The world housing situation [2]

Surveys of world housing conditions undertaken by the United Nations and the Specialised Agencies in recent years have disclosed that with few exceptions housing conditions have not only remained inadequate but have in fact in many cases deteriorated, especially in the less industrialised countries. The causes underlying this negative trend are closely related to the increase in world population, the growing concentration of people in urban and industrial areas, and the general lack of developed resources available for house building. Furthermore current population projections show that housing conditions may in many countries continue to worsen before the rate of house building can be sufficiently expanded. Taking into account the growing housing deficit that will result from the expected population increase, the construction of the needed new dwelling units could alone consume the better part of the world's total investment capital. Even to supply to that part of the world's population which lives in rural areas a durable roof and safe drinking water would in itself constitute a formidable economic burden. The fact is that because of the more dramatic character of slum conditions and squatting in the cities, there has been a relative neglect of the rural housing problem.

The problem of improving housing conditions is made difficult because of the gap between the cost of acceptable housing and the amount that families are able and willing to pay for housing accommodation. In some of the countries which have had rent control legislation, families have throughout most of the post-war period paid on the average less than 5 percent of their income for rent. In some countries in the Asian region it is considered that 10 to 12 and ½ percent of family incomes is a reasonable allowance for rent. Among the more highly industrial countries, between 15 and 20 percent is regarded as normal in some western European countries, while 20 to 25 percent is customary in some countries in North America. The fact is that low income families in most countries find it difficult to obtain adequate housing accommodation without jeopardising other essential needs.

As a result, housing has become an important public issue in most countries and the problems relating to the formulation, financing and execution of low-cost housing programmes have become more pressing from year to year. It is increasingly recognised that poor housing conditions may reduce working efficiency or lead to serious social disruptions,

[1] *Full text of U.N. proposals for a long-range programme of concerted international action 1961 to 1965 (see page 285).*
[2] *Introduction to the proposals.*

and that increased efforts must be made to improve housing and community facilities. Consequently, in a large number of countries measures aimed at promoting the construction of new housing and community facilities and the improvement of the existing structure have been introduced within the framework of national economic and social policies. Among the steps taken in that direction are, first of all, measures of a financial or fiscal nature, such as tax concessions, state-guaranteed mortgages, extension of loans, capital subsidies, direct subsidies to householders and building of rental housing with public funds.

Secondly, a number of governments have stimulated the development and expansion of resources in the building industry with a view to reducing construction costs. National and regional training and research institutes have been or are being established in different parts of the world for study and application of economic and technological improvements.

Thirdly, in several countries steps have been taken to reduce urban congestion and to provide work and accommodation in new industrial or developing rural areas. At the same time, a number of governments have recognised the need to encourage the preparation of master plans for larger urban agglomerations and are beginning to establish planning agencies at the central, provincial and local levels to cope with the problems of organising, financing and administering urban redevelopment and renewal projects.

In some countries, the direct contribution of householders is being mobilised in an effort to increase the production of housing and to reduce building costs. There is also a growing tendency towards governmental support of individual ownership of homes in order to reduce the heavy administrative and economic burden which public housing imposes on central and local authorities.

The developments referred to illustrate some of the approaches towards a solution of the housing problem, and there is no doubt that a great deal of practical experience has been gained in improving the quality and quantity of low-cost housing. Nevertheless, the fact remains that in spite of combined national and international efforts during the past decade, the world has not seen a substantial betterment in the general housing situation, and it may be expected that governments especially in the less industrialised countries will be faced for a long time with a pressing demand for more and better dwellings at reasonable costs. It is evident, therefore, that not only remedial but also preventive measures are called for which go beyond the present more or less conventional methods to solve the housing problem.

It is now generally recognised that such measures should deal not only with the economic aspects of housing and the expansion of the building industry, but should also be concerned with the social welfare aspects of housing. For example, in many cases governmental housing agencies find themselves in charge of a large number of dwelling units involving responsibilities not only for rent collection but also for maintenance and repair of public property; and the social welfare of tenants calls increasingly for special provisions in large scale housing developments whether they are of a public, cooperative or private nature. Without adequate social services and educational programmes for the householders' benefit, these projects often turn prematurely into slums and thus defeat their very purpose of arresting conditions of blight and overcrowding. The building of new towns in different parts of the world has also focussed attention on the fact that shelter cannot be conceived merely in terms of physical needs but must represent in equal measure a fulfillment of communal needs if some kind of social cohesion and civic pride are to be created in the new settlements.

In this connection, the provision of schools, health services, community centres, adequate transportation, safe water, sewage disposal and other essential public utilities and services is acute in developing countries, where the provision of primary education for all is a recognised objective, while the present enrolment is in many cases less than half of the children of school age. There is a need also in the more developed countries as a result of an unprecedented growth of the population in the school age groups. In spite of the fact that during the last ten years many governments, particularly in Asia, Africa and Latin America have made special efforts in extending medical and health services to the rural areas, the needs are still very far from being met. Safe water supply and adequate means of excreta disposal are non-existent in most rural areas in the developing countries, and even in cities of 50,000 population there are rarely adequate provisions for safe water supply and sewage disposal systems.

These and similar needs for community facilities have been recognised by public and private agencies alike and though action has been taken towards providing the essential services and facilities, their cost to the individual householder and to the community as a whole has often been prohibitive and hampered their development. It would, therefore, appear to be desirable to pay increasing attention to the provision of these services as integral parts of national low-cost housing programmes and to develop methods and techniques for reducing their costs.

The effectiveness of the measures taken will depend to a large extent on the administrative machinery available. While most countries have created special agencies to deal with housing and related questions, in many cases further measures are needed to bring about an integrated effort between the various governmental departments concerned, as well as between these and private and voluntary organisations.

A constant review of world housing trends especially in the less industrialised countries as well as certain changes in the concepts of international action, have caused the international programme in housing, building and planning to undergo certain distinct stages in its development. At the request of the Economic and Social Council, an integrated programme in housing and town and country planning was drawn up in 1949 by the United Nations and the specialised agencies concerned. This programme, approved by the Council in 1950, was essentially a programme of study, conceived along broad lines, and designed to be carried out under the leadership of the United Nations working in close consultation with the participating agencies who were responsible for the study of certain aspects of the housing problem according to their specific interests.

The next phase in the development of the international housing programme came in 1953 when the Council requested that high priority be given to housing for low income groups especially in the underdeveloped countries. Thereafter an effort was made to concentrate the resources of the various international organisations on certain fields more directly related to specific pressing needs indicated by Governments. This led to an intensified activity by the regional economic commissions especially with regard to questions relating to government programmes and policies including the financing of housing and the reduction of building costs.

In more recent years, studies, regional meetings of experts and direct assistance to Governments were more closely related to urban and rural housing programmes for low income groups as part of general economic and social development. Attention was also given to the training of technical and administrative personnel and to the establishment of national and regional housing centres. At the same time increasing emphasis was placed on the study of methods and techniques of environmental (physical) planning. This latter development stemmed from a growing number of requests by Governments for advice on the preparation of master plans for capital cities in various parts of the world and from a general awareness of the need to consider the problems of urbanisation and industrial location within a regional framework.

There are certain basic criteria which should be applied in the formulation of long-range international activities for the extension of low-cost housing and community facilities. It is necessary to take into account the essential differences in the housing problem as between urban and rural areas and as between the more and the less industrialised countries. Recent experience has shown that various techniques applied in connection with the urban housing problem cannot be transferred readily to an economically less advanced rural setting. The central problem is that special measures have to be evolved because of the different economic and social conditions prevailing in rural areas and that such measures, in some cases, may call for changes in age-old patterns of living.

Locally available building materials will need to be used more fully and rationally. Houses will need to be improved through introducing certain elementary devices such as sanitation and cooking and heating devices. Community life will need to be reoriented in order to benefit from newly established health and educational facilities. These innovations represent by no means merely a technological advance but rather far-reaching changes in local customs and traditions and their acceptance will depend to a large degree upon the active co-operation of individuals and the community as a whole.

Concerted action designed to deal with the problems set out above, will have to be preceded by field studies and surveys with a view to ascertaining needs and the actual and potential availability of funds, building materials and manpower which could be mobilised most readily in urban and rural areas to fulfil the demand for low-cost housing and community facilities. At the same time, the suitability of remedial measures and techniques applied so far should be evaluated in the light of difficulties encountered and results achieved. In this way it would be possible, on the one hand, to detect those areas which call for greater emphasis, de-emphasis or an entirely different approach and, on the other, to transmit these findings to governments in the form of relevant recommendations for practical action.

In order to strengthen such recommendations and to encourage their application, the resources of the various programmes of technical assistance, including, where appropriate, the Special Fund, should be utilised in a variety of demonstration and pilot projects including seminars, workshops, expert advice and fellowships for the purpose of training, operational research and dissemination of knowledge. Such measures will help facilitate the training of personnel ranging from the highest executive and administrative level to the lowest artisan level and assist governments in staffing the necessary national organisations for the planning, administration and execution of effective housing programmes for the lower income groups.

This general outline for a concerted action programme for the period 1961–1965 points towards certain areas of work which should receive early attention. Fact-finding should be directed in the first place towards regional and national surveys and qualitative evaluations of public and private resources already used in different parts of the world in national efforts to increase the low-cost housing stock. These surveys should underline differences in approach as well as successes and failures directly traceable to the stage of economic, social and technological advancement of the countries concerned.

As a result of the finds thus obtained, the resources of the various international agencies concerned would be combined in undertaking specific projects within this framework in the form of joint and separate studies and promotion of training and research through pilot and demonstration projects, seminars, conferences, etc., on a national and regional basis. The regional economic commissions and regional housing centres where they exist would play an increasingly important role in this connection.

It should be noted that the proposed long-range programme is not a substitute for the continuing programmes of the United Nations and the specialised agencies in the field of housing, building and planning. For example, the field of town and country and regional planning which is an important development in the Social Commission's programme is included in these proposals only in so far as it is related to planning at the community or neighbourhood level. Activities of the regional economic commissions in the field of housing and building also are far broader than those included in this programme. Forestry activities of FAO offer a similar example. Furthermore, broad programmes such as urbanisation, industrialisation and community development have a direct bearing on low-cost housing and community facilities. The principle followed in constructing this programme has been to select those activities of the United Nations and the specialised agencies directly related to the extension of low-cost housing and community facilities and to supplement these activities in such a way that a coherent and effective programme emerges. It is expected that such proposals will serve as a basis for orientation of international activities in this field over a period of years.

The following is a general description of the five areas selected and of the specific projects proposed for concerted action for the extension of low-cost housing and community facilities in the years 1961 to 1965. It should be noted that the areas are not mutually exclusive; they are in fact interrelated and certain aspects of a given project, such as exchange of information, may cut across other areas. Furthermore Area I: Planning, Organisation and Administration of Programmes for Low-Cost Housing and Community Facilities, and Area V: Education and Training are dealing with projects which are of fundamental importance to the other three areas.

Area I: Planning, organisation and administration of programmes for low-cost housing and community facilities
Programmes for extension of low-cost housing and related community

facilities must be planned and carried out through national and local organisations in co-operation with individual and group efforts within each country. These plans and programmes will in most cases be a part of wider programmes for housing and town planning, for rural or urban development, or for social development generally.

The primary role of the international organisations is to assist governments in strengthening their national organisations for planning and execution of such programmes, particularly through providing basic information for planning purposes, through assistance in the organisation of national and local machinery for the administration of such programmes, and through training of administrative and technical personnel.

The place of broad social, scientific and technological research in planning low-cost housing and community facilities should be recognised at both international and national levels. In many cases, particularly in scientific and technological research, it will not be economical to provide research stations covering the whole range of problems in each country. For example, research on forest products widely used throughout whole region (such as bamboo) or research on the sources of energy for heating purposes or sound-proofing can be promoted on a regional basis or in some instances on even a wider basis by the international organisations concerned. The provision of demographic and social data needed for planning, on the other hand, will normally have to be done country by country although international technical assistance is available to national governments in the development of such data.

No standard formula for organisation of programmes for low-cost housing and related community facilities can or should be developed in view of the wide differences in general administrative structure and resources available for such programmes. At the same time, certain general principles can be accepted universally, *e.g.* that low-cost housing and community facilities require consideration from a health point of view as well as from an economic technological point of view and that, if several ministries or departments of governments are concerned with various aspects of the programme, adequate machinery for consultations among these departments should be provided. Furthermore, if special programmes exist for community development, urbanisation problems, etc., ways and means of utilising the resources of these programmes for the extension of low-cost housing and community facilities should be devised.

Projects which might be undertaken in this area over the next five years include the following:

Surveys of housing conditions and programmes   As a part of the normal work programme of the United Nations and specialised agencies, continued efforts should be made to improve the statistical data on housing conditions and the extent of the need for low-cost housing units. New efforts will be made to provide governments with information on the extent and nature of the needs for expansion of community facilities (see Area III), and to report on national programmes for low-cost housing. In this connection, ECE is working on the improvement of the quality and coverage of housing and building statistics in Europe; annual surveys of housing progress and policies; methods of drawing up housing programmes; and periodic quantitative surveys of housing requirements in Europe. Similar work has been initiated in ECAFE and in the Latin American area.

Promotion of scientific and *technological research* To provide governments with a continuing flow of scientific information for application in low-cost housing programmes, the international organisations will promote through national, regional and international scientific bodies basic research on low-cost methods of ensuring healthful housing, for instance, through protection against heat and cold, wind and dust and noise as well as technological research in development and utilisation of building materials. As a first step, a survey would be made of existing scientific and technical research relevant to low-cost housing with a view to identify the major gaps in this scientific and technical work.

Assistance in national surveys directly *related to formulation of policies and programmes* *for low-cost housing and community facilities* On request of governments, the agencies concerned will be prepared to assist in determining through general or sample surveys the extent of the need for low-cost housing in a given country, the manpower and natural resources available, methods of financing and other elements necessary in formulating a national plan.

Public administration aspects of *low-cost housing programmes* In the first instance a comparative study of various patterns of national and local organisations for planning and execution of low-cost housing should be undertaken with a view to establishing criteria and principles to help countries ready to organise such programmes or improve existing efforts. Such a study should be followed by direct assistance to governments in this field.

Area II: Mobilisation of individual and group efforts for extending low-cost housing
Individual and group efforts can bring about immediate and substantial improvement in local housing situations. These human resources, however, remain largely untapped because of lack of incentives, of knowledge and skills, and of funds and organisation.

Two major types of individual effort may be distinguished: self-help in undertaking all or part of the operations involved in preparing the land, producing materials and building the house; and in personal saving with a view to acquiring a home.

Self-help of the former type is particularly appropriate in rural communities in developing countries. Large unused or partially unused labour resources are frequently available as a result of under-employment or seasonal unemployment and suitable building materials can often be obtained and prepared at little or no financial cost. The applicability of self-help methods to rural housing has been demonstrated in widely separated regions of the world and in varying economic and social settings. It would, therefore, seem to be desirable to utilise these methods in those cases where community development programmes are already eliciting the participation of the people in efforts to raise their levels of living and to make self-help housing an integral part of such programmes. In other cases, the improvement of housing may provide an initial impetus to community development.

In urban communities, self-help has more limited application and calls for further research and experience. Nevertheless, there are opportunities for its utilisation in the peripheral areas of congested cities with particular reference to permanent resettlement of squatters. Experimentation and demonstration may also prove that the renewal of central urban slum areas opens up a new field for individual and group efforts once further knowledge has been obtained on the economics of self-help and mutual aid as well as on the social and technological problems involved.

The success of individual and group efforts in improving the housing situation largely depends on effective education and documentation to inform people fully of the purpose of the project and of how they can participate in it, and to elicit their interest and support and their ideas and criticisms. There is also a need to develop methods which would diminish reliance on exceptional conditions and exceptional people to carry out self-help, mutual aid and co-operative housing projects. It is also difficult to envisage a marked increase of individual and group effort without security of tenure or ownership rights.

Self-help in housebuilding requires technical and material aids and training facilities. These may be provided by governments, employers, trade unions or co-operative associations. Local conditions will indicate whether it is more appropriate to organise and train small groups of workers who will carry out the construction, or to train large numbers of future householders to build their own dwellings. Attention may be drawn to the opportunities for stimulating individual efforts by the provision of certain components, *e.g.* doors and windows or roofing and flooring materials, and by the provision of the central core of the house.

There are also large opportunities for improving housing conditions through group action. In some of the more industrialised countries, housing co-operatives and building societies have maintained a high level of housebuilding for a long period and have achieved substantial reductions in housing costs. In many of the other highly industrialised countries and in the less industrialised countries, there is widespread interest in stimulating personal savings and co-operative housing. There are a great many obstacles, however, chief of which are insufficient co-operative experience, limited management capacities and lack of financial resources.

There is need for international action in sponsoring seminars on self-help and non-profit housing, providing assistance in the form of experts, fellowships, lecturers and documentation, and assisting in the establishment of training courses for specialists and administrators concerned with non-profit housing organisations at national, regional and local levels.

Projects which might be undertaken in this area over the next five years include the following:

Evaluation of self-help methods   A comprehensive fact-finding analysis should be made in selected countries of the application of self-help, mutual aid and other methods of co-operation in housing in rural and urban areas, with particular reference to techniques used and problems and difficulties encountered in the execution of such projects. Information should be included on the use of labour, organisation of group work, use of spare time, nature of technical supervision, role of financial and other aids, and health and educational aspects. Attention should also be given to evaluating the role of self-help, mutual aid and co-operative housing in national housing policy and programmes and the extent to which public and private agencies can assist or encourage such efforts. Based on such information an evaluation of methods would be made and their more general applicability assessed.

Demonstration projects in rural areas   Such projects should be undertaken in close co-operation with national and regional housing centres and they should demonstrate the practical experience already gained in house building in rural areas in different parts of the world. They would offer training opportunities for local personnel at the supervisory and workers' levels and might serve as spearheads for the introduction of large-scale, self-help housing programmes, preferably within community development and fundamental education programmes at the village level. Of equal importance for housing in rural areas are projects for improving or extending existing housing accommodations through self-help and mutual aid for the purpose of adding space, separation of man and animal, provision of storage and processing facilities, for farm products and the improvement of cooking stoves, heating, lighting, etc.

Studies and pilot projects in urban areas   Projects under this heading, undertaken in close co-operation with national and regional housing centres, should be directed towards providing more knowledge and experience on the applicability of self-help techniques to urban low-cost housing. Projects might, for example, be undertaken to resettle squatters in urban fringe areas on a permanent basis by using community development methods. Other projects might investigate the feasibility of applying similar methods to improving slums in a central urban area. (Note: Mention may be made, in this connection of particular types of low-cost housing projects using mutual aid, which have been carried out over the past 12 years by "International Voluntary Work Camps" established by youth organisations. UNESCO extends assistance to the co-ordinating committee of the organisations concerned and their yearly planning conference).

Production of audio-visual materials on self-help, mutual aid and co-operation The preparation of audio-visual materials on selected projects to provide (*i*) technical instruction for leaders in the housing field, (*ii*) general education of the public on self-help, mutual aid and co-operative methods.

Seminars and assistance in various forms on housing through non-profit organisations Further joint UN/ILO seminars for the African and Mediterranean countries might be organised. In due course such seminars for Latin American and Asian countries could be organised for the second time. Such seminars would be held every second year. In addition, advice and assistance should be given to governments in encouraging and aiding co-operative and other forms of non-profit housebuilding activities. Such projects might include assistance in training personnel in the organisation and administration of housing co-operatives, including the maintenance of accounts, assistance in preparing model by-laws for the guidance of co-operative housing societies, and assistance in organising pilot co-operative housing projects (see also projects in Area IV under the heading "Productivity of the building industry"). (Note: The more general aspects of financing of housing and the establishment of community facilities within national programmes are included in the regular work programmes of the participating organisations).

Area III: Provision of community facilities
Certain basic community facilities form an integral part of schemes for the extension of low-cost housing. From the point of view of health, the basic requirements of sanitary and health facilities such as safe water supply, adequate sewage and garbage disposal, hospitals, health centres, dispensaries, etc. From the point of view of education, schooling facilities should be within easy reach, including day nurseries. For the pursuit of cultural activities, it is necessary to provide library services, places of entertainment, town halls, community centres, etc., for children and adults who also are in need of a certain amount of open recreational spaces for play, sports and similar activities. In addition, there must be basic

shopping and retail outlets, the essential means of communication by road or rail and a supply of power in one form or another without which no community can exist properly as part of a wider network of human settlements within an industrial or agricultural setting.

Special attention may be given to multi-purpose community centres because they play a special part in low-cost housing programmes. Centres may provide space and equipment for canning, sewing and such carpentry work as will encourage simple home improvement projects; facilities for laundering; a nursery and playground for small children during the period mothers are working at the centre; first aid and emergency equipment in cases where health centres are not available in the vicinity; and an opportunity to demonstrate suitable furnishings and equipment for homes in the neighbourhood, especially if the centre is built during the early stages of the community's development. Voluntary women's organisations have shown great interest in the establishment of community centres and have often played an important part in their financing and building. It is important that the interest of such organisations be sustained and further stimulated and that due consideration be given to the specific needs of the women of the community when the centre and its functions are being planned.

It is a wellknown fact that these fundamental neighbourhood pre-requisities are largely non-existent in the rural areas, particularly in the less industrialised countries. Although the highly industrialised countries are in general better equipped because municipal authorities and interested private agencies have for many years concentrated their efforts in this field on the larger urban and metropolitan areas, there are still serious deficiencies in urban community facilities. It, therefore, would seem to be desirable to direct international action foremost to the rural area where there is such a marked absence of basic amenities. It would be preferable in many cases to improve health and educational facilities as well as roads first before undertaking actual housing improvements.

The need to consider the provision of community facilities and public utility services not as a haphazard component of urban and rural development but rather as an essential element of human settlements has for a long time been recognised as an important objective of town and country planning. But while the underlying principles have been well established on the theoretical level, consistent practical application of these principles has almost exclusively been restricted to new towns especially in the more developed countries. There is, therefore, a large field for utilising proven techniques in the rural areas of the less developed countries and to try and bring them into relationship with community development techniques, not only to stimulate local interest but also to enlist the contribution of individuals and groups in order to reduce the cost to the community of the needed facilities.

Projects which could be undertaken in this area over the next five years include the following:

Existing and potential demand for community facilities in rural areas Fact-finding surveys within the technical assistance programmes should be conducted in selected countries to establish the adequacy and costs of existing basic community facilities and the demand for such facilities at the community level. Such surveys should also examine the role which public and private agencies have played or are prepared to play in the provision of such facilities.

Planning and design of community facilities related to the extension of low-cost housing Within this project, studies and technical assistance should be utilised to assist governments in providing essential community facilities in urban and rural residential neighbourhoods. Studies should be undertaken by the United Nations and the specialised agencies in their respective fields, to show how far physical planning techniques from a local and regional point of view may be utilised in the development of desirable layouts and location within urban and rural neighbourhoods of such community facilities as: schools, sanitary facilities, health centres, maternity homes, nurseries, community and youth centres, recreational facilities, neighbourhood shops and village markets, food storage and processing facilities, transport facilities etc. For conducting these studies full advantage should be taken of the contribution that can be made by the interested professional and voluntary organisations.

Comparative cost of various types of community facilities Studies need to be made of the costs of various types of community facilities at different technological levels in both rural and urban areas, with a view to providing guidance in the formulation and execution of community facility programmes. A study should be made of the actual and potential role which self-help, mutual aid, co-operation and the application of community development techniques has played or may play in increasing community facilities quantitatively and in reducing their cost to the community.

Dissemination of information on community facilities related to the extension of low-cost housing Information sheets, simple guides and other media should be prepared in co-operation with national and regional housing centres and other organisations concerned to encourage the provision and maintenance of essential community facilities in urban and rural residential neighbourhoods. They should include data on typical designs, layout, construction costs and legal aspects, and would be distributed to governments within programmes of technical assistance. (See also "Public administration aspects of low-cost housing programmes" in Area I).

Pilot projects   On request by governments pilot projects, including workshops and seminars, could be organised within the technical assistance programme to demonstrate the possibility of extending self-help, mutual aid and other methods of co-operation for the establishment and maintenance of community facilities.

Area IV: Increasing the productivity and capacity of the building industry
The building and building materials industry, has a strategic role to play in improving housing conditions. The reduction of costs through raising productivity and increasing the supply of building materials not only in urban areas but also in rural districts makes it possible for a greater number of persons to obtain adequate housing and also raises the output of dwelling units produced from existing resources.

Governments, employers and workers in the building industry, and professional persons such as architects and engineers, can all make important contributions to increasing the efficiency of resources already employed within the industry. Detailed planning in advance of construction, the simplification of design and building operations, better programming of operations, the development and use of new building materials, prefabrication of components, the standardisation of building materials, equipment and accessories, the extension of modular co-ordination, improved organisation on the worksite, greater mechanisation of on-site operations, work study, vocational and management training and improvements in labour-management relations are all examples of the wide scope for action for the promotion of greater productivity within the building industry.

While there are many possibilities of increasing productivity through the development of large-scale enterprises using highly mechanised methods, there are also many opportunities for increasing the efficiency of small enterprises through better management, improved organisation, stabilisation of activities on a year-round basis, and the development of suitable arrangements enabling the small contractor to participate more widely in large-scale construction projects.

Another objective in many countries, particularly in the less industrialised countries, is to increase the capacity of the building industry. Many countries cannot possibly meet the urgent demands for various types of new construction, even with greatly increased productivity in the use of existing resources employed in the building industry, without a considerable increase in capacity. In the early stages of expanding capacity in the building industry, it may be necessary in the interest of speeding up the rate of economic development for a large part of the increase to be devoted to non-residential building, for example, industrial and commercial building; but in the later stages this enlarged capacity will be available for a marked increase in housing construction. Expanding the capacity of the building industry means bringing into it new enterprise, new capital, new materials and new labour and raising the technical level of personnel throughout.

In areas where large-scale housing schemes are being undertaken, there are often opportunities for streamlining vocational training of building workers. A reasonably high level of skill in the performance of certain limited tasks can be achieved during a comparatively short period of training when the building process is simplified and broken down and there is an opportunity for the worker to engage in repetitive tasks.

In rural areas, particularly in the less industrialised countries, the building and building materials industries are generally conducted on a small scale and handicraft basis. It is important that all possible encouragement and assistance be given to these infant industries both from the standpoint of supplementing the resources of the highly developed building industries normally found in urban areas, and that of stimulating the expansion of building capacity in the country as a whole. Emphasis should be placed on increasing the local supply of both organic and inorganic building materials such as timber and other forest products including bamboos, clay tiles, mud bricks and cement products.

Attention may be drawn to the possibilities of financing and expansion in the building, building materials and building equipment industries through international movements of capital and of developing programmes for expanding international trade in building materials, particularly on a regional basis.

Projects which could be undertaken in this area over the next five years include the following:

Productivity of the building industry   Increasing the capacity and raising the productivity of the building industry should be the subject of comprehensive examination by the United Nations and the specialised agencies. This should be combined with the provision of advice and assistance to governments, professional personnel, employers and workers in the building industry with a view to raising productivity. The ILO could study and provide assistance on such matters as improvements in organisation of the work site and in working methods; the training of managerial personnel in work study; production planning and control; and personnel management. The ECE through its Housing Committee is making a comprehensive enquiry into Government policies and the cost of building, with as a major underlying theme, promotion of the technological development of the European building industries. Related to this enquiry an examination is being made of Government policies designed to promote greater standardisation and modular co-ordination of building materials and components. A further stage in this work will be a pilot project designed to compare actual building costs in different European countries, particularly of more industrialised methods of construction, using as far as possible the techniques of operational research. It is also intended at an early stage to examine the scope for bringing up-to-date and greater standardisation of building regulations, which are frequently no longer appropriate to the present state of building technology. Similar work has been initiated by the Working Party on Housing and Building of ECAFE. The Sub-Committee on Housing, Building and Planning of the Central American Committee on Economic Co-operation of ECLA has been established for the purpose of integrating the development of the building and building materials industries and establishing a common market for building materials in that area. The regional housing centres in Latin America and Asia are expected to take an increasingly important part in this work in the dissemination of its results, and in the adaptation of the results of research to conditions in their respective areas.

Supply and utilisation of local organic building materials   Further research needs to be carried out on the improved use of forest products for building purposes, particularly non-durable tropical woods and bamboo. Greater attention also needs to be given to the problems of establishing small-scale rural industries, often on a co-operative basis, for exploiting on an economic scale opportunities for expanded use of forest products in housebuilding. Specific activities by the FAO could be directed towards the improved supply of timber, plywood, board products and other organic building materials including bamboos with particular reference to the technical and economic aspects of their availability, processing, fabrication and marketing; seminars and training centres on small sawmills and logging techniques; demonstration centres on bamboo utilisation; consultations on timber seasoning and preservation, particularly for less durable tropical species, and on new methods and materials of construction such as plywood, fibreboards and particle boards.

Supply and utilisation of local inorganic building materials   Further research needs to be carried out on the improved use of inorganic products for building purposes, particularly earth. Greater attention also can be given to the problems of establishing small-scale rural industries, often on a co-operative basis, for exploiting on an economic scale the opportunities for expanded use of inorganic building materials, particularly in the production of clay and cement products and locally available aggregates, frequently from industrial waste, especially for the manufacture of bricks, building blocks, roofing materials and including hollow or other light weight components.

Education and training of personnel Substantially increased efforts are re-
for the building industry quired to promote the education and
training of personnel for the building industry at four levels: the professional level – architects, construction and sanitary engineers and other
professional grades; the management level; the supervisory level on the
site, such as foremen; and the operative level, *i.e.* the development of
craft skills. Institutions for higher training of professional and management
personnel for the building industry, more particularly national and regional
technological institutes, should include in their curricula special training
and refresher courses. Within the general framework of the secondary
education system and at the level of technical and vocational education,
increased technical assistance would be provided for the training of supervisory personnel, particularly general foremen and skilled workers (masons,
wood-workers and carpenters, metal-workers and welders, mechanics,
plumbers, electricians, etc.). Such assistance would apply particularly to
the organisation of short refresher courses. It would include fellowships
particularly for teachers in technical and vocational schools on ways of
adapting their teaching to modern and new techniques of low-cost building.
Fellowships could be provided for further study abroad and for the inservice training of personnel at the higher levels. Technical assistance should
also be available for short training periods within the building industry
for semi-skilled and un-skilled workers. The regional housing centres
should be encouraged to assist in these programmes.

Area V: Education and training
One of the main obstacles in extending low-cost housing and related
community facilities is the lack of trained personnel required for planning,
administering and executing housing programmes. Since professional education shows tangible results only after a considerable period of time, it
would be useful to develop training programmes of shorter duration in
addition to established programmes of higher education for persons performing tasks which require professional training but are lacking such
training. It would also be desirable to provide certain types of additional
training for professional personnel, refresher courses on progress in science
and industry, and training looking toward specialisation in fields in which
personnel is lacking in a given country.

In most rural areas particularly in the less developed countries, there
is an urgent need for a large scale training effort for personnel at the intermediate level. This training should be directed at the local level both in
villages and urban fringe areas. Training should include instruction in
tenant education, home economics, and social services in general in addition to simple technological improvements such as house design, con-

struction and community layout at the village and neighbourhood level including the arrangement and construction of roads, water supply and drainage. In addition trainees should be equipped to provide leadership in encouraging individuals and organising groups of people to build and maintain their dwellings and community facilities.

In planning low-cost housing projects due attention should be given to the education of prospective householders so that they may derive the greatest benefit from their new houses and that the deterioration of such housing projects into new slums may be avoided. In particular, those responsible for planning low-cost housing units should encourage and help families to extend social participation to the new community, to assess their particular needs in relation to proposed house designs and layouts, to utilise the available floor space and amenities effectively, and to furnish and equip the house so as to meet the minimum requirements for healthful living. Such activities are best started when the house is being built. In self-help housing projects, efforts should be made to utilise the spirit of self-help in other types of activities which contribute to the betterment of the family, such as the making of suitable furnishings for the home.

Finally, it is necessary to provide for continuous education of the public generally in accepting the approach offered by self-help, mutual aid and co-operation and in such matters as better methods of family living, more attractive and efficient utilisation of available housing space, and methods of improving community co-operation and social cohesion.

Projects included in this area deal with the training of personnel required for the organisation and administration of programmes designed to extend low-cost housing and community facilities. The professional training of personnel for the building industry at various levels is covered by Project "Education and training of personnel for the building industry" in Area IV.

Projects which could be undertaken in this area over the next five years include the following:

Training of personnel for the organisation and administration of low-cost housing programmes at the higher level — Institutions providing higher training in fields related to housing, building and planning, more particularly national and regional technological institutes, schools of public administration and national and regional housing centres would receive increased technical assistance for special training and refresher courses for the benefit of higher technical and administrative personnel. Special attention would be given in these courses to the relationship between programmes for the extension of low-cost housing and related community facilities and the general national programmes for housing and other social programmes. Fellowships could be provided for further study abroad, and for the inservice training of high level technicians and administrators.

Training of personnel for organising and supervising low-cost housing projects   Technical assistance should be given for establishing centres for training the personnel required to organise and supervise the improvement or extension of low-cost housing and related community facilities in villages and urban fringe areas. In particular, the facilities of national and regional housing centres and fundamental or adult education centres could be utilised for organising short courses on the technical, administrative and educational aspects of projects in this broad field.

Education of the public   Assistance should be extended to various projects of promotional education, to help the community and the public at large understand the purpose, nature and methods of large-scale housing programmes, and the applications of methods of self-help, mutual aid and co-operation. Such projects may be carried out by central or local authorities, teachers' organisations and local teachers, trade-unions and educational workers' associations, non-governmental organisations conducting educational programmes, youth groups and youth-serving agencies. Forms of assistance would include the provision of prototype materials and guides, the services of experts for organising and conducting pilot projects, etc.

Education and training of house-holders   Seminars on the education of householders might be organised by national and regional housing centres, local or national adult education agencies and local authorities. Since housing and home improvement have a direct bearing on family welfare they should be included in the courses of training for welfare workers, home economics teachers, rural extension and community development workers. Increased attention should be given to practical training in these subjects through the organisation of workshops, seminars and training courses for such workers and through collaboration with other international organisations specially concerned with the welfare aspects of housing.

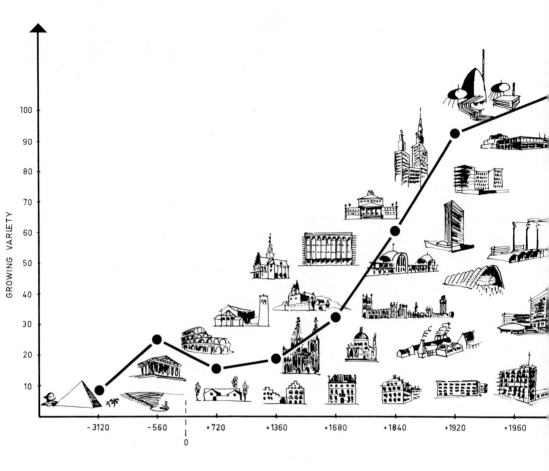

Throughout the ages building has reflected the fundamental aspects of life. The diversity of modern life is therefore clearly illustrated by the appreciable increase in the number of types of buildings.

17   Our building programme

*a thousand million dwellings to be built in this century /
extension low-cost housing in the period 1958–1969 /
distribution of investments / international aid and extra
building programme / towards a habitable world / more
favourable conditions for development of the individual
and the relations between individuals*

More building research and development activity, better building methods, acceleration of transmission of building knowledge are all very important, but all on one overruling condition. The result should not just be more paper, more seminars, more discussions and more resolutions; all these things should lead to more and better building.

By more and better building and civil engineering our planet must be adapted in such a way that the individual and the relations between individuals can develop under more favourable conditions. Socially and economically, building is one of the key problems for man and society. The fundamental unbalance which is making our world more and more uninhabitable is partly due to the fact that it is impossible to build sufficiently, especially in the poorer countries.

With a view to the aim of making the world habitable for all before the end of the present century the most important data of Tables 7 and 8 (page 33) are once more given below.

TABLE 26

PRODUCTION SCHEME FOR HOUSE-BUILDING 1958–1999

Period	Average number of dwellings built per year in millions	Total number of dwellings, in millions
1957	8*	
1958–1969	12	140
1970–1979	21	210
1980–1989	30	300
1990–1999	35	350
1958–1999		1000

* *Rough estimate*

In Chapter 4 it was assumed that with a balanced development the investments in house-building equal the investments made on behalf of other buildings. This implies that it may be assumed as a rough approximation that man requires just as much built-up space inside as outside the dwelling. It was further assumed in Chapter 4 that in terms of money 50 per cent of the amount to be invested in house-building will be required for civil and hydraulic engineering. Naturally, depending on the prevailing conditions, this figure will be different for each country. The short-term and long-term struggle against fundamental unbalance can be successfully waged if equal attention is given to economic growth and to improvement of the social infrastructure. This means that special attention must be given to low-cost housing, both in the poor and in the rich countries. In view of the considerable arrears in the poor countries this problem is particularly urgent there. Hence, it would be desirable if the world house-building programme, for the next ten years could be drawn up roughly as follows.

The initial target has been put at 8 million dwellings in 1957, *i.e.* 3 million in poor countries and 5 million in rich countries (very high estimates). Further, it is assumed that in the years 1958, 1959 and 1960 the number of dwellings built in rich countries will be one million more than three times the number built in 1957.

TABLE 27

EXTENSION LOW-COST HOUSING IN THE PERIOD 1958–1969

Period	Total number of dwellings built, in millions	Poor countries		Rich countries
		basic number own means	extra from international aid for improvement social infrastructure	
1957		3		5
1958–1960	25	9	–	16
1961	9	3	–	6
1962	10	3	1	6
1963	11	3	2	6
1964	12	3	3	6
1965	13	3	4	6
1966	14	3	4	7
1967	15	4	4	7
1968	15	4	4	7
1969	16	5	4	7
1958–1969	140			

Such an additional house-building programme would be possible for the poor countries within the desirable acceleration of capital movement from the rich to the poor countries set out in Table 25. This should be based, however, on the distribution of investments indicated in Table 28.

TABLE 28

DISTRIBUTION OF INVESTMENTS IN %

	House-building	Other buildings	Civil and hydraulic engineering	Other investments
Economic investments (A)	—	10	10	80
Social investments (B)	40	30	10	20
Total as A = B	20	20	10	50

The number of extra dwellings (Table 27) can now be built in the poor countries if on an average one thousand dollars per dwelling is made available for low-cost housing there and the other investments are made in the ratios shown above. The investment programme will then be as follows.

TABLE 29

INTERNATIONAL AID AND EXTRA BUILDING PROGRAMME IN MILLIARDS OF DOLLARS

Year	Economic investments	Social investments	House-building	Other buildings	Civil and hydraulic engineering	Other investments
1961	7.5	1 *	—	0.75	0.75	6
1962	10	2.5	1	1.75	1.25	8.5
1963	10	5	2	2.50	1.50	9
1964	10	7.5	3	3.25	1.75	9.5
1965	10	10	4	4	2	10

* Preparation of extension of low-cost housing and related community facilities.

The execution of such an extensive programme depends to a large extent on the organisational form adopted. The most obvious solution would be to adapt the existing apparatus, which would provide a lot of available experience. The organisations which come to mind in this respect are, of course, the International Bank for Reconstruction and Development and the

Special Fund (Sunfed), which could undertake concerted action. A great deal of attention should also be given to the organisation in the various countries, and, especially in the beginning, a certain amount of centralisation should not be feared.

It is also of great importance that in the developing countries the housing policy should be conducted in such a way that as the level of prosperity rises an increasingly greater part of the cost-price rent is paid by the occupants and that by saving it will gradually become possible to invest a higher percentage of the growing national income. It is only on this basis that the international aid can sufficiently accelerate development.

The aim to achieve a habitable world is not one that is solely of importance for the so-called under-developed countries, nor is it one that can be realised by building alone.

Building can make an essential contribution towards a better functioning of our society for the benefit of man and society alike. We just have to accept that on this God-made earth we live in a man-made environment. The finite life of man and man-made environment are gradually becoming more and more interwoven.

On December 10th, 1948, the General Assembly of the U.N.O. laid down in article 25 of the Universal Declaration of Human Rights: "Everyone has the right to a standard of living adequate for the health and well-being of himself and his family, including food, clothing, housing and medical care . . . ".

This article, however, will remain a dead letter unless by building at a high rate we adapt the space available to us in such a way that our planet becomes habitable for all. And this would be a dangerous dead letter, because on this earth, which – figuratively speaking – is gradually becoming smaller, the poor, who are rapidly growing in number, entertain rising expectations.

Consequently, we are now faced with the decisive choice for the future: destruction or construction. Before making this choice, we must realise that unless we find the right approach by a constructive attack – i.e. materialisation of the human rights – our hope and joy and economic power will decay and we shall be heading for the abyss.

A growing number of people living in slums and hovels will then ask themselves why they live at all and what sense there is in their lives.

There will remain in the end only the nihilist, who is described by Nietzsche in his "Wille zur Macht" as one who thinks that the world as it is should not exist and that the world as it should be does not exist, which brings us to the point where the reality that we experience has become senseless. Senseless and dangerous, because the changing human being with

"All your sons shall be taught by the Lord. And great shall be the prosperity of your sons."

Isiah 54 : 13

his undiscovered self will be confronted with a world which generally does not offer any stimulant to develop the good, the creative in him and to reduce the bad and the destructive in him.

Hence, the only possible choice is: construction. This is a choice that cannot be made solely at the political conference table, but one that concerns us all, because ultimately the problem relates to the individual and the relations between individuals. For this reason this political choice must be followed by a highly intensified international aid and domestic effort, by acceleration of building research, education and training, in order that planners, architects, engineers and the building industry will have optimum means at their disposal. For they will have to build more and better to give our man-made environment the highest possible living value, to create a habitable world fit for all to live in. It is only then that mankind will be freed from its immediate daily worries to the extent that he will gain a clearer insight into the things that really matter.

Photographs have been supplied by:

Automobiles Citroën, Amsterdam, *page 170*
Boer, H. de, Amsterdam, *page 62*
Bouwcentrum, Rotterdam, *pages 119, 143*
Broomfield, Maurice, London, *pages 54, 55, 260, 266*
Collection, Museum of Modern Arts, New York, *page 6*
Coppens, Martin F. J., Eindhoven, *pages 26, 150*
Eckardt, H. O., Rotterdam, *page 169*
Gembouw, The Hague, *page 176*
Huf, Paul, Amsterdam, *pages 38, 60*
Interstate Photographers, New York, *page 151*
I.P.O., Rotterdam, *page 172*
K.L.M. Aerocarto N.V., Amsterdam, *pages 56, 62, 250, 282*
Kowadlo †, Boris, *page 317*
Laboratorio Fotografico G. Gherardi-A. Fiorelli, Rome, *page 171*
Meischke, W. A., Amsterdam, *page 58*
Oorthuis, Cas, Amsterdam, *page 2*
Ratiobouw, Rotterdam, *page 191*
Renes, Arnhem, *page 151*
Schilthuizen, J., Vlaardingen, *page 46*
Unesco, *page 12*
U. S. Information Service, Press Section, The Hague, *pages 60, 76, 96, 128, 206*
Vrijhof, J. A., Rotterdam, *page 150*
Wanink H., Bouwcentrum, Rotterdam, *pages 60, 104, 125, 126, 169, 222, 236, 238, 240, 257, 258, 259, 260, 261, 262, 263, 264, 265, 291*